THE APPAREL PRODUCTION SOURCEBOOK

Solving your domestic production sourcing needs.

contractors

AMERICAN EDITION

2014

fashiondex.com

COATS SLEEPWEAR
STITCHINGEMBROIDERY
SCREENPRINTINGLINGERIE
SWIMWEAR CUSTOMS BROKERROOMS
QUILTINGSPORTSWEAR WOVENSSAMPLE
INTIMATE TRIM APPLICATION SWEATERS
CONTRACTORS UNDERWEAR
FUSINGBLOUSES BRIDAL WEARWAREHOUSESHIRTS
FINISHING KNITWEAR
LEATHERPRODUCTION SOURCING
COATING SPORTSWEAR KNITS TEE SHIRTS
DYEING INSPECTIONHOME FURNISHINGSSHORTS
CUTTING
TOPS DRESSESFREIGHT FORWARDER
PANTSLAUNDRYATHLETIC WEAR DENIMWEAR
SMALLACTIVE WEARDISTRIBUTION JACKETS
GRADINGSWEAT SHIRTS ACCESSORIES
TAILORED GARMENTS JEANS
DANCEWEAR SUITS
PRODUCTION CHILDRENS WEAR
SUEDE FACTORY AGENTSPLEATING
UNIFORMSEVENING WEAR REWORK
MARKING
PATTERNMAKING TUCKING
WASHING ROBES
SKIRTS

Dear Fashiondex Owner,

Fashiondex is pleased to provide you with the most up-to-date resource guide in the apparel industry today.

Every effort has been made to provide you with the must accurate information possible. If you do find an error please let us know so we can correct it for the next edition.

As always our support staff at 212 647 0051 or info@fashiondex.com is ready to answer your questions and take your suggestions and comments or to help you find a source, so we can make Fashiondex even more useful to you.

Sincerely,

The Fashiondex

P.S. Please let the supplier know that you found them with Fashiondex.

Legal Stuff

The Fashiondex, Inc.
212 647 0051
info@fashiondex.com
fashiondex.com

Printed in the United States of America

Jan 2014

TABLE OF CONTENTS

TABLE OF CONTENTS

Notes

ACCURATE FLANNEL BAG COMPANY
468 Totowa Avenue
Paterson, NJ 07522

(1) (973) 720 1800   Fax: (1) (973) 689 6774
E-Mail: *service@accuratebags.com*
Web Site: *www.accuratebags.com*
Description: *Bags and pouches contractor using all fabrics such as flannel, suede,*
velvet, canvas, silk, satin, nylon and more.
Markets: *Accessories market.*

AETNA SHIRT/ON CALL MEDICAL COATS
620 Franklin Avenue
Baltimore, MD 21221
Dan Kohn
(1) (410) 574 2657   Fax: (1) (410) 574 6307
E-Mail: *customerservice@medicalcoats.com*
Web Site: *www.medicalcoats.com*
Description: *CMT contractors of high quality*
formalwear accessories.
Year Est: *1916*
Categories: *Shirts/Tops*
Specialties: *Cummerbunds & bowties for formalwear.*
Markets: *Menswear, Womenswear*
Machinery: *Over 50 sewing machines: single needle, felling,*
embroidery, formal shirt pleating & more.
Packages: *Sewing, CMT & Complete packages available.*
Export to: *Japan*
Agent: *Dan or Wayne. Tel: 877-355-2898.*
Minimums: *None*
Factory Locals: *Baltimore, MD*
Production Capacity: *250 labcoats/week, 1500-2000 woven shirts/week*

AMERICAN SEWING DYNAMICS, INC.
2441 Vermont Avenue #154
Blue Island, IL 60406
Bob Choi
(1) (773) 394 9544   Fax: (1) (773) 394 9610
E-Mail: *sales@americansewingdynamics.com*
Web Site: *www.americansewingdynamics.com*
Description: *Sewing, cutting & assembly services for military & commercial*
uniforms, casual wear, shoe uppers, leather goods, home & specialty.
Categories: *Uniforms, Casual Wear, Coats/Jackets*
Specialties: *Specialize in coveralls, pants, combat uniforms, casual shirts,*
sportswear, leather & military shoe & boot uppers, leather goods.
Markets: *Menswear, Womenswear, Accessories.*
Machinery: *Multiple - Single needle, double needle, walking, cylinder, felling,*
pattern tacker, riveting, grommeting, eyeletting, snap, splitting,
skiving, button hole, button sewing, bartacker, die cutting, table
cutting, puritan, autobarr, zigzag, web cutting, folding, trimming.
Minimums: *Vary*

| Factory Locals: | Chicago, IL |
| Production Capacity: | 500 - 25,000 units/month depending on material & design. |

ARTEX KNITTING MILLS INC.

300 Harvard Avenue
Westville, NJ 08093
Jill Ann Bal
(1) (856) 456 2800   Fax: (1) (856) 456 4111

E-Mail:	sales@artexknit.com
Web Site:	www.artexknit.com
Description:	Knitting contractor of hats, leg warmers, gloves, men's ties and more.
Year Est:	1926
Categories:	Sweaters/Knitwear, Embroidery
Specialties:	Specialize in custom knitted accessories, embroidery and custom color.
Machinery:	Knitting, embroidery and sewing machines. Production done in-house.
Minimums:	None
Factory Locals:	Above
Production Capacity:	100,000 doz/month

DAVE PRESSLEY DESIGN

456 Greenwich Street
New York, NY 10013
David T. Pressley
(1) 917 771 9557

E-Mail:	jewelman65@gmail.com
Web Site:	www.djphandmade.com
Description:	Hardware model maker (proto-type), also does custom work & assists in design development for handbag hardware, belt buckles & jewelry.
Specialties:	Specialize in mechanical handbag locks. Production consultant.
Markets:	Menswear, Womenswear, Children, Accessories, Home.
Packages:	CMT
Minimums:	Small runs for sales samples.

DREAMBAGS INC

2441 Vermont Avenue #154
Blue Island, IL 60406
Bob Choi
(1) (773) 394 3136   Fax: (1) (773) 394 9610

E-Mail:	sales@dreambags.com
Web Site:	www.dreambags.com
Description:	Manufacturer & contractor of leather goods, handbags, backpacks, totes, travelware, computer cases, pet carriers, specialty cases.
Categories:	Leather Accessories, Fashion Accessories, Home Accessories
Specialties:	Leather shoe/boot uppers, sample development services.
Markets:	Mid-high range women, men, commercial accounts
Machinery:	Multiple single needle, double needle, zigzag, walking, cylinder, splitting, skiving, rivet, eyelet, grommet, snap, clickers, travel head, table cutting knives, web cutter, pattern tacker
Minimums:	Varies per model and color
Factory Locals:	Chicago, IL

F & M HAT CO., INC.
103 Walnut Street
Denver, PA 17517
Fred Fichthorn
(1) (717) 336 5505   Fax: (1) (717) 336 0501

E-Mail:	*customerservice@fmhat.com*
Web Site:	*www.fmhat.com*
Description:	*Contractor of men's & women's wool, felt, straw & western hats.*
Specialties:	*Wool, straw & cloth hats from start to finish.*
Machinery:	*Cording, pressing, decorating & boxing equipment.*
Packages:	*Complete packages*
Minimums:	*Vary*
Factory Locals:	*1-800-953-4287*

H.T.T. HEADWEAR LTD.
41185 Raintree Court
Murrieta, CA 92562

(1) (951) 304 0400   Fax: (1) (951) 304 0420

E-Mail:	*contact@httapparel.com*
Web Site:	*www.httapparel.com*
Description:	*Manufacturer & contractor of caps, visors and bags.*
Categories:	*Shirts/Tops, Outerwear*
Specialties:	*Our factories offer the latest technology such as stain resistant and organic materials along with cutting edge embellishments.*
Markets:	*Womenswear & Menswear.*
Packages:	*All packages.*
Export to:	*United Kingdom & Australia*
Minimums:	*288 pcs.*
Factory Locals:	*Have own domestic plants & can import through Taiwan, China & Pakistan.*
Production Capacity:	*Hats: 5,000 dozen/month & Shirts: 120,00 units/month*

HENSCHEL HAT CO.
1706 Olive Street
St. Louis, MO 63103
Tarek Deiab, President
(1) (314) 421 0009   Fax: (1) (314) 421 1317

E-Mail:	*usahat@aol.com*
Web Site:	*www.henschelhats.com*
Description:	*Hat manufacturer open for contract work of all hat styles.*
Year Est:	*1947*
Exporting Since:	*1985*
Specialties:	*Men's high fashion, classic & leather hats.*
Markets:	*Menswear, Accessories.*
Packages:	*All*
Export to:	*Germany, Holland, Austria, France, Spain, Japan, Mexico & Korea.*
Minimums:	*Special orders: 6 doz/style; regular orders: 1 doz/style.*
Factory Locals:	*Factory in Missouri.*
Production Capacity:	*200-400 dozen/week*

KAM MANUFACTURING INC.
PO Box 407
Van Wert, OH 45891

(1) (419) 238 6037   Fax: (1) (419) 238 3489
E-Mail: *ollie@kammfg.com*
Web Site: *www.kammfg.com*
Description: *Cut, sew, ship contractor specializing in quilted fashion purses.*
Packages: *Full Package*

KEMESTRY
1221 Stirling Road
Dania Beach, FL 33004
Fred Kinigsberg
(1) (954) 922 2802   Fax: (1) (954) 922 2012
E-Mail: *elj1978@aol.com*
Web Site: *www.kemestryonline.com*
Description: *Custom contracting house specializing in belts &*
leather, suede or fabric covered buckles & hair accessories.
Markets: *Middle to high-end.*
Minimums: *None*

MANZELLA PRODUCTIONS
80 Sonwil Drive
Buffalo, NY 14225

(1) (716) 681 8880   Fax: (1) (716) 681 6888
E-Mail: *info@manzella.com*
Web Site: *www.manzella.com*
Description: *Glove designer, manufacturing, contracting &*
production sourcing.
Categories: *Accessories, Production Sourcing/Factory Agent.*
Packages: *CMT & complete packages available.*

NEW CONCEPTS OF NEW YORK LLC
313 West 37th Street
New York, NY 10018
Mel Weiss
(1) (212) 695 4999   Fax: (1) (212) 695 4513
E-Mail: *sales@newconceptsllc.com*
Web Site: *www.newconceptsllc.com*
Description: *Belt & hat band contractor & manufacturer.*
Categories: *Accessories, Trim Application*
Specialties: *Nailhead & rhinestone design work.*
Minimums: *one*

NOVELTY POM POM COMPANY

247 West 37th Street
New York, NY 10018
John Jones
(1) (212) 391 9175   Fax: (1) (212) 575 9688

Description:	*Contractor of macrame & corded belts, tassels, pom poms fringes, frogs, braiding & accessories. Domestic.*
Markets:	*Womenswear, Childrenswear. All price points.*
Machinery:	*Braiding & knitting machinery in house.*
Minimums:	*Low*

PARIS ACCESSORIES

1385 Broadway
New York, NY 10018

(1) (212) 868 0500   Fax: (1) (212) 967 4936

E-Mail:	*info@parisacc.com*
Description:	*Domestic contractor & manufacturer of women's belts, gloves, hats & scarves.*
Categories:	*Accessories*
Specialties:	*Better priced belts & accessories.*
Minimums:	*None*

PORTCHESTER, USA

42-24 Orchard Street
Long Island City, NY 11101
Kulwant Chouhan
(1) (718) 937 4200   Fax: (1) (718) 937 4223

E-Mail:	*portchester_usa@verizon.net*
Web Site:	*www.portchesterusa.com*
Description:	*Handbag sample maker and manufacturer - we find solutions to your problems when it comes to making a line of handbags.*
Year Est:	*1985*
Specialties:	*From pattern making to samples to production of handbags & belts. Sourcing all kinds of leather, lining & hardware. Made in the USA.*
Packages:	*Complete & CMT packages.*

QUINTIN CO.

2630 Humboldt Street
Los Angeles, CA 90031

(1) (323) 221 9202   Fax: (1) (323) 221 7304

E-Mail:	*info@quintinco.com*
Web Site:	*www.quintinco.com*
Description:	*Wide selection of fully customized hat styles.*
Categories:	*Embroidery, Screenprinting*
Specialties:	*We produce hats of the highest quality with superior fit & finish.*
Markets:	*Menswear & Womenswear, Childrenswear, Infants*
Machinery:	*Large plant with wide variety of machinery.*
Minimums:	*200 pieces/style*

R & N HEADWEAR

544 Park Avenue
Brooklyn, NY 11211
Fay Green
(1) (718) 522 6990   Fax: (1) (718) 522 3924

Description:	*Contractors & importers of children's hats & accessories.*
Categories:	*Accessories, Childrenswear*
Markets:	*Boyswear, Girlswear, Infantwear.*
Machinery:	*Plant equipped with over 150 sewing machines.*
Packages:	*Sewing.*
Minimums:	*Vary*

SHURCO MANUFACTURING INC.

4638 North Ravenwood Avenue
Chicago, IL 60640
Seymour Ferdman
(1) (773) 907 8400   Fax: (1) (773) 907 8476

E-Mail:	*sy924@sbcglobal.net*
Description:	*Contractor of accessories, handbags, bags & apparel items in leather, suede, plastic, vinyl & cloth.*
Year Est:	*1950*
Specialties:	*We provide embossing, embroidery & silk screening. Quick delivery & quick turn-around.*
Markets:	*Accessories*
Machinery:	*Kick-press, 5 die-cutting & 25 sewing machines.*
Packages:	*Cutting & Sewing & CMT.*
Minimums:	*None*
Production Capacity:	*8,000 pcs/month*

SUNCOAST TRENDS CORP.

2860 21st Avenue North
St. Petersburg, FL 33713
Rosanna Carl
(1) (727) 321 4948   Fax: (1) (727) 321 4320

Description:	*Cut & sew contractor of all types of cosmetic bags, dog line and accessories.*
Categories:	*Sportswear/Knits, Sportswear/Wovens, Patternmaking Services*
Markets:	*Menswear, Womenswear, Childrens, Accessories.*
Minimums:	*12 dozen*

UNWRAPPED, INC.

95 Rock Street
Lowell, MA 01854
Steven Katz
(1) (978) 441 0242   Fax: (1) (978) 441 0929

E-Mail:	*skatz@unwrappedinc.com*
Web Site:	*www.unwrappedinc.com*
Description:	*Sewing factory specializing in contract manufacturing of stitched goods including mesh, nylon & canvas bags & OEM production.*
Specialties:	*Cosmetic bags, toy bags, shoe bags, gear bags, pillows & pillow liners.*
Markets:	*Accessories, Home Furnishings.*

W.Y. SHUGART

405 Beeson Gap Road
Fort Payne, AL 35968
Tim Shugart
(1) (256) 845 1251   Fax: (1) (256) 845 4502

E-Mail:	*tshugart@wyshugart.com*
Web Site:	*www.wyshugart.com*
Description:	*Makers of fine gauge hosiery since 1937.*
Specialties:	*Man-made & natural fibers. Basic, fashion, fancy and novelty socks.*
	Also, custom-design capabilities & dye and finishing facilities.
Markets:	*Womens & Childrens.*

WELLS HOSIERY MILLS, INC.

1758 South Fayetteville Street
Asheboro, NC 27205

(1) (336) 633 4881   Fax: (1) (336) 633 4862

E-Mail:	*info@wellshosiery.com*
Web Site:	*www.wellshosiery.com*
Description:	*Cut and sew operations specializing in womens high end knit tops.*
Categories:	*Shirts/Tops*
Specialties:	*Ladies hosiery. Brand name & private label products. Seamless lines.*
Markets:	*Womenswear.*

info@fashiondex.com © The Fashiondex, Inc.

manufacture your creative efforts.

Markets: Menswear, Womenswear & Childrenswear.
Minimums: 600 pcs per color

ACTIVE APPAREL INC.
11076 Venture Drive
Mira Loma, CA 91752

5,royal

(1) (951) 361 0060   Fax: (1) (951) 361 3120

E-Mail: sales@activeapparel.net
Web Site: www.activeapparel.net
Description: All types of tees, tops and bottoms.
Categories: Sample Rooms/Small Production
Specialties: Specialize in custom creations and have full capabilities to
manufacture your creative efforts.
Markets: Menswear, Womenswear & Childrenswear.
Minimums: 600 pcs per color

AMERICAN TEXTILE & APPAREL INC.
10408 W State Road 84
Davie, FL 33324
Luis Mejia
(1) (954) 734 9988   Fax: (1) (954) 734 9966

E-Mail: luis.mejia@ata-usa.com
Web Site: www.ata-usa.com
Description: Contractor of knits & woven athletic sportswear, tee shirts,
polo shirts and ladies underwear.
Year Est: 2002
Specialties: Specialize in private label manufacturing in both knits
and woven apparel.
Markets: Menswear, Womenswear, Childrenswear.
Packages: CMT & Full Packages
Factory Locals: Davie Florida plus a network of the best apparel and
textile manufacturers from both hemispheres.
Production Capacity: T-Shirts 50,000 doz/month, Polo Shirts 35,000 doz/month,
Sportwear 10,000 doz/month, Underwear 100,000 doz/month

BOULDER PATH DESIGNS
110 E. 2nd Street
The Dalles, OR 97058
Luise Langheinrich
(1) (541) 296 4470   Fax: (1) (541) 298 5067

E-Mail: info@boulderpathdesigns.com
Web Site: www.boulderpathdesigns.com
Description: Full service contractor. Product development, specifications, patterns,
CAD service, grading, marker making, samples, production runs.
Categories: Patternmaking, Samples/Small Production, Sportswear/Wovens
Specialties: Problem solving. Experience in work wear, sportswear, hospital gowns,
active wear, and more. Can do all styles of tops, bottoms and jackets.
Markets: Menswear, Womenswear & Childrenswear.
Packages: Full service, prototype, development, samplemaking

Minimums:	None
Factory Locals:	Oregon, USA

COTTON & ELSE INC.
2921 N.W. 28th Street
Lauderdale Lakes, FL 33311

(1) (954) 677 8010   Fax: (1) (954) 677 0270

E-Mail:	cottonet@bellsouth.net
Web Site:	www.cottonandelse.net
Year Est:	1992
Categories:	Dyeing, Sleepwear/Robes
Specialties:	Specialize in knitting, dyeing and sewing of cotton knitted garments. We offer a wide range of Tee-Shirts.
Markets:	Menswear, Womenswear & Childrenswear.
Export to:	Canada, Europe, Middle East, South America
Factory Locals:	Florida
Production Capacity:	10,000 doz/week (garments)

FASHIONS UNLIMITED, INC.
1100 Wicomico Street
Baltimore, MD 21230
Mary Murphy
(1) (410) 783 1584

E-Mail:	fashionsu@verizon.net
Web Site:	www.fashionsu.net
Description:	Contractor of athletic bodywear. Patternmaker & sample room on premises.
Year Est:	1976
Categories:	Active/Athleticwear, Lingerie/Intimate Apparel, Sportswear-Knits, Swimwear/Dancewear.
Specialties:	We specialize in seamless development. We have seamless knitting capabilities on Santoni Machines. Bras, tops, pants, underwear, swim.
Markets:	Womenswear, Childrenswear
Machinery:	Overlock, single needle, coverstitch (1 and 2 needle) zig zag, walking foot machines, flat locks.
Packages:	Full service, CMT & complete packages.
Minimums:	None
Factory Locals:	Baltimore MD, Hellam PA, Charlotte NC (Seamless)
Production Capacity:	Swim: 1,000 units/week, Activewear: 1,500 units/week, Dance: 1,500 units/week, Sportswear: 1,000 units/week

GRANITE KNITWEAR/DBA CAL CRU
805 S Salisbury Avenue
Granite Quarry, NC 28072
Mike Jones, President
(1) (704) 279 5526   Fax: (1) (704) 279 8205

E-Mail:	calcru@mindspring.com
Web Site:	www.calcru.com
Description:	1-800-476-9944. Contractor & manufacturer of knit apparel & tee shirts using Coolmax & Dri-Release performance knit fabrics.

Year Est:	1968
Exporting Since:	1980
Categories:	Sportswear-Knits, Tee Shirts
Specialties:	Private labeling, custom design & manufacturing, stock inventory & final packaging.
Markets:	Menswear, Womenswear, Children/Infantwear.
Machinery:	1 flatlock, 30 overedger, 4 coverseam, 4 covertape, 4 single needle, 1 button hole, 1 snap machine, 1 pocket, 1 shirring.
Packages:	Full package, screenprinting, embroidery, pattern making.
Export to:	Japan
Minimums:	60 dozen/color/style
Production Capacity:	2,000 doz/month

GRIFFIN MANUFACTURING CO., INC.

502 Bedford Street
Fall River, MA 02722
Gene Laudon
(1) (508) 677 0048   Fax: (1) (508) 674 1268

E-Mail:	sales@griffinmanufacturing.com
Web Site:	www.griffinmanufacturing.com
Description:	Cut & sew contractor plus design, development, patternmaking, sample making & warehousing.
Year Est:	1936
Categories:	Samples/Small Production
Specialties:	Athleticwear, performance knits, knit & woven sportswear & outerwear.
Markets:	Menswear, Womenswear & Childrenswear.
Machinery:	Sewing machines, flatlock stitch machines, automatic cutting machines, in-house embroidery & heat transfers.
Minimums:	200 to 2,000 pieces
Factory Locals:	Fall River, MA & Costa Rica

HAGINS INDUSTRIES, INC.

2128 Marion Stage Road
Fairmont, NC 28340
Johnnie Hagins
(1) (910) 628 6777   Fax: (1) (910) 628 5160

E-Mail:	haginsinds@bellsouth.net
Description:	Contractor specializing in sweatpants.
Year Est:	1989
Categories:	Shirts/Tops, Rework/Inspection
Specialties:	All type of rework and re-labeling capabilities.
Markets:	Menswear, Womenswear & Childrenswear.
Machinery:	Overlock & flatlock machines. Full cutting room.
Packages:	CMT & complete packages available.
Minimums:	None
Production Capacity:	4800 pcs/month

INDU FASHIONS

220 West 25th Street
National City, CA 91950
Shashi Pal
(1) (619) 336 4638   Fax: (1) (619) 336 4122

E-Mail:	*shashi@indufashions.com*
Web Site:	*www.indufashions.com*
Description:	*Full service contractor specializing in running shorts, yoga wear, cycle & tri-wear plus all types of athletic sportswear.*
Specialties:	*Specialize in flatlock seam construction and excel with fabrics such as lycra and modal fabrics.*
Markets:	*Menswear, Womenswear*
Packages:	*CMT & Full. Cutting, marking & grading in house.*
Minimums:	*250-500 pieces/style*
Production Capacity:	*40,000 pieces/month*

J.P. SPORTSWEAR/AARON CORP.

1820 East 41st Street
Los Angeles, CA 90058
Paul/Paco
(1) (323) 235 5959   Fax: (1) (323) 235 2999

E-Mail:	*jppaul2@pacbell.net*
Web Site:	*www.jpsportswear.net*
Description:	*Contractor of high-end activewear.*
Year Est:	*1979*
Exporting Since:	*1995*
Specialties:	*In house pattern makers, sample department, full inspection.*
Markets:	*Menswear, Womenswear*
Machinery:	*40 flat seam, 50 overlock, 35 single needle, 25 coverstitch, 7 bartack, 5 button, 4 zigzag, 5 double & 4 multi-needle.*
Packages:	*CMT & Full packages available.*
Minimums:	*1,000 pieces - steady volume only.*
Factory Locals:	*Los Angeles*

MIAMI STYLE INC.

7480 NW 52nd Street
Miami, FL 33166
Amnon Bensimon/Sofia Rincon
(1) (305) 805 1168   Fax: (1) (305) 805 0075

E-Mail:	*sofia@miamistyle.com*
Web Site:	*www.miamistyle.com*
Description:	*Sourcing agent for all types of active wear, bottoms, tops, tee shirts, knit sportswear, beachwear, sports bras, basics and children's wear.*
Year Est:	*1997*
Categories:	*Pants/Shorts/Skirts, Shirts/Tops, Tee Shirts/Sweat Shirts*
Specialties:	*Production services: Private label, sewing, cutting, patternmaking, printing, embroidery, screenprinting, samplemaking, dyeing, beading & more.*
Markets:	*Menswear, Womenswear, Boyswear, Girlswear.*
Factory Locals:	*Bangladesh and China*
Production Capacity:	*3 million pcs per month*

MONALISA FASHIONS INC.

650 East Green Street
Allentown, PA 18109
Mereille Najm
(1) (610) 770 0806   Fax: (1) (610) 770 0823

E-Mail:	*monalisamfg@gmail.com*
Web Site:	*www.monalisamfg.com*
Description:	*Family-owned CMT contractor. The 15,000SF facility includes cutting, sewing, trimming, shipping/storage.*
Year Est:	*1984*
Categories:	*Active & Athletic wear, Childrens Wear, Shirts & Tops, Swimwear, T-Shirts, Sportswear-knits, Sample Rooms/Small Production.*
Specialties:	*Garment dye, organic, contemporary knitwear, infantwear.*
Markets:	*Menswear, Womenswear, Childrens*
Machinery:	*Over-lock, safety, 2-ndl and 3-ndl cover stitch, straight stitch, single needle, neck tape, double needle, metal snaps, elastic cover stitch, binding, button hole, button sewer, picot machine, flatlock, heat press, fusing.*
Packages:	*CMT, Sewing*
Export to:	*Canada, Europe, Asia*
Minimums:	*200 units/style*
Production Capacity:	*50,000 pcs/month*

NEW ICM, LP

220 Sam Bishkin Road
El Campo, TX 77437
R. C. Whitson, Projects Coordinator
(1) (979) 578 0543   Fax: (1) (979) 578 0503

E-Mail:	*rcwhitson@newicm.com*
Web Site:	*www.newicm.com*
Description:	*Manufacturer, designer & contractor of children's activewear.*
Year Est:	*1948*
Markets:	*Childrenswear*
Machinery:	*Over 400 serger, safety stitch, double & triple needle, cover stitch, single needle, zig-zag & numerous other special-operations machines.*
Export to:	*Piece goods & trims for various programs exported to countries in Latin America & Asia.*
Minimums:	*Domestic - none, overseas - negotiable.*
Factory Locals:	*El Campo, TX. Also affiliated with factories in Mexico, Dominican Republic, China & Southeast Asia.*
Production Capacity:	*4,000 units/day for domestic. Virtually unlimited for overseas.*

NORTHRIDGE MILLS INC.

1901 First Street
San Fernando, CA 91340
Rocio Maldonado
(1) (818) 361 7373   Fax: (1) (818) 365 5369

E-Mail:	*rocio@northridgemills.com*
Description:	*Sewing, cutting, logo heat-transfer & computer sewing,*

specialty stitching.

Specialties:	*Specialize in activewear, bikewear, swimwear, pants, tops & bottoms in knits, lycra, cotton-lycra, nylon, cotton & nylon flatlock stitching.*
Markets:	*Menswear, Womenswear & Childrenswear.*
Machinery:	*Over 300 various sewing machines and equipment.*
Minimums:	*400 pieces*

ROYAL APPAREL INC.

65 Commerce Street
Hauppauge, NY 11788
Morey Mayeri
(1) (631) 213 8299

See our ad on page 9, 113, 129

Fax: (1) (631) 922 8438

E-Mail:	*sales@royalapparel.net*
Web Site:	*www.royalapparel.net*
Description:	*Manufacturer & private label contractor/converter of premium knit apparel. Made to order custom programs.*
Year Est:	*1993*
Exporting Since:	*1993*
Categories:	*Tee Shirts, Sportswear-Knits, Sample Room, Shirts & Tops, Embroidery, Cutting/Fusing*
Specialties:	*Active sportswear styles in knit jersey, ribs, cotton blends. We produce organic blanks and products.*
Markets:	*Menswear, Womenswear & Childrenswear.*
Packages:	*Full service, complete packages.*
Export to:	*Canada & Europe*
Minimums:	*100 dozen per size/per color*

SARAH LYNN SPORTSWEAR, INC.

431 N. Jordan Street
Allentown, PA 18102
Richard Koury
(1) (610) 770 1702

Fax: (1) (610) 770 1785

E-Mail:	*rkoury@slsportswear.com*
Web Site:	*www.slsportswear.com*
Description:	*Contractor of all types of active & athletic wear.*
Year Est:	*1985*
Categories:	*Active/Athletic Wear, Sportswear-Knits, Childrenswear, Tee-Shirts*
Specialties:	*Experience with stretch fabrics & all types of knits. All work done in-house. Also, patternmaking, sample making & rework/inspection.*
Markets:	*Menswear, Womenswear & Childrenswear.*
Machinery:	*20 overlock, 20 safety, 8 coverstitch, 4 button, 4 binding, 9 flat-seam and more.*
Packages:	*Sewing only, Complete & CMT packages.*
Production Capacity:	*75,000 pcs/month*

SOLID STONE FABRICS

26 Fayette Street
Martinsville, VA 24112
David Stone
(1) (276) 634 0115

Fax: (1) (276) 632 8986

E-Mail:	*dstone@solidstonefabrics.com*

Web Site:	*www.solidstonefabrics.com*
Description:	*Cut and sew contractor of dancewear and clothing for athletes such as gymnasts.*
Categories:	*Dancewear, Small Production*
Specialties:	*Small production lots.*
Markets:	*Menswear & Womenswear.*
Minimums:	*Small*

SWEENIE MANUFACTURING CORPORATION

34 Sedgwick Avenue
Yonkers, NY 10705
Diane Walker
(1) (646) 825 5027   Fax: (1) (646) 825 5027

E-Mail:	*diane@sweeniemanufacturing.com*
Web Site:	*www.sweeniemanufacturing.com*
Description:	*Branded manufacturer. Specialize in design/merchandising, sourcing and production of activewear, swimwear and cut/sew knits.*
Specialties:	*Specialize in swimwear, activewear, tee-shirts, knit & woven sportswear, sportsbags, gym bags, cosmetic bags. Printed & logo trims.*
Markets:	*Menswear, Womenswear, Childrenswear.*
Machinery:	*Flat bed, button holer, spaghetti strap*
Packages:	*Full package or CMT only*
Factory Locals:	*Domestic & Overseas Production Capabilities.*

VAPOR APPAREL

2120 Noisette Boulevard
North Charleston, SC 29405
Christopher Bernat
(1) (843) 747 4200   Fax: (1) (843) 747 4211

E-Mail:	*sales@sourcesubstrates.com*
Web Site:	*www.vaporapparel.com*
Description:	*High quality performance apparel specifically engineered for digital decorating, screenprinting & embroidery.*
Specialties:	*Offer cut & sew custom garment services as well as full private label programs.*
Markets:	*Menswear, Womenswear, Childrenswear.*
Factory Locals:	*Bogota, Colombia*

DALMA DRESS MFG CO INC

251 West 39th Street
New York, NY 10018
Michael Dipalma
(1) (212) 391 8296

Description:	*Cut and sew contractor of women's dresses & evening wear.*
Categories:	*Sample Rooms/Small Production, Dresses/Blouses*
Markets:	*Womenswear*

J.L.S.C./SYDNEY BUSH

728 East 136th Street
Bronx, NY 10454
Michael
(1) (718) 742 9629   Fax: (1) (718) 742 1379

E-Mail:	*michaelraske@msn.com*
Description:	*Contractor of underpinnings & petticoats for wedding & formal dresses.*
Specialties:	*Domestic*
Markets:	*Womenswear, Girlswear.*
Packages:	*Complete & CMT.*
Minimums:	*None*

Notes

BLOOM FASHION USA

5589-B Guinea Road
Fairfax, VA 22032

(1) (703) 323 6793   Fax: (1) (703) 323 6795
E-Mail: sales@bloomfashionusa.com
Web Site: www.bloomfashionusa.com
Description: Sewing contractor of childrens dresses, t-shirts, uniforms & pants.
Categories: Uniforms, Pants/Shorts/Skirts
Specialties: We can help you start your new business.
100% of our products are made in the USA.
Markets: Menswear, Womenswear, Childrenswear.
Minimums: Low Minimums

IN.STYLE EXCHANGE™   See our ad on page 75

1844 W. Division Street
Arlington, TX 76012
Sales Manager
(1) (817) 886 9222
E-Mail: info@instyleexchange.com
Web Site: www.instyleexchange.com
Description: Full service, 'one-stop-shop' for children's wear, including
design, patterns, grading/marking, samples & small run production.
Categories: Sample Rooms/Small Production, Production Sourcing, Shirts & Tops,
Patternmaking, Dresses & Blouses, Lingerie, Sleepwear & Robes.
Packages: Private label & full packages.
Minimums: 50 pieces per color per style
Production Capacity: 50,000 pcs/month

L.S.W. CUTTING & SEWING SERVICE

670 Ninth Street
Oakland, CA 94607
Lana Wong
(1) (510) 891 9246
E-Mail: lswcuttingandsewing@hotmail.com
Description: Contractor of dresses for the children's market.
Specialties: Complete patternmaking services.
Markets: Girlswear.
Packages: Full service, CMT & complete packages.
Minimums: 300 units/style
Production Capacity: 30,000 pcs/month

MONALISA FASHIONS INC.

650 East Green Street
Allentown, PA 18109
Mereille Najm
(1) (610) 770 0806   Fax: (1) (610) 770 0823
E-Mail: monalisamfg@gmail.com
Web Site: www.monalisamfg.com
Description: Family-owned CMT contractor. The 15,000SF facility
includes cutting, sewing, trimming, shipping/storage.

Year Est:	1984
Categories:	Active & Athletic wear, Childrens Wear, Shirts & Tops, Swimwear, T-Shirts, Sportswear-knits, Sample Rooms/Small Production.
Specialties:	Garment dye, organic, contemporary knitwear, infantwear.
Markets:	Menswear, Womenswear, Childrens
Machinery:	Over-lock, safety, 2-ndl and 3-ndl cover stitch, straight stitch, single needle, neck tape, double needle, metal snaps, elastic cover stitch, binding, button hole, button sewer, picot machine, flatlock, heat press, fusing.
Packages:	CMT, Sewing
Export to:	Canada, Europe, Asia
Minimums:	200 units/style
Production Capacity:	50,000 pcs/month

NEW ICM, LP

220 Sam Bishkin Road
El Campo, TX 77437
R. C. Whitson, Projects Coordinator
(1) (979) 578 0543   Fax: (1) (979) 578 0503

E-Mail:	rcwhitson@newicm.com
Web Site:	www.newicm.com
Description:	Manufacturer, designer & contractor of children's sleepwear, dresses, sportswear & activewear.
Year Est:	1948
Specialties:	Flame resistant children's sleepwear, undergarments & slips.
Markets:	Childrenswear
Machinery:	Over 400 serger, safety stitch, double & triple needle, cover stitch, single needle, zig-zag & numerous other special-operations machines.
Export to:	Piece goods & trims for various programs exported to countries in Latin America & Asia.
Minimums:	Domestic - none, overseas - negotiable.
Factory Locals:	El Campo, TX. Also affiliated with factories in Mexico, Dominican Republic, China & Southeast Asia.
Production Capacity:	4,000 units/day for domestic. Virtually unlimited for overseas.

R & N HEADWEAR

544 Park Avenue
Brooklyn, NY 11211
Fay Green
(1) (718) 522 6990   Fax: (1) (718) 522 3924

Description:	Contractors & importers of children's hats & accessories.
Categories:	Accessories
Markets:	Boyswear, Girlswear, Infantwear.
Machinery:	Plant equipped with over 150 sewing machines.
Packages:	Sewing.
Minimums:	Vary

ROYAL APPAREL INC.

See our ad on page 9, 113, 129

65 Commerce Street
Hauppauge, NY 11788
Morey Mayeri
(1) (631) 213 8299   Fax: (1) (631) 922 8438

E-Mail:	*sales@royalapparel.net*
Web Site:	*www.royalapparel.net*
Description:	*Manufacturer & private label contractor/converter of premium knit apparel. Made to order custom programs.*
Year Est:	*1993*
Exporting Since:	*1993*
Categories:	*Tee Shirts, Sportswear-Knits, Activewear/Athleticwear, Embroidery, Cutting/Fusing*
Specialties:	*Active sportswear styles in knit jersey, ribs, cotton blends. We produce organic blanks and products.*
Markets:	*Menswear, Womenswear & Childrenswear.*
Packages:	*Full service, complete packages.*
Export to:	*Canada & Europe*
Minimums:	*100 dozen per size/per color*

SARAH LYNN SPORTSWEAR, INC.

431 N. Jordan Street
Allentown, PA 18102
Richard Koury
(1) (610) 770 1702   Fax: (1) (610) 770 1785

E-Mail:	*rkoury@slsportswear.com*
Web Site:	*www.slsportswear.com*
Description:	*Contractor of children's sportswear, active wear & tee shirts.*
Year Est:	*1985*
Categories:	*Active/Athletic Wear, Sportswear-Knits, Childrenswear, Tee-Shirts*
Specialties:	*Experience with stretch fabrics & all types of knits. All work done in-house. Also, patternmaking, sample making & rework/inspection.*
Markets:	*Menswear, Womenswear & Childrenswear.*
Machinery:	*20 overlock, 20 safety, 8 coverstitch, 4 button, 4 binding, 9 flat-seam and more.*
Packages:	*Sewing only, Complete & CMT packages.*
Production Capacity:	*75,000 pcs/month*

SEW PRECISE COMPANY

3212 N. Kilpatrick Avenue
Chicago, IL 60641

(1) (773) 481 1400   Fax: (1) (773) 481 1335

E-Mail:	*info@sewprecise.com*
Web Site:	*www.sewprecise.com*
Description:	*Full service cutting and sewing contractor of all types of apparel.*
Categories:	*Grading/Marking, Small Production*
Specialties:	*Grading/marker, pressing/finishing, embroidery.*
Markets:	*Menswear, Womenswear, Childrenswear.*
Machinery:	*80 machines of all types including fusing machines, pressing equipment, and 2 40ft. cutting tables.*

CANDILEJAS CLOTHING CO.

742 South Hill Street
Los Angeles, CA 90014
Angelina Munoz
(1) (213) 489 2855   Fax: (1) (213) 489 1845

Description:	*Full service contractor.*
Categories:	*Coats/Jackets, Suits/Tailored Apparel.*
Specialties:	*Women's jackets, pants, skirts, skorts in all fabrics.*
Markets:	*Womenswear.*
Packages:	*CMT & complete packages. Sample room on premises.*
Minimums:	*None*

CHATHAM KNITTING MILLS, INC.

P.O. Box 152
Chatham, VA 24531
Matt Harris
(1) (434) 432 4701 x11   Fax: (1) (434) 432 3742

E-Mail:	*mattharris2006@gmail.com*
Description:	*Contract sewing of men's & women's outerwear. Also, outerwear.*
Year Est:	*1951*
Categories:	*Coats/Jackets, Uniforms.*
Packages:	*Sewing only.*
Minimums:	*None*

DYNOTEX INC.

236 Greenpoint Avenue
Brooklyn, NY 11222
Annie Kwan
(1) (917) 532 9068

E-Mail:	*dynotexinc@gmail.com*
Web Site:	*www.dynotex.com*
Description:	*Manufacture ladies and mens woven & knit bottoms, tops and outerwear. More than just cut & sew services. Quality conscious.*
Year Est:	*1999*
Specialties:	*We can provide patternmaking services, cutting room in-house, sample making, grading & marking, 100% inspection,*
Markets:	*Menswear & Womenswear*
Machinery:	*18 Single Needle, 8 Merrow, 1 Double Needle, 2 Blind Stitch, 2 Double Needle Cover Stitch, 1 Zig Zag, 2 Purl Stitch, 2 Button, 1 Button Hole Straight, 1 Button Hole Keyhole, 2 Snap Machines, 3 Thread Trimmer, 1 Fabric Steamer, 2 Cutting Tables and more.*
Packages:	*Comprehensive technical knowledge of fabrics.*
Minimums:	*None*
Factory Locals:	*All work is done in-house.*
Production Capacity:	*Knitwear: 15,000 units/month, Pants: 10,000 units/month, Blouses: 10,000 units/month, Blazers: 5,000 units/month.*

H.T.T. HEADWEAR LTD.
41185 Raintree Court
Murrieta, CA 92562

(1) (951) 304 0400   Fax: (1) (951) 304 0420

E-Mail:	*contact@httapparel.com*
Web Site:	*www.httapparel.com*
Description:	*Manufacturer & contractor of fleece pullovers, 3 in one jackets, wind jackets.*
Categories:	*Accessories, Shirts/Tops*
Specialties:	*Our factories offer the latest technology such as stain resistant and organic materials along with cutting edge embellishments.*
Markets:	*Womenswear & Menswear.*
Packages:	*All packages.*
Export to:	*United Kingdom & Australia*
Factory Locals:	*Have own domestic plants & can import through Taiwan, China & Pakistan.*
Production Capacity:	*Hats: 5,000 dozen/month & Shirts: 120,00 units/month*

ID4U JACKETS WITH IDENTITY
344 Hostetter Road
Manheim, PA 17545
Daryl Schumacher
(1) 888 968 4348   Fax: (1) 717 644 4397

E-Mail:	*daryl@id4u-jackets.com*
Web Site:	*www.id4u-jackets.com*
Description:	*1-888-968-4348. Full package contractor & manufacturer of custom jackets. Also offer dye sublimation type decoration on shirts & jackets.*
Year Est:	*1991*
Categories:	*Leather/Suede*
Specialties:	*Specialize in full customization of leather, wool & twill jackets as well as team shirts. Prototypes are offered for a minimal charge.*
Markets:	*Menswear & Womenswear*
Packages:	*CMT, samples, embroidery, screenprinting & dyeing.*
Minimums:	*25 pcs/style*
Factory Locals:	*Pennsylvania & Madras, India.*
Production Capacity:	*Variable. Can fill small & large orders.*

LEONORA FASHIONS, INC.
1095 East 15th Street
Hialeah, FL 33010
Michael Fiorilli
(1) (305) 885 8148   Fax: (1) (305) 885 8148

E-Mail:	*mike@leonorafashions.com*
Web Site:	*www.leonorafashions.com*
Description:	*Contractor specialized in active outerwear, coats, blazers & lined & unlined jackets & sportcoats.*
Categories:	*Coats/Jackets, Active Outerwear, Uniforms, Suits/Formal*
Specialties:	*Designing, pattern making and grading.*
Markets:	*Menswear, Womenswear.*
Machinery:	*State-of-the-art machinery.*

Packages:	Full package.
Factory Locals:	20,000 sq. ft. factory with warehouse in Hialeah, FL.
Production Capacity:	5,000 pieces/week

MCBEE MANUFACTURING COMPANY

347 West Cypress Avenue
McBee, SC 29101
John/Tom Campolong
(1) (843) 335 8234   Fax: (1) (843) 335 8236

E-Mail:	vinci@shtc.net
Web Site:	www.vinciclothiers.com
Description:	Contractor of ladies woven jackets.
Year Est:	1960
Markets:	Womenswear
Machinery:	Complete range of machinery.
Packages:	CMT & Full packages available.
Minimums:	Vary
Factory Locals:	McBee & Camden, South Carolina

PRIMO COAT COMPANY

43-15 Queens Street
Long Island City, NY 11101

(1) (718) 349 2070   Fax: (1) (718) 349 7150

E-Mail:	alan@alandavidnyc.com
Description:	Contractor of men's & ladies jackets, topcoats, overcoats & all formal wear.
Categories:	Coats/Jackets, Sample Rooms/Small Production
Specialties:	Small production lots & special orders. Top quality.
Markets:	Menswear & Womenswear
Machinery:	Sergers, bartack & buttonhole machinery.
Packages:	Cutting & CMT packages avail. Design service avail.
Minimums:	None. Will do singles.

RAYLON CORPORATION

267 Fifth Avenue
New York, NY 10016
Jay Pollak
(1) (212) 221 3633   Fax: (1) (212) 889 3283

E-Mail:	jpollak@rayloncorp.com
Description:	Full package contractor/factory agent & textile converter.
Year Est:	1948
Specialties:	Specialize in board shorts & warm-up jackets.
Markets:	Menswear, Womenswear, Boyswear, Girlswear.
Minimums:	500-1,000 pcs/style
Factory Locals:	Asia

SCHOTT BROTHERS, INC.
1000 Jefferson Avenue
Elizabeth, NJ 07201
Don King
(1) (908) 527 0011   Fax: (1) (908) 527 6185

E-Mail:	*schott@schottnyc.com*
Web Site:	*www.schottnyc.com*
Description:	*Contractor of leather & wool jackets & outerwear.*
Year Est:	*1913*
Exporting Since:	*1970*
Specialties:	*Specialize in flight, bomber & motorcycle jackets.*
Machinery:	*Over 80 single needle, double needle & safety stitch machines. 20 leather cutters in house.*
Packages:	*Cutting & Sewing & CMT.*
Export to:	*Europe, Asia & Middle East.*
Minimums:	*200 pieces/style*

SOARING EAGLE OUTERWEAR, INC.
1916 20th Avenue S.E.
Minot, ND 58701
Austin Hall
(1) (701) 838 2110   Fax: (1) (701) 852 4941

E-Mail:	*seagle@srt.com*
Description:	*Contractor of outerwear, parka jackets, smocks, life jackets & more.*
Categories:	*Uniforms*
Machinery:	*Sergers, cover stitch, multi-needle & pressing machinery.*
Packages:	*Sewing & CMT packages.*
Minimums:	*None. Can handle small & large production lots.*

STERLINGWEAR OF BOSTON, INC.
175 McClellan Highway
East Boston, MA 02128
David Fredella
(1) (617) 567 6465   Fax: (1) (617) 567 6472

E-Mail:	*dfredella@sterlingwear.com*
Web Site:	*www.sterlingwear.com*
Description:	*Manufacturers of quality outerwear for men, women & children plus military outerwear clothing.*
Categories:	*Uniforms*
Specialties:	*Will do contract work for private label uniforms.*
Minimums:	*Vary*

WORLD SOURCE
224 West 35th Street
New York, NY 10001
Alan Novie/Jack Mann
(1) (212) 594 9129   Fax: (1) (212) 202 5298

E-Mail:	*info@worldsourcenyc.com*
Description:	*All types of apparel production services.*

Year Est:	1993
Categories:	Production Sourcing/Factory Agent, Leather/Suede, Dresses/Blouses
Specialties:	Specialize in leather and suede outerwear, embellished, embroidered and lace dresses and blouses.
Markets:	Menswear & Womenswear.
Packages:	Complete
Factory Locals:	China and India
Production Capacity:	Leather garments: 200 pcs/month per style/color, Sequin Dresses: 150 pcs/month, Blouses: 300 pcs/month.

Notes

DIDI OF CALIFORNIA
5816 Piedmont Avenue
Los Angeles, CA 90042
Aldo Garrolini
(1) (323) 256 4514   Fax: (1) (323) 256 4514

Description:	*Contractor of better ladies dresses, skirts & blouses.*
Markets:	*Womenswear.*
Machinery:	*Over 50 machines on premises.*
Packages:	*Sewing & CMT.*
Minimums:	*100-200 pieces/style*

G.S. FASHION
2765 Randolph Street
Huntington Park, CA 90255
George Simonian
(1) (323) 581 0764   Fax: (1) (323) 581 1253

E-Mail:	*ssimonn@aol.com*
Description:	*Sewing contractor of dresses, evening/formal, skirts, blouses & pants. Interested in partnering with a freelance designer.*
Year Est:	*1988*
Categories:	*Sample Rooms/Small Production*
Specialties:	*Sewing, finishing, bagging, tagging, repair & change labels. Also fulfillment services for offshore containers.*
Markets:	*Womenswear*
Machinery:	*Single Needle, Double Needle, Overlock, Cover Stitch*

IN STYLE USA, INC.
307 West 36th Street
New York, NY 10018
James Mallon
(1) (212) 631 0278   Fax: (1) (212) 631 0279

E-Mail:	*instyleusa@instyleusa.net*
Description:	*Contractor & private label manufacturer.*
Categories:	*Patternmaking, Sample Room/Small Production, Suits/Tailored Garments*
Specialties:	*Expert with women's dresses, blouses, shirts, suits, tailored garments. On-time delivery.*
Markets:	*Womenswear*
Machinery:	*Over 100 new machines.*
Packages:	*All*
Minimums:	*None*
Factory Locals:	*New York City.*
Production Capacity:	*12,000 to 20,000 pcs/month*

IN.STYLE EXCHANGE™
See our ad on page 75
1844 W. Division Street
Arlington, TX 76012
Sales Manager
(1) (817) 886 9222

E-Mail:	*info@instyleexchange.com*
Web Site:	*www.instyleexchange.com*

Description:	Full service, 'one-stop-shop' for dresses & blouses, including design, patterns, grading/marking, samples & small run production.
Categories:	Sample Rooms/Small Production, Production Sourcing, Shirts & Tops, Childrens Wear, Patternmaking, Lingerie, Sleepwear & Robes.
Packages:	Private label & full packages.
Minimums:	50 pieces per color per style
Production Capacity:	50,000 pcs/month

JADE APPAREL

1017 Race Street
Philadelphia, PA 19107
Anh Thai
(1) (215) 922 3953   Fax: (1) (215) 922 7231

E-Mail:	jadey989@aol.com
Description:	Cut and sew moderate size lot contractor.
Year Est:	1995
Categories:	Shirts/Tops
Specialties:	Specialize in better knits & woven tops, blouses, dresses and men's button down shirts, pants.
Markets:	Menswear, Womenswear & Childrenswear.
Machinery:	40 single needle, 4 double needle coverstitch, zig zag, pearl stitch, safety stitch, blind stitch & bar tack machines, welt pocket machine, smocking.
Packages:	CMT
Minimums:	200 unit per style.
Factory Locals:	Philadelphia, PA
Production Capacity:	30,000 pieces

L.S.W. CUTTING & SEWING SERVICE

670 Ninth Street
Oakland, CA 94607
Lana Wong
(1) (510) 891 9246

E-Mail:	lswcuttingandsewing@hotmail.com
Description:	Contractor of dresses.
Specialties:	Complete patternmaking services.
Markets:	Womens & childrens markets.
Packages:	Full service, CMT & complete packages.
Minimums:	300 units/style
Production Capacity:	30,000 pcs/month

LEFT IN STITCHES INC.

55 Ericson Court
Arcata, CA 95521

(1) (707) 822 3041   Fax: (1) (707) 822 3042

E-Mail:	info@leftinstitches.com
Web Site:	www.leftinstitches.com
Description:	Over 29 years of patternmaking, grading and sewing. Samples, prototypes. Work with knits and wovens.
Categories:	Grading/Marking, Patternmaking, Samples/Small Production

Specialties:	*Creative design and development from concept to production. Specialize in working with small and startup companies.*
Markets:	*Menswear, Womenswear & Childrenswear.*

REST IN BEAUTY, INC.

771 Bridge Street
Bamberg, SC 29003
Teresa Dansby
(1) (803) 245 5126   Fax: (1) (803) 245 5665

E-Mail:	*restinbeauty@bellsouth.net*
Web Site:	*www.restinbeauty.com*
Description:	*Design & manufacturers of ladies burial garments. Dresses, gowns, accessories, hankies, slippers and gloves.*
Categories:	*Accessories, Miscellaneous.*
Specialties:	*Design, engineering, cutting room & sourcing available. Quick delivery.*
Markets:	*Womenswear, Accessories.*
Machinery:	*Single needle, double needle, sergers, zig-zag & cover stitch machinery.*
Packages:	*Sewing & CMT.*
Minimums:	*250 pieces/style*

WORLD SOURCE

224 West 35th Street
New York, NY 10001
Alan Novie/Jack Mann
(1) (212) 594 9129   Fax: (1) (212) 202 5298

E-Mail:	*info@worldsourcenyc.com*
Description:	*All types of apparel production services.*
Year Est:	*1993*
Categories:	*Production Sourcing/Factory Agent, Leather/Suede, Coats/Jackets*
Specialties:	*Specialize in leather and suede outerwear, embellished, embroidered and lace dresses and blouses.*
Markets:	*Menswear & Womenswear.*
Packages:	*Complete*
Factory Locals:	*China and India*
Production Capacity:	*Leather garments: 200 pcs/month per style/color, Sequin Dresses: 150 pcs/month, Blouses: 300 pcs/month.*

info@fashiondex.com © The Fashiondex, Inc.

5 KIDS EMBROIDERY GROUP LLC

37 Highway 35
Neptune City, NJ 07753
Phil Miller
(1) (732) 774 5331   Fax: (1) (732) 774 3311

E-Mail:	*philm@5kidsembroidery.com*
Web Site:	*www.5kidsembroidery.com*
Description:	*Multi head embroidery. Domestic.*
Specialties:	*First samples. Digitizing. Overseas sourcing of all promotional products.*
Markets:	*Cater to all production runs of all sizes.*

A PROMOS USA DBA THE IMAGEMAKER & AARROW PROMOTIONS

143 East Merrick Road
Freeport, NY 11520
Mindy Younger
(1) (516) 377 0186   Fax: (1) (516) 377 0198

E-Mail:	*sales@imagemakerus.com*
Web Site:	*www.apromosusa.com*
Description:	*Screenprinted custom t-shirts, embroidery and promotional items. All work done in-house.*
Year Est:	*1990*
Categories:	*Screenprinting*
Specialties:	*Embroidery on polo shirts, golf shirts, t-shirts, sweaters, hats/caps. Oversized printing, specialty inks, 3D embroidery.*
Markets:	*Menswear, Womenswear, Childrenswear.*
Machinery:	*Automated presses*
Production Capacity:	*T-shirts: 15,000/day*

AA WORLD CLASS EMBROIDERY & EMBELLISHMENT CO.

450 Murray Hill Parkway
East Rutherford, NJ 07073
Ben Amoruso
(1) (201) 313 0022   Fax: (1) (201) 313 0044

E-Mail:	*bena@aaworld.com*
Web Site:	*www.aaworld.com*
Description:	*Toll-free: 1-800-526-0411. Contractor expert with all types of new embroidery & embellishments.*
Year Est:	*1986*
Exporting Since:	*1990*
Specialties:	*Loloft embroidery, PVC, hi-resolution transfers, appliques,, novelties & many exciting processes. Any design can be made.*
Markets:	*Menswear, Womenswear, Childrenswear, Accessories.*
Export to:	*Worldwide*
Minimums:	*250-1,000/style per size*
Production Capacity:	*Unlimited*

ALL AMERICAN EMBROIDERY

2228 Noblestown Road
Pittsburg, PA 15205
Lou Fani
(1) (412) 922 8999   Fax: (1) (412) 922 7712

E-Mail:	*aae2000@aol.com*
Description:	*Contract embroidery work on finished garments or pieces, plus sweatshirts, hats, tees, etc.*
Year Est:	*1980*
Specialties:	*Applique embroidery*
Markets:	*Menswear, Womenswear, Childrenswear, Accessories.*
Minimums:	*4 dozen/style*
Factory Locals:	*Two plants in the Pittsburg area.*
Production Capacity:	*600 dozen/week*

ALL U, INC.

9 Interstate Avenue
Albany, NY 12205
Tina Benson
(1) (518) 438 2558   Fax: (1) (518) 438 7282

E-Mail:	*sales@allu.com*
Web Site:	*www.allu.com*
Description:	*Quality custom screenprinting and embroidery.*
Year Est:	*1986*
Categories:	*Screenprinting*
Specialties:	*Our in-house digitizing allows us to reproduce even the most demanding designs quickly and accurately.*
Machinery:	*8 color and two 12 color automatic presses, and 6 color and 2 color manual presses for screenprinting.*

ARTEX KNITTING MILLS INC.

300 Harvard Avenue
Westville, NJ 08093
Jill Ann Bal
(1) (856) 456 2800   Fax: (1) (856) 456 4111

E-Mail:	*sales@artexknit.com*
Web Site:	*www.artexknit.com*
Description:	*Knitting contractor of hats, leg warmers, gloves, men's ties and more.*
Year Est:	*1926*
Categories:	*Sweaters/Knitwear, Accessories*
Specialties:	*Specialize in custom knitted accessories, embroidery and custom color.*
Machinery:	*Knitting, embroidery and sewing machines. Production done in-house.*
Minimums:	*None*
Factory Locals:	*Above*
Production Capacity:	*100,000 doz/month*

ARTWEAR EMBROIDERY, INC.
621 A Indeneer Drive
Kernersville, NC 27284
Cindy Cox Wilson
(1) (336) 992 2166   Fax: (1) (336) 992 2167

E-Mail:	*artwear@artwearinc.com*
Web Site:	*www.artwearinc.com*
Description:	*High quality embroidery contractor. On time, every time.*
Year Est:	*1992*
Exporting Since:	*1994*
Specialties:	*Embroidery, applique, names personalization & multi-media applications on any type of apparel, piece goods or cut pieces.*
Machinery:	*51 Tajima embroidery heads, Pulse signature digitizing equipment.*
Export to:	*England*
Minimums:	*48 pieces/style*
Factory Locals:	*Kernersville, NC*
Production Capacity:	*100,000 pieces/month*

BLANKET BOSS
87 Windermere Avenue
Greenwood Lake, NY 10925
Barney Lopilato
(1) (845) 477 4774

E-Mail:	*blanketboss@aol.com*
Web Site:	*www.theblanketboss.com*
Description:	*Embroidery and silk screening on tee shirts and polo shirts.*
Categories:	*Sweaters/Knitwear, Embroidery*
Markets:	*Mens, womens & childrens*
Minimums:	*None*

BONNAZ EMBROIDERY CO.
6000 Adams Street
West New York, NJ 07093
Alex Faraj
(1) (201) 552 94 94

E-Mail:	*embroideryusa@msn.com*
Description:	*Embroidery contract work. Also do theatrical custom embroidery.*
Year Est:	*1983*
Markets:	*Designer & couture markets.*
Machinery:	*10 Cornely embroidery machines, 2 Tajima multi-head, 10 fancy stitching machines.*
Minimums:	*Sample & small production lot capabilities.*
Production Capacity:	*1,000 pcs/month*

BRANDED EMBLEM
7920 Foster
Overland Park, KS 66024
Danny
(1) (913) 648 7920   Fax: (1) (913) 648 7444

E-Mail:	*dannys@campdavid.com*

Web Site:	*www.campdavid.com*
Description:	*Toll free:#1-800-747-7920. Contract embroidery, embroidered emblems, appliques & imported woven labels.*
Year Est:	*1969*
Exporting Since:	*1997*
Specialties:	*Laser cut, heat seal embroidered emblems & appliques for the direct embroidery look.*
Minimums:	*50 pieces/style*

CAROLACE EMBROIDERY CO., INC.

450 Murray Hill Parkway
East Rutherford, NJ 07073
Howard Mann
(1) (201) 945 2151   Fax: (1) (201) 943 1990

E-Mail:	*info@carolace.com*
Web Site:	*www.carolace.com*
Description:	*Contract embroiderer.*
Specialties:	*Custom embroideries, embroidered nets, novelties & Schiffli laces. Cater to all price points.*
Markets:	*Lingerie, blouse & childrens markets.*
Minimums:	*Low*

CREATIVE EMBROIDERY CORP.

305 Third Avenue
Newark, NJ 07107
Steven Diamond
(1) (973) 497 5700   Fax: (1) (973) 497 5520

E-Mail:	*sdiam43091@aol.com*
Description:	*Contract embroidery, appliques & decorative embroidery. Cut pieces or finished garments.*
Categories:	*Embroidery*
Markets:	*All apparel markets & all price points.*
Minimums:	*None*

CROOKED BROOK

901 Broad Street
Utica, NY 13501
Ray
(1) (315) 733 1992   Fax: (1) (315) 292 1901

E-Mail:	*info@crookedbrook.com*
Web Site:	*www.crookedbrook.com*
Description:	*Apparel & design & reproduction studio offering knit & woven pattern making from spec sheets or renderings, samples.*
Categories:	*Sample Rooms/Small Production*
Specialties:	*Small lot production for men's, women's & children's sportswear. Custom embroidery, applique and tackle twill.*
Machinery:	*Juki Straight Stitch, Juki Serge, Reece Key Hole, Singer Straight Button Hole, Kansai Coverstitch, Juki Feed Off the Arm, Melco EMT 10 Em broidery Machine*
Minimums:	*None*

CUSTOM CHENILLE EMBROIDERY

11330 Hillguard
Dallas, TX 75243
Ken Gilmer, President
(1) (214) 343 0888   Fax: (1) (214) 349 8884

E-Mail:	*kgilmer@chenille.com*
Web Site:	*www.chenille.com*
Description:	*1-800-227-2040. Garment decoration, including traditional chenille embroidery appliques & emblems on any type of apparel.*
Specialties:	*Sportswear & uniform decoration .*
Markets:	*Menswear, Womenswear, Childrenswear & Home.*
Machinery:	*80 embroidery, 80 chenille embroidery machines.*
Minimums:	*12 dozen/style*
Production Capacity:	*600,000 units/month*

ELEGANT EMBROIDERY/MELON INK SCREEN PRINT

100 B Oakwood Road
Lake Zurich, IL 60047
Nancy Needham
(1) (847) 540 8003   Fax: (1) (847) 540 8477

E-Mail:	*nancy@elegantembroidery.com*
Web Site:	*www.elegantembroidery.com*
Description:	*Custom embroidery & screen printing.*
Year Est:	*1995*
Specialties:	*Specialize in embroidery & screen printing on towels, linens, table linens & outerwear.*
Markets:	*Accessories, Home Furnishings.*
Machinery:	*SWF four-head, 2 SWF single-head embroidery machines. (2) 6 Color & 6 Station Screen Print, one automatic, one manual heat transfer presses, rhinestone.*
Minimums:	*None*

EMBROIDERED CORPORATE IMAGE

10318 North U.S. Highway 95
Hayden Lake, ID 83835
Robert Allen, Owner
(1) (208) 772 4044   Fax: (1) (208) 772 4723

E-Mail:	*rla@eci-embroidery.com*
Web Site:	*www.eci-embroidery.com*
Description:	*High quality, high speed contract embroidery for all apparel & accessory markets.*
Year Est:	*1989*
Specialties:	*Embroidery on accessories, jackets, caps, polos, sweats & athletic wear.*
Markets:	*All*
Machinery:	*Operate Tajima, Barudan & Melco equipment 24 hours a day & 7 days a week.*
Minimums:	*Vary*
Factory Locals:	*1-800-858-4044*

EMBROIDERY CONCEPTS

231 South College Street
Washington, PA 15301
Kevin Booth
(1) 724 225 3644   Fax: (1) 724 225 3609

E-Mail:	*kevin@1clickshirts.com*
Web Site:	*www.1clickshirts.com*
Description:	*One stop source for embroidering your corporate apparel, business logos, and team wear on tee shirts, denim shirts, jackets & hats.*
Specialties:	*Specialize in computerized embroidery.*
Markets:	*Menswear, Womenswear & Childrenswear.*
Machinery:	*10 Brother Machines*
Production Capacity:	*4,000/pcs.*

EMBROIDERY ONE CORPORATION

1359 Channing Street
Los Angeles, CA 90021

(1) (213) 572 0280   Fax: (1) (213) 572 0283

E-Mail:	*emb1@pacbell.net*
Web Site:	*www.embroidery-one.com*
Description:	*Embroidery and screenprinting contractor.*
Specialties:	*Fast turnaround, high quality, reliable and committed to excellence.*

EXPLOSION SPORTSWEAR/ IMAGE SOURCE

4814 South 35th Street
Phoenix, AZ 85040

(1) (602) 243 2728   Fax: (1) (602) 276 4315

E-Mail:	*info@explosionsportswear.com*
Web Site:	*www.explosionsportswear.com*
Year Est:	*1998*
Categories:	*Screenprinting*
Specialties:	*One stop shop for all apparel, screenprint, embroidery and promotional needs.*
Markets:	*Menswear, Womenswear, Childrenswear, Infants, Accessories.*
Machinery:	*90+ Tajima & Brother machines in factory; plus subcontract and overseas. Also, embroidery, laundering, washing, printing & screenprinting equipment.*
Packages:	*CMT & sewing, finishing & packing.*
Minimums:	*36 pieces/style*

FIBERLOK, INC.

811 Stockton Avenue
Fort Collins, CO 80522
Brown Abrams
(1) (970) 221 1200   Fax: (1) (970) 221 0200

E-Mail:	*info@fiberlok.com*
Web Site:	*www.fiberlok.com*
Description:	*Exclusive sew-on or heat applied Lextra® and TackleKnit™ and ChromaFlex® Graphics.*

Specialties:	Distribution limited to select-up market brands and partners, ChromaFlex brand metallized and die-formed graphics.
Markets:	All apparel & uniform markets.
Machinery:	5 - Lextra, 6 TackleKnit, 8 ChromaFlex
Export to:	Europe, Asia, Latin America
Production Capacity:	7 million units/month

GIMASPORT

241 Ledyard Street
Hartford, CT 06114
Roberto S. Giansiracusa
(1) (860) 296 4441 Fax: (1) (860) 296 8423

E-Mail:	sales@gimasport.com
Web Site:	www.gimasport.com
Description:	Custom embroidery on hats, jackets, tee shirts, polos, bags etc. Fulfillment services.
Year Est:	1992
Categories:	Screenprinting
Specialties:	Quality, delivery and attention to detail are our specialties.
Machinery:	55 Barudan Embroidery Multi-head.
Packages:	All work done in house.
Factory Locals:	25,000 sq. ft. building in Hartford, CT.
Production Capacity:	75,000 pcs/month

HAMILTON EMBROIDERY CO.

907-909 21st Street
Union City, NJ 07087
Frank Blaso
(1) (201) 867 4084 Fax: (1) (201) 867 2066

E-Mail:	fblaso@cs.com
Description:	Schiffli embroidery contract work on customer's fabrics or ours.
Year Est:	1935
Specialties:	We can do custom designs & have an extensive library of existing designs.
Markets:	All apparel, accessory & home markets.
Machinery:	10 Schiffli machines, 10 Saurer, 1 Epoca plus sample machine.
Export to:	China 65%, Turkey 5%
Production Capacity:	5,000 yds/day

HENDERSON ADVERTIZING

2508 East Cook Street
Springfield, IL 62703
Leon Henderson
(1) (217) 544 9419 Fax: (1) (217) 522 8155

E-Mail:	hendersonart@ameritech.net
Web Site:	www.henderson-advertising.com
Description:	We provide a variety of custom embroidery, embossing, or silk-screening to help you create your product.
Categories:	Screenprinting
Specialties:	A large selection of promotional products. Custom shirts, hats, jackets,

            sportswear, aprons.

Markets:	*Menswear, Womenswear, Childrens & Accessories.*

JOCASSEE DESIGNS INC.
311 Tucapau Road
Duncan, SC 29334
Julie Edwards
(1) (864) 433 1113   Fax: (1) (864) 433 1204

E-Mail:	*julie@jocasseedesigns.com*
Web Site:	*www.jocasseedesigns.com*
Description:	*Embroidery contractor*
Year Est:	*1985*
Specialties:	*Custom embroidery on piece or finished goods.*
Markets:	*All*
Machinery:	*In-house digitizing, 452 embroidery heads & a complete packing line.*

JUST JEN
23510 Telo Avenue
Torrance, CA 90505
Lawrence Smith/Jennifer Smith
(1) 310 539 6000   Fax: (1) 323 903 0308

E-Mail:	*jennifer@justjen.com*
Web Site:	*www.justjen.com*
Description:	*Rhinestone setter plus embroidery decoration. Designs on t-shirts can be made with a combo of embroidery and Swarovski crystal.*
Categories:	*Trim Application*
Specialties:	*Wholesale rhinestone t-shirt orders from retailers, organizations and individuals. We also do embroidery decoration.*
Markets:	*Menswear, Womenswear, Childrens/Infantwear.*
Minimums:	*None*

LATITUDES
2425 NE Riverside Way
Portland, OR 97211

(1) (503) 248 2060   Fax: (1) (503) 248 2134

E-Mail:	*info@latitudespdx.com*
Web Site:	*www.latitudespdx.com*
Description:	*Custom screen printing, embroidery, design, promotional products. We can accommodate all your design needs from concept to production.*
Categories:	*Screen Printing*
Specialties:	*Other services provided - tagging, UPC bar coding, folding, poly-bagging, boxing, palletizing, full service shipping worldwide.*
Markets:	*Menswear, Womenswear, Childrens, Accessories.*
Machinery:	*Embroidery: 15 head Tajima, 6 head Tajima, 1 head Melco*
Packages:	*Full Package Programs including private label product.*
Factory Locals:	*In-house*
Production Capacity:	*150,000 prints/weekly*

MOONLITE GRAPHICS CO., INC.

951 Broadway
Fall River, MA 02724
Bill Boudreau
(1) (508) 676 6674   Fax: (1) (508) 679 8128

E-Mail:	*moonlite79@verizon.net*
Description:	*Embroidery on all types of apparel plus screenprinting.*
Year Est:	*1979*
Categories:	*Screenprinting*
Specialties:	*In-house graphics. Four-color process, cut part printing, familiar with hi-tech fabrics & large volume.*
Markets:	*All apparel markets & all price points.*
Machinery:	*2 automatics & 6 manuals*
Factory Locals:	*14,000 sq. ft. facility*

OREGON SCREEN IMPRESSIONS

3580 NE Broadway
Portland, OR 97232

(1) (503) 231 0181   Fax: (1) (503) 231 9756

E-Mail:	*tiffanyf@oregonscreen.com*
Web Site:	*www.oregonscreen.com*
Description:	*Excellence in screenprinting and embroidery. We offer a broad range of garments - tees, sweats, polos, dress shirts, jackets & bags.*
Categories:	*Screenprinting*
Specialties:	*We also provide the following services: labeling, hang tags, packaging, fulfillment services, shipping.*
Markets:	*Menswear, Womenswear, Childrens, Accessories.*
Minimums:	*Screen Printing 24 pcs, Embroidery 12 pcs.*
Factory Locals:	*Our factory is in Oregon but we assist customers throughout the US*

PENN & FLETCHER, INC.

21-07 41st Avenue
Long Island City, NY 11101
Ernie Smith
(1) (212) 239 6868   Fax: (1) (212) 239 6914

E-Mail:	*pennandfletcher@aol.com*
Web Site:	*www.pennandfletcher.com*
Description:	*Contractor of custom embroideries by hand or by machine.*
Year Est:	*1986*
Markets:	*Higher-end manufacturers.*
Minimums:	*None. Small & large production lots & samples.*
Production Capacity:	*Modest*

QUINTIN CO.
2630 Humboldt Street
Los Angeles, CA 90031

(1) (323) 221 9202   Fax: (1) (323) 221 7304

E-Mail:	*info@quintinco.com*
Web Site:	*www.quintinco.com*
Description:	*Apply embroidery on a wide variety of garments from our custom hats to personalized polos.*
Categories:	*Accessories, Screenprinting*
Specialties:	*We do all digitizing in house. Traditional single color, multi-color, and applique.*
Markets:	*Menswear & Womenswear, Childrenswear, Infants*
Machinery:	*Large plant with wide variety of machinery.*

ROYAL APPAREL INC.
See our ad on page 9, 113, 129

65 Commerce Street
Hauppauge, NY 11788
Morey Mayeri
(1) (631) 213 8299   Fax: (1) (631) 922 8438

E-Mail:	*sales@royalapparel.net*
Web Site:	*www.royalapparel.net*
Description:	*Embroidery & screen printing contract work.*
Year Est:	*1993*
Exporting Since:	*1993*
Categories:	*Tee Shirts, Sportswear-Knits, Activewear/Athleticwear, Childrenswear, Cutting/Fusing*
Specialties:	*Simple text or complex multi-color artwork.*
Markets:	*Menswear, Womenswear & Childrenswear.*
Packages:	*Full service, complete packages.*
Export to:	*Canada & Europe*
Minimums:	*100 dozen per size/per color*

SEMEL'S EMBROIDERY, INC.
1078 Route 46 West
Clifton, NJ 07013
Dolly Semel
(1) (973) 473 3959   Fax: (1) (973) 473 8895

E-Mail:	*embroideri@aol.com*
Web Site:	*www.semelsembroidery.com*
Description:	*Multi-head embroidery contractor.*
Year Est:	*1935*
Exporting Since:	*1990*
Categories:	*Embroidery, Screenprinting Contractors.*
Specialties:	*Same day samples & on-demand delivery. Screen applique, chenille embroidery & bonnaz vintage embroidery.*
Minimums:	*Low. small & large runs okay. Also, do samples.*

SQUEEGEE PRINTERS

4067 VT Route 102
Canaan, VT 05903
Pat Beauregard
(1) (802) 266 3426   Fax: (1) (802) 266 3654

E-Mail:	*squeegee@together.net*
Description:	*Toll-free: 1-800-962-0252. Cater to corporate, special events, advertising specialties & resortwear.*
Year Est:	*1984*
Categories:	*Embroidery, Screenprinting Contractors*
Specialties:	*Full service contract embroiderer. Up to 9 colors.*
Machinery:	*M & R Challenger 8-color & M & R Gauntlet II 10-color. 2 Automatic press, 1 14-head embroidery machine.*
Minimums:	*12 dozen*
Production Capacity:	*Screenprinting: 350 units/hour, Embroidery: Varies*

STAR EMBROIDERY

305 3rd Avenue West
Newark, NJ 07107
Dean Ganet
(1) (973) 481 4300   Fax: (1) (973) 481 1267

E-Mail:	*dwiley921@gmail.com*
Web Site:	*www.star-embroidery.com*
Description:	*Embroidered promotional apparel, printed custom clothing, custom tee shirts, custom polo shirts, embroidered towels.*
Specialties:	*Embroidered sportswear, outerwear, team wear, bags & accessories.*
Markets:	*Menswear, Womenswear, Childrenswear & Home.*
Minimums:	*Low*

STITCH DESIGNERS

1601 Crums Lane
Louisville, KY 40216
John Home
(1) (502) 637 8619

E-Mail:	*marketing@dbswebsite.com*
Web Site:	*www.stitchdesigners.com*
Description:	*Premier contract embroiderer in the United States.*
Specialties:	*Full range of embroidery services to promotional products distributors & various other resellers of embroidered goods.*

STUCKI EMBROIDERY

Box 185, Route 28
Boiceville, NY 12412
Murray Fenwick
(1) (845) 657 2308   Fax: (1) (845) 657 2860

E-Mail:	*mail@stuckiembroidery.com*
Web Site:	*www.stuckiembroidery.com*
Description:	*Custom embroidery and screenprinting.*
Specialties:	*Expert with embroidered trims, edges, all-overs, emblems & specialty motifs, ie: animals.*
Machinery:	*10 Swiss embroidery looms in house.*

Minimums:	*20 yds.*
Factory Locals:	*Plants in Boiceville, NY & Fairview, NJ.*

TODD RUTKIN

5801 South Alameda Street
Los Angeles, CA 90001
Abe Garcia
(1) (323) 584 9225   Fax: (1) (323) 584 9295

E-Mail:	*jan@toddrutkin.com*
Web Site:	*www.toddrutkin.com*
Description:	*A complete source for cutting, fusing, grading, marking, slitting & embroidery.*
Categories:	*Cutting & Fusing, Grading & Marking*
Machinery:	*Tajima machinery*

TOUCH OF LACE, INC.

333 Bergen Boulevard
Fairview, NJ 07022
Marvin Greenburg/Gabriel Sasson
(1) (201) 943 1082   Fax: (1) (201) 943 7163

E-Mail:	*sales@touchoflace.com*
Web Site:	*www.touchoflace.com*
Description:	*1-800-742-7506. Schiffli embroidery on various fabrics & puckered all-overs.*
Specialties:	*Custom designs.*
Markets:	*Children's, intimate apparel, bridal, dress & sportswear.*

USA BEADING/FARAJ INC.

422 Cliff Street
Fairview, NJ 07022
Zackary Faraj, President
(1) (201) 313 4480   Fax: (1) (201) 313 4485

E-Mail:	*farajinc@aol.com*
Web Site:	*www.farajinc.com*
Description:	*Manual & automatic bonnaz embroidery, embellishment, trims & beading (www.usabeading.com).*
Specialties:	*Specialize in bonnaz embroidery, laser cutting, caviar beads, glitter, rhinestones, trims & beading.*

WEBER & DOEBRICH

119 61st Street
West New York, NJ 07093
Jane Zellweger
(1) (201) 867 1540   Fax: (1) (201) 854 5564

E-Mail:	*wedoembroidery@gmail.com*
Description:	*Schiffli & multi-head embroideries.*
Markets:	*Lingerie, Seventh Avenue & home furnishing trades.*
Minimums:	*None*

WINGOLD EMBROIDERY LLC

5 Monarch Lane
Freehold, NJ 07728
Thomas Figliolino
(1) (201) 945 2727

E-Mail:	*tfigliolino@aol.com*
Web Site:	*www.wingoldembroidery.com*
Description:	*Schiffli embroidery.*
Specialties:	*Domestic & overseas production from China.*
Markets:	*Apparel, lingerie, intimate apparel & home furnishings.*
Minimums:	*Varies*

YOONIMEX INC. DBA/U.S. EMBROIDERY

13953 Valley View Avenue
La Mirada, CA 90638
Edward Yoon, President
(1) (562) 906 2100   Fax: (1) (562) 906 2330

E-Mail:	*info@us-embroidery.com*
Web Site:	*www.us-embroidery.com*
Description:	*Embroidery and applique on finished garment or cut pieces. Best creative & experienced in-house digitizers in the industry.*
Specialties:	*Quick turnaround. Custom patches, embroidered patches & heat seal patches available.*
Machinery:	*1,000 heads*
Factory Locals:	*25,000 sq. ft. plant in Santa Fe Springs, CA.*
Production Capacity:	*400,000 pcs/month*

info@fashiondex.com © The Fashiondex, Inc.

AIKEN INDUSTRIES, INC.

1910 Richland Avenue
Aiken, SC 29801
Sarah Friedman/Cary Friedman
(1) (803) 648 5467   Fax: (1) (803) 648 5469

E-Mail:	*carysarah@aol.com*
Web Site:	*www.aikenind.com*
Description:	*Contractor of duvets, sheets, pillows and pillowcases. Expert with knit & woven fabrications.*
Year Est:	*1962*
Categories:	*Pants/Shorts/Skirts*
Markets:	*Home Furnishings*
Packages:	*Cutting & Sewing, Complete & CMT packages available.*
Minimums:	*100 dozen/style*
Factory Locals:	*Aiken factory also has a controlled environment cleanroom for assembly of sewn & non-sewn health care products.*
Production Capacity:	*10,000 pcs/month*

BJ CON-SEW

321 Industrial Park Avenue
Asheboro, NC 27205
Barbara/Jerry Trotter
(1) (336) 629 4550   Fax: (1) (336) 629 2078

E-Mail:	*bjconsew@triadbiz.rr.com*
Web Site:	*www.bjconsew.com*
Description:	*Services include cutting and sewing, slitting, product development, and pattern design.*
Year Est:	*1992*
Specialties:	*Specialize in bedding and pillows. ISO 9001 certified.*
Markets:	*Home Furnishings.*

GENESIS IMPORTS

2408 Royal Lytham Drive
Austin, TX 64500
Art Kimbel
(1) (512) 292 4000   Fax: (1) (512) 292 4515

E-Mail:	*akimbel@aol.com*
Web Site:	*www.genesismexico.com*
Description:	*Cut & sew contractors of aprons, napkins, pillowcases & laundry bags.*
Year Est:	*1993*
Exporting Since:	*1995*
Categories:	*Uniforms, Accessories*
Machinery:	*160 sewing machines. Single needle, overlocking, double needle, bar tack, flat safety stitch, button, buttonholers & cutting knives, plus 2 20-ton die cut presses & 2 50-foot cutting tables.*
Export to:	*USA & Canada.*
Minimums:	*None*
Factory Locals:	*Promotora Genesis in Monterrey, Mexico. Two locations with over 30,000 sq ft. Registered with the FDA in USA.*

HARRIS PILLOW SUPPLY INC.

3026 Trask Parkway
Beaufort, SC 29906
John Harris
(1) 800 845 8240   Fax: (1) 843 846 4196

E-Mail:	*john@harrispillow.com*
Web Site:	*www.harrispillow.com*
Description:	*Contractor & manufacturer specializing in pillows. Quick turn-around.*
Year Est:	*1958*
Exporting Since:	*1980*
Specialties:	*Feather & down pillows & synthetic down (Comforel) pillows.*
Markets:	*Home Furnishings*
Machinery:	*Sewing, spreading, custom built pillow blower & pillow filling machines in house.*
Packages:	*Full packages available.*
Export to:	*Canada 3%, Europe 2%*
Minimums:	*None*
Production Capacity:	*20,000 pcs/month*

HOSPI-TEL MANUFACTURING COMPANY

545 North Arlington Avenue
East Orange, NJ 07017

(1) (973) 678 7100   Fax: (1) (973) 678 1482

E-Mail:	*info@hospitel.com*
Web Site:	*www.hospitel.com*
Description:	*Manufacturer/contractor of Safe-t-top shower curtains, drapery treatments, bedspreads, window curtains & vertical blinds.*

INTEDGE INDUSTRIES INC.

1875 Chumley Road
Woodruff, SC 29388

(1) (864) 969 9601   Fax: (1) (864) 969 9604

E-Mail:	*sales@intedge.com*
Web Site:	*www.intedge.com*
Description:	*Contractor of sewn kitchen products.*
Year Est:	*1914*
Categories:	*Uniforms, Home Furnishings.*
Markets:	*Mainly restaurant industry, but open to more.*
Machinery:	*3 overlock, 10 single needle, 1 double needle, 1 bartack, 2 buttonhole, & multi-needle quilting machinery.*
Packages:	*Sewing*
Export to:	*Canada 10%, Puerto Rico 2%*
Minimums:	*None*

L.S.W. CUTTING & SEWING SERVICE

670 Ninth Street
Oakland, CA 94607
Lana Wong
(1) (510) 891 9246

E-Mail:	*lswcuttingandsewing@hotmail.com*
Description:	*Contractor of all types of bedding, bedding accessories, draperies & curtains.*
Specialties:	*Complete patternmaking services.*
Packages:	*Full service, CMT & complete packages.*
Minimums:	*300 units/style*
Production Capacity:	*30,000 pcs/month*

LACORP/LEBANON APPAREL CORP.

70 Thornhill Drive
Lebanon, VA 24266
Jeoff Bodenhorst
(1) (276) 889 3656   Fax: (1) (276) 889 2830

E-Mail:	*jeoff@lacorpusa.com*
Web Site:	*www.lacorpusa.com*
Description:	*Contractor of home furnishings.*
Year Est:	*1968*
Categories:	*Pants/shorts/skirts, Childrenswear, Uniforms, Rework & Inspection Services.*
Specialties:	*Specialize in mattress zipper covers, pillows, pillow covers & bedding accessories.*
Markets:	*Menswear, Womenswear, Childrenswear & Home.*
Machinery:	*Over 500 various sewing machines & electronic cutting, embroidery & besum pocket equipment on site.*
Packages:	*CMT, Sewing, Cutting, Sample Making & Embroidery.*
Minimums:	*Will adjust to fit your needs.*
Factory Locals:	*All work is done in-house.*

RAYLON CORPORATION

267 Fifth Avenue
New York, New York 10016
Jay Pollak
(1) (212) 221 3633   Fax: (1) (212) 889 3283

E-Mail:	*jpollak@rayloncorp.com*
Description:	*Full package contractor/factory agent & textile converter. Home products ranging from bedding to shower curtains & window.*
Year Est:	*1948*
Categories:	*Production Sourcing/Factory Agent, Pants/Shorts, Rainwear/Outerwear.*
Markets:	*Menswear, Womenswear, Boyswear, Girlswear.*
Minimums:	*500-1,000 pcs/style*
Factory Locals:	*Asia*

Notes

info@fashiondex.com © The Fashiondex, Inc.

A&S CLOTHING

1130 Ada Street, Suite C
Blue Ridge, GA 30513
Salma Adam
(1) (706) 632 2133   Fax: (1) (706) 632 8638

E-Mail:	*asclothing@tds.net*
Description:	*Sewing contractor of mens and womens jeans & chinos.*
Year Est:	*1989*
Categories:	*Pants/Shorts/Skirts*
Markets:	*Menswear & Womenswear.*
Machinery:	*12 straight needle, 8 double needle, 7 serger, 2 bander, 1 auto belt loop, 2 waistband end u-tack, 2 bar tacker, 1 zig-zag, 1 auto label sewer, 1 monogram, 2 belt loop maker, 1 heat sealer, 2 needle chain stitch, 2 felling, 2 bulldog hem, 1 rivet, 4 walking foot*
Packages:	*CMT packaages.*
Factory Locals:	*Our 20,000 sq ft facility is equipped with a warehouse and loading dock.*
Production Capacity:	*20,000 units/monthly*

ALL AMERICAN WASH CO.

2932 East 11th Street
Los Angeles, CA 90023
Alex Kahen
(1) (323) 265 2626   Fax: (1) (323) 265 3307

E-Mail:	*alexkahen@allamericanwashco.com*
Description:	*Cut and sew contractor of jeans, denim skirts, denim jackets and tee shirts.*
Categories:	*Laundry/Wash Contractor, Dyeing Contractor, Small Production/Sample Room,*
Specialties:	*Premimum denim wash and garment dyeing. All work is done in house.*
Markets:	*Menswear, Womenswear, Childrenswear.*
Packages:	*Complete & CMT packaging available.*
Minimums:	*Low*

COLLECTIVE APPAREL

750 East Gage Avenue
Los Angeles, CA 90001
Don Valenzuela
(1) 310 770 1093   Fax: (1) 323 750 5010

E-Mail:	*contact@collectiveapparel.us*
Web Site:	*www.collectiveapparel.us*
Description:	*One stop. We design, sketch, prepare patterns, do samples and production.*
Year Est:	*2009*
Categories:	*Pants/Shorts/Skirts, Laundry/Washing*
Specialties:	*We specialize in new and innovative wash techniques as well as organic wash and dye processes.*
Markets:	*Menswear, Womenswear, Childrenswear.*
Packages:	*Full packages - premium denim, tops & knits.*
Production Capacity:	*48,000 pcs/month*

ROOCHI TRADERS INC.

6393 East Washington Blvd
City of Commerce, CA 90040
Mickey Sachdeva
(1) (323) 722 5592   Fax: (1) (323) 724 0045

E-Mail:	*mickey@roochi.com*
Web Site:	*www.cottonheritage.com*
Description:	*Over 25+ years of sportswear and activewear sourcing for men, women and children, also junior knits.*
Categories:	*Production Sourcing/Factory Agent, Tee Shirts/Sweat Shirts, Outerwear, Polo Shirts*
Specialties:	*We stock blank inventory in our DC's NJ, FL and CA for at once delivery.*
Markets:	*Menswear, Womenswear & Childrenswear.*
Export to:	*Europe, Mexico, Central America, Canada*
Production Capacity:	*100,000 doz/month + per category*

ROUND HOUSE MANUFACTURING

One American Way
Shawnee, OK 74801
Jim Antosh
(1) (405) 273 0510   Fax: (1) (405) 273 0511

E-Mail:	*info@round-house.com*
Web Site:	*www.round-house.com*
Description:	*Contractor specializing in bib overalls.*
Categories:	*Jeans/Denimwear, Uniforms.*
Specialties:	*All work is produced in the USA.*
Packages:	*CMT & complete packages. Cutting room in house.*
Minimums:	*50 dozen/style*

SKY BLUE SEWING

960 Mission Street
San Fransicso, CA 94103
Steven
(1) (415) 777 9978   Fax: (1) (415) 777 9938

E-Mail:	*skyblueswg@sbcglobal.net*
Description:	*Private label manufacturer. Provides CMT, sample making, hand pressing, tagging, poly bagging and packing.*
Year Est:	*1988*
Categories:	*Sample Rooms/Small Production*
Specialties:	*Specialize in the cutting and sewing of denim, and other medium and heavy weight woven fabrics.*
Markets:	*Menswear, Womenswear & Childrenswear.*
Machinery:	*Electric cutting knife, keyhole, automatic belt loop, hemming, side seam serger, open seam press.*
Packages:	*CMT & private label.*
Production Capacity:	*20,000-30,000 units/month (basic five pocket jeans)*

TRINITY SPORTS INC.

2067 East 55th Street
Vernon, CA 90058
Kate McHale Jensen
(1) (323) 277 9288   Fax: (1) (323) 277 9883

E-Mail:	*info@trinitysportsinc.com*
Web Site:	*www.trinitysportsinc.com*
Description:	*Jean specialist. Five bottoms jeans, low waist jeans, fray jeans, carpenter plus skirts, shorts.*
Specialties:	*Cut & sew contractor at competitive prices & exceptional quality.*
Markets:	*Menswear, Womenswear & Childrenswear.*
Machinery:	*Automatic back pocket setter, belt loop machine, design machine, label machine, welt pocket, double needele, single needle overlock*
Packages:	*CMT & Full packages available.*

Notes

info@fashiondex.com © The Fashiondex, Inc.

ID4U JACKETS WITH IDENTITY

344 Hostetter Road
Manheim, PA 17545
Daryl Schumacher
(1) 888 968 4348   Fax: (1) 717 644 4397

E-Mail:	*daryl@id4u-jackets.com*
Web Site:	*www.id4u-jackets.com*
Description:	*1-888-968-4348. Full package contractor & manufacturer of custom jackets. Also offer dye sublimation type decoration on shirts & jackets.*
Year Est:	*1991*
Categories:	*Coats/Jackets*
Specialties:	*Specialize in full customization of leather, wool & twill jackets as well as team shirts. Prototypes are offered for a minimal charge.*
Markets:	*Menswear & Womenswear*
Packages:	*CMT, samples, embroidery, screenprinting & dyeing.*
Minimums:	*25 pcs/style*
Factory Locals:	*Pennsylvania & Madras, India.*
Production Capacity:	*Variable. Can fill small & large orders.*

SCHOTT BROTHERS, INC.

1000 Jefferson Avenue
Elizabeth, NJ 07201
Don King
(1) (908) 527 0011   Fax: (1) (908) 527 6185

E-Mail:	*schott@schottnyc.com*
Web Site:	*www.schottnyc.com*
Description:	*Contractor of leather jackets & outerwear.*
Year Est:	*1913*
Exporting Since:	*1970*
Specialties:	*Specialize in flight, bomber & motorcycle jackets.*
Machinery:	*Over 80 single needle, double needle & safety stitch machines. 20 leather cutters in house.*
Packages:	*Cutting & Sewing & CMT.*
Export to:	*Europe, Asia & Middle East.*
Minimums:	*200 pieces/style*

SHURCO MANUFACTURING INC.

4638 North Ravenwood Avenue
Chicago, IL 60640
Seymour Ferdman
(1) (773) 907 8400   Fax: (1) (773) 907 8476

E-Mail:	*sy924@sbcglobal.net*
Description:	*Contractor of apparel items in leather, suede, plastic, vinyl & cloth.*
Year Est:	*1950*
Specialties:	*We provide embossing, embroidery & silk screening. Quick delivery & quick turn-around.*
Markets:	*Accessories*
Machinery:	*Kick-press, 5 die-cutting & 25 sewing machines.*
Packages:	*Cutting & Sewing & CMT.*
Minimums:	*None*
Production Capacity:	*8,000 pcs/month*

STUDIO ONE LEATHER DESIGN INC.

270 West 39th Street
New York, NY 10018
Arthur Cohen
(1) (212) 760 1701   Fax: (1) (212) 760 1702

E-Mail:	arthur@studio1leather.com
Description:	A full service sample room working in the development of men's and women's sportswear and outerwear.
Categories:	Patternmaking, Sample Room/Small Production, Production Sourcing,
Specialties:	Specialize in leather and suede.
Markets:	Menswear, Womenswear
Machinery:	5 sewing machines, buttonhole, fur sewing machine and merrow.
Minimums:	25 pcs/style (leather garments, woven)
Factory Locals:	All work in done in the USA.
Production Capacity:	800-1,000 units/month

TANNERY DIRECT

40 West 37th Street
New York, NY 10018
Anne Sampson
(1) (212) 465 1503   Fax: (1) (212) 465 1512

E-Mail:	asampson@tannerydirect.com
Description:	Offer full garment packages with production in Turkey, China and India and limited production in the United States.
Specialties:	Our New York sample studio takes our customers from patternmaking, fit sessions to final production.
Factory Locals:	Shearling coats/jackets are made in Turkey, leather coats & sportswear & dresses are done in China or India.

WORLD SOURCE

224 West 35th Street
New York, NY 10001
Alan Novie/Jack Mann
(1) (212) 594 9129   Fax: (1) (212) 202 5298

E-Mail:	info@worldsourcenyc.com
Description:	All types of apparel production services.
Year Est:	1993
Categories:	Production Sourcing/Factory Agent, Dresses/Blouses, Coats/Jackets
Specialties:	Specialize in leather and suede outerwear, embellished, embroidered and lace dresses and blouses.
Markets:	Menswear & Womenswear.
Packages:	Complete
Factory Locals:	China and India
Production Capacity:	Leather garments: 200 pcs/month per style/color, Sequin Dresses: 150 pcs/month, Blouses: 300 pcs/month.

AFAP
12000 Slauson Avenue
Santa Fe Springs, CA 90670
Ann Huang
(1) (626) 330 6376

E-Mail:	*sales@afapfashion.com*
Web Site:	*www.afapfashion.com*
Year Est:	*2001*
Specialties:	*Specialize in seamless undergarments and shapewear.*
Markets:	*Womenswear*
Minimums:	*300 dz/style, 150 dz/color*
Production Capacity:	*150,000 units/month*

AMERICAN TEXTILE & APPAREL INC.
10408 W State Road 84
Davie, FL 33324
Luis Mejia
(1) (954) 734 9988   Fax: (1) (954) 734 9966

E-Mail:	*luis.mejia@ata-usa.com*
Web Site:	*www.ata-usa.com*
Description:	*Contractor of knits & woven athletic sportswear, tee shirts, polo shirts and ladies underwear.*
Year Est:	*2002*
Specialties:	*Specialize in private label manufacturing in both knits and woven apparel.*
Markets:	*Womenswear.*
Packages:	*CMT & Full Packages*
Factory Locals:	*Davie Florida plus a network of the best apparel and textile manufacturers from both hemispheres.*
Production Capacity:	*T-Shirts 50,000 doz/month, Polo Shirts 35,000 doz/month, Sportwear 10,000 doz/month, Underwear 100,000 doz/month*

CHESTER LINE CORP.
9820 Bell Ranch Drive
Santa Fe Springs, CA 90670
Soung Kim, Owner
(1) (562) 944 2777   Fax: (1) (562) 944 2233

E-Mail:	*soungkim@chesterline.com*
Web Site:	*www.chesterline.com*
Description:	*Factory group specializing in high quality intimate apparel, lingerie, sleepwear & women's foundation apparel.*
Year Est:	*1999*
Specialties:	*Textile design, new product design, molding & more.*
Markets:	*Womenswear & Girlswear.*
Packages:	*Full packages, patterns, samples, embroidery, beading & more.*
Minimums:	*3,000 units/style, but negotiable*
Factory Locals:	*Shantou & Shenzhen China & Seoul, South Korea*
Production Capacity:	*200,000 pcs/month*

COVILLE INC.

8065-0 North Point Boulevard
Winston-Salem, NC 27106
Kevin Williams
(1) (336) 759 0115   Fax: (1) (336) 759 2229

E-Mail:	*kwilliams@covilleinc.com*
Web Site:	*www.covilleinc.com*
Description:	*Full package cut and sew facility producing thermal underwear, performance underwear, Henleys and nightshirts.*
Specialties:	*Contract services, CMT and knitting of cloth.*

DYNASHAPE INTIMA CORPORATION

2121 Orange Street
Alhambra, CA 91803

(1) (626) 289 8418   Fax: (1) (626) 289 8309

E-Mail:	*stewart@dynashapeintima.com*
Web Site:	*www.dynashapeintima.com*
Description:	*Manufacturer of bras, nursing bras, panties, seamless intimate/ yoga apparel and sleepwear.*
Year Est:	*1984*
Specialties:	*Our design team works closely with our overseas office to produce samples based on the customer's design, concept and budget.*
Markets:	*Womenswear*
Factory Locals:	*Domestic design center, warehouse and showroom. Import from 12 overseas certified factories.*

FASHIONS UNLIMITED, INC.

1100 Wicomico Street
Baltimore, MD 21230
Mary Murphy
(1) (410) 783 1584

E-Mail:	*fashionsu@verizon.net*
Web Site:	*www.fashionsu.net*
Description:	*Contractor of women's innerwear, daywear & body shaping apparel. Patternmaker & sample room on premises.*
Year Est:	*1976*
Categories:	*Active/Athleticwear, Lingerie/Intimate Apparel, Sportswear-Knits, Swimwear/Dancewear.*
Specialties:	*We specialize in seamless development. We have seamless knitting capabilities on Santoni Machines. Bras, tops, pants, underwear, swim.*
Markets:	*Womenswear, Childrenswear*
Machinery:	*Overlock, single needle, coverstitch (1 and 2 needle) zig zag, walking foot machines, flat locks.*
Packages:	*Full service, CMT & complete packages.*
Minimums:	*None*
Factory Locals:	*Baltimore MD, Hellam PA, Charlotte NC (Seamless)*
Production Capacity:	*Swim: 1,000 units/week, Activewear: 1,500 units/week, Dance: 1,500 units/week, Sportswear: 1,000 units/week*

HEMINGWAY APPAREL MFG., INC.

Highway 41 North, P.O. Box 459
Hemingway, SC 29554
Jack Marsh
(1) (843) 558 3482   Fax: (1) (843) 558 9530

E-Mail:	*jmarsh@hemingwayapparel.com*
Web Site:	*www.hemingwayapparel.com*
Description:	*Sewing contractor of ladies panties, intimate apparel & sleepwear.*
Year Est:	*1978*
Specialties:	*Service for product development.*
Markets:	*Womenswear*
Machinery:	*200 overlock, 20 zig-zag, 80 coverstitch, single needle, double needle, multi-needle, all types of hemmers & more.*
Packages:	*Sewing & CMT. Cutting room on premises.*
Minimums:	*1,000 dozen/style*
Production Capacity:	*32,000 dozen/month*

IN.STYLE EXCHANGE™   See our ad on page 75

1844 W. Division Street
Arlington, TX 76012
Sales Manager
(1) (817) 886 9222

E-Mail:	*info@instyleexchange.com*
Web Site:	*www.instyleexchange.com*
Description:	*Full service, 'one-stop-shop' for lingerie, intimate & underwear. Design, patterns, grading/marking, samples & small run production.*
Categories:	*Sample Rooms/Small Production, Production Sourcing, Shirts & Tops, Childrens Wear, Dresses & Blouses, Patternmaking, Sleepwear & Robes.*
Packages:	*Private label & full packages.*
Minimums:	*50 pieces per color per style*
Production Capacity:	*50,000 pcs/month*

LLU INC.

108-28 46th Avenue
Corona, NY 11368
James
(1) (718) 271 3228   Fax: (1) (718) 271 3228

E-Mail:	*lluinc@hotmail.com*
Description:	*Cut and sew contractor of womens underwear, lingerie and bras.*
Year Est:	*1997*
Specialties:	*All work is done in-house.*
Markets:	*Womenswear*
Machinery:	*Sewing machines, needle sewing, horizontal sewing*

A&S CLOTHING
1130 Ada Street, Suite C
Blue Ridge, GA 30513
Salma Adam
(1) (706) 632 2133   Fax: (1) (706) 632 8638

E-Mail:	*asclothing@tds.net*
Description:	*Sewing contractor of mens and womens jeans & chinos.*
Year Est:	*1989*
Categories:	*Jeans/Denimwear*
Markets:	*Menswear & Womenswear.*
Machinery:	*12 straight needle, 8 double needle, 7 serger, 2 bander, 1 auto belt loop, 2 waistband end u-tack, 2 bar tacker, 1 zig-zag, 1 auto label sewer, 1 monogram, 2 belt loop maker, 1 heat sealer, 2 needle chain stitch, 2 felling, 2 bulldog hem, 1 rivet, 4 walking foot*
Packages:	*CMT packaages.*
Factory Locals:	*Our 20,000 sq ft facility is equipped with a warehouse and loading dock.*
Production Capacity:	*20,000 units/monthly*

AIKEN INDUSTRIES, INC.
1910 Richland Avenue
Aiken, SC 29801
Sarah Friedman/Cary Friedman
(1) (803) 648 5467   Fax: (1) (803) 648 5469

E-Mail:	*carysarah@aol.com*
Web Site:	*www.aikenind.com*
Description:	*Contractor of ladies & mens pants & shorts, plus ladies skirts. Expert with knit & woven fabrications.*
Year Est:	*1962*
Categories:	*Home Furnishings*
Markets:	*Menswear & Womenswear.*
Packages:	*Cutting & Sewing, Complete & CMT packages available.*
Minimums:	*100 dozen/style*
Factory Locals:	*Aiken factory also has a controlled environment cleanroom for assembly of sewn & non-sewn health care products.*
Production Capacity:	*10,000 pcs/month*

APPAREL PRODUCTION INC.
270 West 39th
New York, NY 10018
Teddy Sadaka
(1) (212) 278 8362   Fax: (1) (212) 278 8357

E-Mail:	*teddyapparelprod@aol.com*
Web Site:	*www.apparelproductionny.com*
Description:	*Manufacture any type of top or bottom from pattern to production.*
Year Est:	*1993*
Categories:	*Shirts/blouses/tops*
Markets:	*Menswear, Womenswear, Boyswear, Girlswear.*
Packages:	*Full service, CMT & Complete.*
Factory Locals:	*Hangzhou China, most patterns however are made in*

our pattern facility in New York City.

BLOOM FASHION USA

5589-B Guinea Road
Fairfax, VA 22032

(1) (703) 323 6793   Fax: (1) (703) 323 6795

E-Mail:	*sales@bloomfashionusa.com*
Web Site:	*www.bloomfashionusa.com*
Description:	*Sewing contractor of all types of casual wear. Pants, t-shirts, skirts and shorts.*
Categories:	*Uniforms, Childrens Wear*
Specialties:	*We can help you start your new business. 100% of our products are made in the USA.*
Markets:	*Menswear, Womenswear, Childrenswear.*
Minimums:	*Low Minimums*

CATAWBA CREATIONS

PO Box 1159
Hildebran, NC 28637
Doris Houston
(1) (828) 397 7088   Fax: (1) (828) 397 2357

E-Mail:	*catawbacreations@msn.com*
Description:	*Cut and sew family-owned business specializing in knit tops and bottoms for men, women and children.*
Categories:	*Shirts/Tops*
Minimums:	*Will do small quantities*

COLLECTIVE APPAREL

750 East Gage Avenue
Los Angeles, CA 90001
Don Valenzuela
(1) 310 770 1093   Fax: (1) 323 750 5010

E-Mail:	*contact@collectiveapparel.us*
Web Site:	*www.collectiveapparel.us*
Description:	*One stop. We design, sketch, prepare patterns, do samples and production.*
Year Est:	*2009*
Categories:	*Jeans/Denimwear, Laundry/Washing*
Specialties:	*We specialize in new and innovative wash techniques as well as organic wash and dye processes.*
Markets:	*Menswear, Womenswear, Childrenswear.*
Packages:	*Full packages - premium denim, tops & knits.*
Production Capacity:	*48,000 pcs/month*

COLORADO CONTRACT CUT & SEW

2300 West 2nd Avenue, Unit 3
Denver, CO 80223

(1) (303) 733 5376   Fax: (1) (303) 777 6117

E-Mail:	*jane@coloradocut.com*

Web Site:	*www.coloradocut.com*
Description:	*Cut and sew contractor of all types of yoga pants.*
Year Est:	*1989*
Categories:	*Samples/Small Production*
Specialties:	*Prototyping & sample run production available.*
Markets:	*Menswear, Womenswear*
Minimums:	*250+*
Factory Locals:	*USA*

DYNOTEX INC.

236 Greenpoint Avenue
Brooklyn, NY 11222
Annie Kwan
(1) (917) 532 9068

E-Mail:	*dynotexinc@gmail.com*
Web Site:	*www.dynotex.com*
Description:	*Manufacture ladies and mens woven & knit bottoms, tops and outerwear. More than just cut & sew services. Quality conscious.*
Year Est:	*1999*
Specialties:	*We can provide patternmaking services, cutting room in-house, sample making, grading & marking, 100% inspection,*
Markets:	*Menswear & Womenswear*
Machinery:	*18 Single Needle, 8 Merrow, 1 Double Needle, 2 Blind Stitch, 2 Double Needle Cover Stitch, 1 Zig Zag, 2 Purl Stitch, 2 Button, 1 Button Hole Straight, 1 Button Hole Keyhole, 2 Snap Machines, 3 Thread Trimmer, 1 Fabric Steamer, 2 Cutting Tables and more.*
Packages:	*Comprehensive technical knowledge of fabrics.*
Minimums:	*None*
Factory Locals:	*All work is done in-house.*
Production Capacity:	*Knitwear: 15,000 units/month, Pants: 10,000 units/month, Blouses: 10,000 units/month, Blazers: 5,000 units/month.*

GEMBA GROUP, INC.

501 N Bridge Street
Hidalgo, TX 78557
Jorge Avila Trevino
(1) (956) 607 0890

E-Mail:	*joavila@gembagroup.com*
Description:	*Contract manufacturer of fire retardant garments & Arc Flash Suits up to HRC4.*
Categories:	*Shirts/Tops, Uniforms*
Specialties:	*Coveralls, hoods, bibs, jackets, pants & lab coats out of FR fabrics like Nomex, Westex Indura/Ultrasoft, Milliken Amplitude, Itex & Keviar fabrics.*
Factory Locals:	*Mexico tel#899 132-6161*

GRECO APPAREL

420 North Spring Garden St.
Ambler, PA 19002

(1) (215) 628 2557   Fax: (1) (215) 352 0464

E-Mail: *joe@grecoapparel.com*

Web Site:	www.grecoapparel.com
Description:	Contract to order - full package or CMT - from product development to delivery duty paid.
Year Est:	1951
Categories:	Suits/Tailored Garments, Shirts/Tops, Uniforms, Outerwear
Specialties:	Specialize in pants (dress, work & casual), jeans, tailored clothing, shirts (woven & knit), skirts, dresses, outerwear, flame retardant.
Markets:	Menswear, Womenswear & Childrenswear.
Packages:	Full packages
Factory Locals:	USA (Berry Amendment Compliant for US Government), Dominican Republic, Central America, Far East.
Production Capacity:	125,000 units/week

L.S.W. CUTTING & SEWING SERVICE

670 Ninth Street
Oakland, CA 94607
Lana Wong
(1) (510) 891 9246

E-Mail:	lswcuttingandsewing@hotmail.com
Description:	Contractor of pants, shorts & skirts.
Specialties:	Complete patternmaking services.
Markets:	Menswear, Womenswear, Childrenswear.
Packages:	Full service, CMT & complete packages.
Minimums:	300 units/style
Production Capacity:	30,000 pcs/month

LACORP/LEBANON APPAREL CORP.

70 Thornhill Drive
Lebanon, VA 24266
Jeoff Bodenhorst
(1) (276) 889 3656   Fax: (1) (276) 889 2830

E-Mail:	jeoff@lacorpusa.com
Web Site:	www.lacorpusa.com
Description:	Contractor of all types of bottoms: pants, shorts and skirts.
Year Est:	1968
Categories:	Childrenswear, Uniforms, Home Furnishings, Rework & Inspection Services.
Specialties:	Specialize in high-end casual khaki pants.
Markets:	Menswear, Womenswear, Childrenswear & Home.
Machinery:	Over 500 various sewing machines & electronic cutting, embroidery & besum pocket equipment on site.
Packages:	CMT, Sewing, Cutting, Sample Making & Embroidery.
Minimums:	Will adjust to fit your needs.
Factory Locals:	All work is done in-house.

MCBEE MANUFACTURING COMPANY

347 West Cypress Avenue
McBee, SC 29101
John/Tom Campolong
(1) (843) 335 8234   Fax: (1) (843) 335 8236

E-Mail:	vinci@shtc.net

Web Site:	www.vinciclothiers.com
Description:	Contractor of ladies woven bottoms, pants & skirts.
Year Est:	1960
Categories:	Sportswear-Wovens, Coats/Jackets, Pants/Shorts/ Skirts.
Markets:	Womenswear
Machinery:	Complete range of machinery.
Packages:	CMT & Full packages available.
Minimums:	Vary
Factory Locals:	McBee & Camden, South Carolina

MIAMI STYLE INC.

7480 NW 52nd Street
Miami, FL 33166
Amnon Bensimon/Sofia Rincon
(1) (305) 805 1168   Fax: (1) (305) 805 0075

E-Mail:	sofia@miamistyle.com
Web Site:	www.miamistyle.com
Description:	Sourcing agent for all types of active wear, bottoms, tops, tee shirts, knit sportswear, beachwear, sports bras, basics and children's wear.
Year Est:	1997
Categories:	Active/Athletic Wear, Shirts/Tops, Tee Shirts/Sweat Shirts
Specialties:	Production services: Private label, sewing, cutting, patternmaking, printing, embroidery, screenprinting, samplemaking, dyeing, beading & more.
Markets:	Menswear, Womenswear, Boyswear, Girlswear.
Factory Locals:	Bangladesh and China
Production Capacity:	3 million pcs per month

RAYLON CORPORATION

267 Fifth Avenue
New York, NY 10016
Jay Pollak
(1) (212) 221 3633   Fax: (1) (212) 889 3283

E-Mail:	jpollak@rayloncorp.com
Description:	Full package contractor/factory agent & textile converter.
Year Est:	1948
Specialties:	Specialize in board shorts & warm-up jackets.
Markets:	Menswear, Womenswear, Boyswear, Girlswear.
Minimums:	500-1,000 pcs/style
Factory Locals:	Asia

ADVANCE PLEATING & BUTTON CO.

750 Florida Street
San Francisco, CA 94110
Greg Cruz, Manager
(1) (415) 648 3111   Fax: (1) (415) 648 7284

Description:	*Contractor of textile trimmings. Custom trimming and covered buttons for apparel and accessories.*
Specialties:	*Fancy stitching: pearl & shell edge, shirring, tucking, smocking, strapping, ruching, ruffling & elastic shirring.*
Minimums:	*$25.00/order*

APPAREL SOLUTIONS CORP.

249 West 34th Street
New York, NY 10001
John Harihar
(1) (212) 868 1700   Fax: (1) (212) 868 1701

E-Mail:	*john@usapparelsolutions.com*
Web Site:	*www.usapparelsolutions.com*
Description:	*Pleating, special stitching, cutting & finishing, embroidery, digitizing & trimming contractor.*
Year Est:	*1975*
Categories:	*Pleating/Tucking/Stitching, Cutting & Fusing, Finishing/Coating.*
Specialties:	*Machine & table pleating.*

NEW YORK BINDING COMPANY

43-01 22nd Street
Long Island City, NY 11101

(1) 718 729 2454

Description:	*All kinds of pleating, elastic, ruffles, tucking & samples orders.*
Markets:	*Womenswear, Childrenswear, Costumes & Home Furnishings.*
Minimums:	*None*

REGAL ORIGINALS, INC.

43-01 22nd Street
Long Island City, NY 11101
Rodger Cohen
(1) (201) 569 2144   Fax: (1) (201) 569 2246

E-Mail:	*rodger@regaloriginals.com*
Web Site:	*www.regaloriginals.com*
Description:	*Pleating, stitching, novelty trim factory for all types of apparel and accessories.*
Year Est:	*1952*
Specialties:	*Over 60 years experience. All products made on site.*
Markets:	*Menswear, Womenswear, Childrens, Accessories.*
Production Capacity:	*10,000 pcs/month*

SAN FRANCISCO PLEATING CO.

233 23rd Avenue
San Mateo, CA 94403
Rusty O'Keefe
(1) (415) 982 3003

E-Mail:	*rustysfpleating@comcast.net*
Description:	*All types of pleating on all types of fabric.*
Markets:	*Womenswear & home furnishing fabrics.*
Minimums:	*None*

VISIONAIRE PLEATING LLC.

1155 Manhattan Avenue
Brooklyn, NY 11222
John Dziewit
(1) 917 520 4100   Fax: (1) 718 349 3309

E-Mail:	*john@visionairepleating.com*
Web Site:	*www.visionairepleating.com*
Year Est:	*2004*
Specialties:	*All types of pleating.*
Machinery:	*21 different types of pleating machines*
Production Capacity:	*100,000 pcs/month*

VOGUE TOO PLEATING STITCHING AND EMBROIDERY

265 West 37th Street
New York, NY 10018
Larry Geffner
(1) (212) 354 8976   Fax: (1) (212) 354 8975

E-Mail:	*larry@voguetoo.com*
Web Site:	*www.voguetoo.com*
Description:	*Pleating, tucking, decorative & novelty stitching for the apparel trade.*
Year Est:	*2001*
Specialties:	*We can manufacture all types of trimmings. Specialize in tucking, pleated ruffles, picot trim stitching, flower & novelty trims.*

ANTAKY QUILTING COMPANY

1849 East 50th Street
Los Angeles, CA 90058
Derek Antaky
(1) (323) 233 2500   Fax: (1) (323) 233 2570

E-Mail:	*sales@antakyquilting.com*
Web Site:	*www.antakyquilting.com*
Description:	*Quilting specialists for all types of apparel, robes, jackets, uniforms, sportswear & more.*
Year Est:	*1917*
Specialties:	*Quilted nylon packages in stock.*
Packages:	*Can do samples & small & large production lots.*
Minimums:	*None, any size quilting orders workable.*

FABRI-QUILT INC.

901 East 14th Avenue
North Kansas City, MO 64116
John Linam
(1) (816) 421 2000   Fax: (1) (816) 471 2853

E-Mail:	*jhlinam@msn.com*
Web Site:	*www.fabri-quilt.com*
Description:	*Toll-Free#1-800-279-0622. Contractor of custom quilting on your fabric or Fabri-Quilt can supply the fabric on custom packages.*
Year Est:	*1962*
Exporting Since:	*1986*
Specialties:	*All types of quilting patterns & printed cottons for fabric stores.*
Export to:	*France, Germany, Australia, Netherlands, Canada, Spain, Korea, England, Denmark, Italy & Finland.*
Agent:	*Distributors throughout Europe, North America & Asia.*
Minimums:	*$250.00/order*

info@fashiondex.com © The Fashiondex, Inc.

A RIFKIN COMPANY

1400 Sans Souci Parkway
Wilkes-Barre, PA 18706
Joe Bachkosky
(1) (570) 825 9551   Fax: (1) (570) 825 5282

E-Mail:	*jbachkosky@arifkin.com*
Web Site:	*www.rifkinsewing.com*
Description:	*Apparel & garment contract sewing. Samples & small runs.*
	Finishing, inspection, fold and bag.
Specialties:	*Private label services available using your patterns and fabric.*
	All work done in-house.

ABSOLUTELY! DESIGN SERVICE

210 West 80th Street
New York, NY 10024
Nora Littman
(1) (212) 769 0548

E-Mail:	*nlittman@mindspring.com*
Web Site:	*www.batlledesign.com*
Description:	*Full packages with graded specs and samples*
Specialties:	*Specialize in sewing of all types. We make samples vs production*
	unless small quantities.

ACTIVE APPAREL INC.

11076 Venture Drive
Mira Loma, CA 91752

(1) (951) 361 0060   Fax: (1) (951) 361 3120

E-Mail:	*sales@activeapparel.net*
Web Site:	*www.activeapparel.net*
Description:	*All types of tees, tops and bottoms.*
Categories:	*Active/Athletic Wear*
Specialties:	*Specialize in custom creations and have full capabilities to*
	manufacture your creative efforts.
Markets:	*Menswear, Womenswear & Childrenswear.*
Minimums:	*600 pcs per color*

ALL AMERICAN WASH CO.

2932 East 11th Street
Los Angeles, CA 90023
Alex Kahen
(1) (323) 265 2626   Fax: (1) (323) 265 3307

E-Mail:	*alexkahen@allamericanwashco.com*
Description:	*Cut and sew contractor of jeans, denim skirts, denim jackets and tee shirts.*
Categories:	*Laundry/Wash Contractor, Dyeing Contractor, Jeans/Denimwear*
Specialties:	*Premimum denim wash and garment dyeing. All work is done in house.*
Markets:	*Menswear, Womenswear, Childrenswear.*
Packages:	*Complete & CMT packaging available.*
Minimums:	*Low*

ATLANTA SEWING & PATTERN-MAKING SERVICE

1930 Airport Industrial Park Drive
Marietta, GA 30060
Myriam Belasse
(1) (770) 952 9211

E-Mail:	*info@asapsewingservice.com*
Web Site:	*www.asapsewingservice.com*
Description:	*Designing, patternmaking, sample making, fabric sourcing and production sewing. Your idea from concept to final product.*
Specialties:	*We also do label changes in small and large quantities. Qualified to do garment inspection and repairs. By appointment only.*
Markets:	*All markets*
Minimums:	*None*
Factory Locals:	*Cell Number: 404-849-0473*

AVB DESIGNS

1628 Palm Avenue
San Mateo, CA 94402
Alexandria von Bromssen
(1) (650) 346 1533

E-Mail:	*vonbromssen@mac.com*
Web Site:	*www.avbdesigns.com*
Description:	*Fashion design, fashion illustration, patternmaking, sample making, sourcing, small production runs, grading & consulting.*
Year Est:	*2004*
Categories:	*Patternmaking*
Markets:	*Womenswear, Mens, Childrens and Home Furnishings.*
Packages:	*Complete packages available.*
Agent:	*Production Sourcing: USA, China, Brazil*
Minimums:	*None*
Production Capacity:	*Depends on the project.*

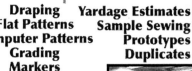

PATTERN DESIGN UNLIMITED, INC.
TOTAL Product Development Service

Design Consults	Draping	Yardage Estimates
Detailed Sketches	Flat Patterns	Sample Sewing
Sourcing	Computer Patterns	Prototypes
Size/Sew Specs	Grading	Duplicates
	Markers	

Tel: 717 336-0500 • Fax: 717 336-0309
550 West Rt. 897 • Reinholds, Pa. 17569
E-mail: pdu@patterndesign.com • Web: www.patterndesign.com

AXIS MOON DESIGN AND PRODUCTION

809 S. Brighton
Dallas, TX 75208
Ellen Kreager
(1) (214) 395 1277

E-Mail:	*ellenkreager@gmail.com*
Web Site:	*www.axismoon.com*
Description:	*Sewing contractor of all types of apparel. Small and large production runs. Also, design, consulting and sourcing.*
Year Est:	*1986*
Specialties:	*Patternmaking, production, sourcing, cutting & graphic art work. Own Cutting Room on premises.*
Markets:	*Menswear, Womenswear, Children, Accessories, Home.*
Machinery:	*4 single needle, 1 buttonhole, 3 serger, 1 button, 2 merrow, 1 leather/walking foot, 1 blindstitch.*
Packages:	*Complete & CMT packages.*
Minimums:	*50*
Production Capacity:	*3000 pcs/monthly*

BLANKET BOSS

87 Windermere Avenue
Greenwood Lake, NY 10925
Barney Lopilato
(1) (845) 477 4774

E-Mail:	*blanketboss@aol.com*
Web Site:	*www.theblanketboss.com*
Description:	*Specialize in making patterns & samples of knit sweaters & cards for production knitting machines.*
Categories:	*Sweaters/Knitwear, Embroidery*
Specialties:	*Personalized photo blankets & pillows and unique scarves. Sublimation - print high quality photos on apparel & shoulder bags.*
Markets:	*Mens, womens & childrens sweater makers.*

Machinery:	*Knitting machines: Stoll 7 gg, Stoll 10 gg, Shima 7 gg, Shima 10 gg.*
Production Capacity:	*1,000 units/month*

BOULDER PATH DESIGNS

110 E. 2nd Street
The Dalles, OR 97058
Luise Langheinrich
(1) (541) 296 4470   Fax: (1) (541) 298 5067

E-Mail:	*info@boulderpathdesigns.com*
Web Site:	*www.boulderpathdesigns.com*
Description:	*Full service contractor. Product development, specifications, patterns, CAD service, grading, marker making, samples, production runs.*
Categories:	*Patternmaking, Active wear, Sportswear/Wovens*
Specialties:	*Problem solving. Experience in work wear, sportswear, hospital gowns, active wear, and more. Can do all styles of tops, bottoms and jackets.*
Markets:	*Menswear, Womenswear & Childrenswear.*
Packages:	*Full service, prototype, development, samplemaking*
Minimums:	*None*
Factory Locals:	*Oregon, USA*

BRIARCLIFF APPAREL TECHNOLOGIES LTD.

246 West 38th Street
New York, NY 10018
Edward Kostyra, President
(1) (212) 840 7666   Fax: (1) (212) 840 7168

E-Mail:	*fashionprofessor@hotmail.com*
Description:	*Over 30 years experience in apparel development & production. Small & large production lots okay.*
Year Est:	*1994*
Categories:	*Active/Athleticwear, Knit Sportswear, Woven Sportswear, Outerwear, Tee Shirts, Dresses/Suits, Robes/Sleepwear.*
Markets:	*Menswear, Womenswear, Childrens & Infantwear.*
Packages:	*Full, CMT, Samples, Patterns & all production services.*
Minimums:	*Flexible*
Factory Locals:	*New York, NY & throughout tri-state area.*
Production Capacity:	*No limit*

CALIFORNIA APPAREL SERVICE

2109 S. Standard Avenue
Santa Ana, CA 92707
Tom Lo/Helen Lo
(1) (714) 222 1970   Fax: (1) (714) 442 2788

E-Mail:	*tom@californiaapparelservice.com*
Web Site:	*www.californiaapparelservice.com*
Description:	*We provide complete apparel manufacturing from pattern through finishing. We specialize in smaller run productions.*
Year Est:	*2003*
Categories:	*T-Shirts, Shirts/Tops, Pants/Shorts/Skirts, Childrenswear, Dresses/Blouses, Sportswear*
Specialties:	*Full service apparel manufacturing from design, patterns and grading*

in.Style eXchange™

Patterns. Samples. Production. Distribution.

Division of IXENTI

www.InStyleExchange.com
info@instyleexchange.com

One-Stop Provider of Private Label Manufacturing Services:

► apparel design services

► product development

► contract manufacturing

► fulfillment services

► fashion business consulting

817.886.9222
1844 W. Division Street
Suite 201
Arlington, Texas 76012

© 2003 - 2012 Copyrights In.Style Exchange™. All Rigths Reserved.

CHERIE BIXLER

See our ad on page 71

135 Fort Lee Road
Leonia, NJ 07605
Cherie Bixler
(1) (201) 944 2886

E-Mail:	*cheriebixler@verizon.net*
Web Site:	*www.cheriebixler.com*
Description:	*Patternmaking and consulting service. We take you from your initial idea through production process. Production done in USA.*
Categories:	*Sample Room/Small Production*
Specialties:	*Product Development, patterns of all types with flat sketch & fittings. Work with people new to the industry.*
Markets:	*Menswear, Womenswear, Childrenswear.*

COLORADO CONTRACT CUT & SEW

2300 West 2nd Avenue, Unit 3
Denver, CO 80223

(1) (303) 733 5376

Fax: (1) (303) 777 6117

E-Mail:	*jane@coloradocut.com*
Web Site:	*www.coloradocut.com*
Description:	*Cut and sew contractor of all types of yoga pants.*

Year Est:	*1989*
Categories:	*Pants/Shorts/Skirts*
Specialties:	*Prototyping & sample run production available.*
Markets:	*Menswear, Womenswear*
Minimums:	*250+*
Factory Locals:	*USA*

CRAVATTA MANUFACTUERS

110 Harmon Drive, Unit 205
Blackwood, NJ 08012
Donielle Martorano
(1) (856) 302 1151

E-Mail:	*info@cravattamfg.com*
Web Site:	*www.cravattamfg.com*
Description:	*American based apparel manufacturer offering small to medium production runs. Specialize in patternmaking, prototypes/SMS & CMT.*
Specialties:	*Consulting services for fashion designers. Branding, wholesale fabric and trim sourcing worldwide.*
Markets:	*Menswear, Womenswear & Childrenswear.*
Minimums:	*25 pcs per style/size/color*
Factory Locals:	*100% made in the USA.*

CREATIVE PATTERN AND SAMPLE

112 West 9th Street
Los Angeles, CA 90015
Isabel Martinez
(1) (213) 233 0253   Fax: (1) (213) 233 4857

E-Mail:	*contact@creativepatternandsample.com*
Web Site:	*www.creativepatternandsample.com*
Description:	*Grades & marker, showroom samples, mock ups, sewing, sample making, design consultation, prototypes, fittings.*
Categories:	*Swimwear, jeans, dresses, suits, lingerie*
Specialties:	*Quality crafted patterns,1st patterns, production patterns, spec sheets, pattern corrections. By appointment only.*
Markets:	*Womenswear*

CROOKED BROOK

901 Broad Street
Utica, NY 13501
Ray
(1) (315) 733 1992   Fax: (1) (315) 292 1901

E-Mail:	*info@crookedbrook.com*
Web Site:	*www.crookedbrook.com*
Description:	*Apparel & design & reproduction studio offering knit & woven pattern making from spec sheets or renderings, samples.*
Categories:	*Embroidery*
Specialties:	*Small lot production for men's, women's & children's sportswear. Custom embroidery, applique and tackle twill.*
Machinery:	*Juki Straight Stitch, Juki Serge, Reece Key Hole, Singer Straight Button Hole, Kansai Coverstitch, Juki Feed Off the Arm, Melco EMT 10 Em broidery Machine*

Minimums: None

CUSTOM-SEWING-SERVICES
117 11th Street
Brooklyn, NY 11215
Edwin
(1) (516) 499 7304

E-Mail:	customsewingservices@yahoo.com
Description:	Single garments and bridal for men, women and children.
Specialties:	Samples, patternmaker and small production.
Factory Locals:	Alternate tel number: 718-314-2041

CYCLE FASHION PATTERN INC.
306 West 37th Street, 2nd Floor
New York, NY 10018

(1) (212) 216 9668

Web Site:	www.cyclefashionpattern.com
Description:	We are a sample room dedicated to making patterns & samples using draping. We provide small lot production service to meet your needs.
Categories:	Patternmaking Services
Specialties:	We specialize in jackets, pants, jeans, dresses, skirts & eveningwear.
Markets:	Womenswear

DALMA DRESS MFG CO INC
251 West 39th Street
New York, NY 10018
Michael Dipalma
(1) (212) 391 8296

Description:	Cut and sew contractor of women's dresses & evening wear.
Categories:	Dresses/Blouses, Bridal/Eveningwear
Markets:	Womenswear

DARWOOD MANUFACTURING CO.
620 West Railroad Street
Pelham, GA 31779
Allen Burford, President
(1) (229) 294 4932   Fax: (1) (229) 294 9323

E-Mail:	darwood@bellsouth.net
Web Site:	www.darwoodmfg.com
Description:	A complete solution to your design, fabric & trim sourcing, pattern development, production, warehousing and distribution.
Year Est:	1960
Categories:	Grading/Marking, Patternmaking, Sample Rooms, Washing, Embroidery
Specialties:	Expertise with all kinds of shirts, tops, pants, shorts, skirts, uniforms & outerwear.
Markets:	Menswear, Womenswear, Boyswear & Accessories.
Packages:	CMT & complete packages available.
Minimums:	5 dozen/style
Factory Locals:	Pelham, GA

DESIGN PRINCIPLES LLC, THE

1914 Cordova Road
Ft. Lauderdale, FL 33316
Hollis Dominick
(1) 727 488 8162   Fax: (1) 954 756 7325

E-Mail:	*hollis@thedesignprinciples.com*
Web Site:	*www.thedesignprinciples.com*
Description:	*Design, sketching, patternmaking, samples, marking/grading, sourcing and production services.*
Categories:	*Patternmaking*
Specialties:	*Specialize in servicing the startup to emerging designer brands for their production needs.*
Markets:	*Menswear, Womenswear, Childrens & Accessories.*
Factory Locals:	*Development Office: 305 879 6863*

EAST BAY GARMENT CUTTING & SEWING SERVICE

3315 Farnam Street
Oakland, CA 94601
Kelvin Lam
(1) (510) 261 6688   Fax: (1) (510) 261 6888

E-Mail:	*annielam6688@gmail.com*
Description:	*Patterns, cutting, grading, marking, samples & production sewing.*
Categories:	*Sample Rooms/Small Production Contractors, Cutting/Fusing Contractors.*
Specialties:	*Great with shirts, outerwear, dresses, lingerie, sportswear, uniforms & vests.*
Markets:	*Menswear, Womenswear*
Minimums:	*None*

FACTORY 212, THE

306 West 38th Street
New York, NY 10018
Angela Kim
(1) (212) 944 6900   Fax: (1) (212) 944 6909

E-Mail:	*angela@thefactory212.com*
Web Site:	*www.thefactory212.com*
Description:	*We make samples for runway & showroom, duplicates, small production lots with no minimums. All work done in-house.*
Year Est:	*2010*
Specialties:	*We can make anything from tee shirts to jeans to dresses & jackets. Patternmaking, design assistance & consulting.*
Markets:	*Menswear & Womenswear.*
Machinery:	*Straight stitch, double needle, merrow, coverstitch, bartack.*
Packages:	*Complete Packages*
Minimums:	*None*

FLEXSYSTEMS USA INC.

727 West Main Street
El Cajon, CA 92020
Gary Smith
(1) (619) 401 1858   Fax: (1) (619) 401 1848

E-Mail:	*sales@flexsystems.com*
Web Site:	*www.flexsystems.com*
Description:	*Manufacturer of custom PVC, corn plastic labels, zip pulls, promotional products.*
Year Est:	*1994*
Categories:	*Trim Application*
Specialties:	*Sourcing, assembly, fulfillment, custom R&D, sewing, warehousing and packaging.*
Markets:	*Menswear, Womenswear, Children, Accessories, Home.*
Export to:	*Canada 8%, Mexico 2%*
Minimums:	*None*

G.S. FASHION

2765 Randolph Street
Huntington Park, CA 90255
George Simonian
(1) (323) 581 0764   Fax: (1) (323) 581 1253

E-Mail:	*ssimonn@aol.com*
Description:	*Sewing contractor of dresses, evening/formal, skirts, blouses & pants. Interested in partnering with a freelance designer.*
Year Est:	*1988*
Categories:	*Dresses/Blouses*
Specialties:	*Sewing, finishing, bagging, tagging, repair & change labels. Also fulfillment services for offshore containers.*
Markets:	*Womenswear*
Machinery:	*Single Needle, Double Needle, Overlock, Cover Stitch*

GRIFFIN MANUFACTURING CO., INC.

502 Bedford Street
Fall River, MA 02722
Gene Laudon
(1) (508) 677 0048   Fax: (1) (508) 674 1268

E-Mail:	*sales@griffinmanufacturing.com*
Web Site:	*www.griffinmanufacturing.com*
Description:	*Cut & sew contractor plus design, development, patternmaking, sample making & warehousing.*
Year Est:	*1936*
Categories:	*Active/Athleticwear*
Specialties:	*Athleticwear, performance knits, knit & woven sportswear & outerwear.*
Markets:	*Menswear, Womenswear & Childrenswear.*
Machinery:	*Sewing machines, flatlock stitch machines, automatic cutting machines, in-house embroidery & heat transfers.*
Minimums:	*200 to 2,000 pieces*
Factory Locals:	*Fall River, MA & Costa Rica*

GWEN'S CREATIVE SEWING

108 W Bizzell Street
Laurinburg, NC 28352
Gwen Baker
(1) (910) 276 2121

E-Mail:	*gebaker@roadrunner.com*
Description:	*Patternmaking, fabric sourcing, cut and sew, samples, small production.*
Specialties:	*All types and styles. Menswear, bridal, costums, sportswer, pillows, drapery treatments for the home.*
Markets:	*Menswear, Womenswear, Home Furnishings.*

IN STYLE USA, INC.

307 West 36th Street
New York, NY 10018
James Mallon
(1) (212) 631 0278   Fax: (1) (212) 631 0279

E-Mail:	*instyleusa@instyleusa.net*
Description:	*Contractor & private label manufacturer.*
Categories:	*Dresses/Blouses, Patternmaking, Suits/Tailored Garments*
Specialties:	*First samples, patternmaking, duplicates & production. On-time delivery.*
Markets:	*Womenswear*
Machinery:	*Over 100 new machines.*
Packages:	*All*
Minimums:	*None*
Factory Locals:	*New York City.*
Production Capacity:	*12,000 to 20,000 pcs/month*

IN.STYLE EXCHANGE™   See our ad on page 75

1844 W. Division Street
Arlington, TX 76012
Sales Manager
(1) (817) 886 9222

E-Mail:	*info@instyleexchange.com*
Web Site:	*www.instyleexchange.com*
Description:	*Private label sampling and production for men's, women's & kid's apparel & accessories.*
Categories:	*Production Sourcing, Shirts & Tops, Patternmaking Services, Childrens Wear, Dresses & Blouses, Lingerie, Sleepwear & Robes.*
Specialties:	*Product development, fabric sourcing, sampling, grading/marking, patternmaking, production, embroidery & screenprinting.*
Packages:	*Private label & full packages.*
Minimums:	*50 pieces per color per style*
Production Capacity:	*50,000 pcs/month*

JONCO INDUSTRIES INC.
2501 West Hampton Avenue
Milwaukee, WI 53209

(1) (414) 449 2000   Fax: (1) (414) 449 5200

E-Mail:	*tom.ryan@joncoind.com*
Web Site:	*www.joncoind.com*
Description:	*Industrial sewing contractor.*
	Also provide packaging & complete warehousing.
Year Est:	*1980*
Categories:	*Distribution/Warehouse, Uniforms, Accessories*
Specialties:	*Open for all your apparel sewing needs. All work done in-house.*
Markets:	*Menswear & Womenswear*
Machinery:	*5 Juki, 3 Consew, 3 Singer, 1 Melco Amaya, 1 Pegasus*
	2 Path Finder Cutters, 1 Kongsberg, 1 5' x 10' Laser.
Minimums:	*None*
Production Capacity:	*Varies by Item*

KATRINA PATTERNS
555 Eighth Avenue
New York, NY 10018
Valentina
(1) (212) 563 7332   Fax: (1) (212) 563 7394

Web Site:	*www.katrinapatterns.com*
Description:	*Samples & duplicates. Fast delivery & turn-around.*
Categories:	*Patternmaking, Sample Room/Small Production.*
Specialties:	*Specialize in women's woven sportswear.*
Markets:	*Womenswear*
Machinery:	*6 sewing, 3 merrow, 3 irons, hindstitch & cutting machine.*
Minimums:	*None*
Production Capacity:	*20 units/week (jackets, dresses), 30 units/week (pants, blouses)*

KRISTABEN
233 Yorktown Street
Dallas, TX 75208
Dinh Yang
(1) (214) 760 9796   Fax: (1) (214) 760 9744

E-Mail:	*dinhyang@hotmail.com*
Web Site:	*www.kristaben.com*
Description:	*Open to small production. Specializing in lingerie, baby and childrenswear.*
Specialties:	*Start-up companies welcome! Product development and Consulting work provided.*
Markets:	*Ladies, baby & childrenswear markets.*
Packages:	*Full Packages.*
Minimums:	*100 pieces*
Factory Locals:	*Vietnam*

L.I. CUTTING

2523 Merrick Road
Bellmore, NY 11710
Peter Romeo
(1) (516) 826 6138   Fax: (1) (516) 826 6148

E-Mail:	*info@licutting.com*
Web Site:	*www.licutting.com*
Description:	*Private label contractor of all types of sportswear knits, swimwear, uniforms & more. Pattern through production.*
Categories:	*Sportswear/Knits, Swimwear, Uniforms*
Specialties:	*All work done in-house. Screenprinting & sublimation on site.*
Markets:	*Womens & childrens markets.*
Packages:	*CMT, Patternmaking, Samplemaking & Grading.*
Minimums:	*None*

LEAHPATRA KNITTING

7543 Trask Avenue
Los Angeles, CA 90293
Leah Walton
(1) 310 951 9095

E-Mail:	*leahpatra@leahpatra.com*
Web Site:	*www.leahpatra.com*
Description:	*Domestic knitting contractor. Design, sample making services, small & large production capabilities. By appointment only.*
Categories:	*Sweaters/Knitwear*
Specialties:	*Specialty is cashmere & high end novelty knitwear, scarves, handbags, sweaters.*
Minimums:	*None*
Production Capacity:	*1500 units/month*

LEFT IN STITCHES INC.

55 Ericson Court
Arcata, CA 95521

(1) (707) 822 3041   Fax: (1) (707) 822 3042

E-Mail:	*info@leftinstitches.com*
Web Site:	*www.leftinstitches.com*
Description:	*Over 29 years of patternmaking, grading and sewing. Samples, prototypes. Work with knits and wovens.*
Categories:	*Grading/Marking, Patternmaking, Dresses/Blouses*
Specialties:	*Creative design and development from concept to production. Specialize in working with small and startup companies.*
Markets:	*Menswear, Womenswear & Childrenswear.*

M.S.R. CUSTOM MADE SHIRTS

600 Broad Avenue
Ridgefield, NJ 07657
Mike/Robert
(1) (201) 941 7970   Fax: (1) (201) 941 7994

E-Mail:	*msrcostumshirt@verizon.net*
Web Site:	*www.msrcustomshirtmakers.com*

Description:	Samples & patterns for sport, stretch & dress shirts, costumes & shirt-waist dresses. Custom shirts & blouses made to order.
Year Est:	1990
Categories:	Shirts & Tops, Costumes, Sample Rooms/Small Productions
Specialties:	Specialize in samples from scratch. Custom work & copying of existing design application.
Markets:	Menswear & Womenswear
Machinery:	Patternmaking, sewing, cutting & grading all in house. 10 Single Needle, 5 Irons, 1 Button Hole, 2 Cutting
Packages:	Full service contractor, all packages available.
Minimums:	Vary
Factory Locals:	Manufacturing done in-house.
Production Capacity:	1,000 pcs/month

ME'LANSON PATTERNS

870 N Richmond
Chicago, IL 60622
Maribel Melanson
(1) (702) 742 3082

E-Mail:	thepatternmaker14@gmail.com
Web Site:	www.coroflot.com/marfig
Description:	Pattern draft, initial first samples and small production. Will do runs of 6 pieces to 2 dozen for start-up companies.
Categories:	Patternmaking, Product Development
Specialties:	Design studio that offers patternmaking, fabric sourcing, technical flat drawings, fittings, grading, marker making, tech packs & branding.
Markets:	Menswear, Womenswear, Childrens & Accessories.
Minimums:	None

MEHERA SHAW TEXTILES PVT LTD.

3307 Trice Atwater Road
Chapel Hill, NC 27516
Shari Keller
(1) (919) 969 2572   Fax: (1) (919) 969 6909

E-Mail:	info@meherashaw.com
Web Site:	www.meherashaw.com
Description:	We are a full production company offering pattern making and grading, including designer support, fabric sourcing, sampling & CMT services.
Year Est:	2007
Exporting Since:	2008
Categories:	Patternmaking
Specialties:	Specialize in small-scale designers wishing to produce private label collections using natural fibers, artisan textiles and/or organic fabrics.
Markets:	Womenswear & Girlswear.
Export to:	USA, Europe, Japan
Minimums:	Small minimums & lots of start-up support
Factory Locals:	India

MICHAEL CALDERONE, INC.
265 West 37th Street
New York, NY 10018
Michael
(1) (212) 465 1093   Fax: (1) (212) 868 0628

E-Mail:	mcpatterns@aol.com
Web Site:	www.mcpatternservice.com
Description:	Expert patternmaking service. Samples and small production capabilities.
Categories:	Grading/Marking, Sample Room/Small Production
Specialties:	Specialize in plaids, stripes & cemetric type of prints.
Markets:	All.

MONALISA FASHIONS INC.
650 East Green Street
Allentown, PA 18109
Mereille Najm
(1) (610) 770 0806   Fax: (1) (610) 770 0823

E-Mail:	monalisamfg@gmail.com
Web Site:	www.monalisamfg.com
Description:	Family-owned CMT contractor. The 15,000SF facility includes cutting, sewing, trimming, shipping/storage.
Year Est:	1984
Categories:	Active & Athletic wear, Childrens Wear, Shirts & Tops, Swimwear, T-Shirts, Sportswear-knits, Sample Rooms/Small Production.
Specialties:	Garment dye, organic, contemporary knitwear, infantwear.
Markets:	Menswear, Womenswear, Childrens
Machinery:	Over-lock, safety, 2-ndl and 3-ndl cover stitch, straight stitch, single needle, neck tape, double needle, metal snaps, elastic cover stitch, binding, button hole, button sewer, picot machine, flatlock, heat press, fusing.
Packages:	CMT, Sewing
Export to:	Canada, Europe, Asia
Minimums:	200 units/style
Production Capacity:	50,000 pcs/month

NY STUDIO LLC
213 West 35th Street
New York, NY 10001
Robert Forehand
(1) (212) 244 1269   Fax: (1) (212) 244 4788

E-Mail:	robert@nystudiollc.com
Web Site:	www.nystudiollc.com
Description:	New York sample room for 1st proto & dups, pattern scanning/plotting, hand-made patterns or digital pattern service.
Year Est:	1998
Specialties:	Tech packs for China can be created in our New York facility.
Packages:	Full service, CMT & complete packages.
Factory Locals:	Shenzhen & Nantong, China
Production Capacity:	3,000 pcs/month

PATTERN DESIGN UNLIMITED, INC.

See our ad on page 73

550 West Rt. 897
Reinholds, PA 17569
Pamela Urban
(1) (717) 336 0500   Fax: (1) (717) 336 0309

E-Mail:	*pdu@patterndesign.com*
Web Site:	*www.patterndesign.com*
Description:	*20+years in business constructing cut and sew apparel & items with 30 industrial machines. All stitch & folder applications available.*
Year Est:	*1987*
Categories:	*Patternmaking, Grading/Marking*
Specialties:	*Offering complete ""one-stop"" product development; designing, patterns, grading, marking, samples & small production runs available.*
Markets:	*Menswear, Womenswear & Childrenswear.*
Packages:	*Complete & CMT packages.*
Minimums:	*None*

PRIMO COAT COMPANY

43-15 Queens Street
Long Island City, NY 11101

(1) (718) 349 2070   Fax: (1) (718) 349 7150

E-Mail:	*alan@alandavidnyc.com*
Description:	*Sample room specializing in jackets, topcoats, overcoats, pants & formal wear.*
Categories:	*Coats/Jackets, Sample Rooms/Small Production*
Specialties:	*Small production lots & special orders. Top quality.*
Markets:	*Menswear & Womenswear*
Machinery:	*Sergers, bartack & buttonhole machinery.*
Minimums:	*None. Will do singles.*

PROSTER FASHION

265 West 37th Street
New York, NY 10018
Cecilia
(1) (212) 730 8503   Fax: (1) (212) 730 8348

E-Mail:	*prosterlock23@gmail.com*
Description:	*Cut and Sew contractor.*
Year Est:	*2002*
Specialties:	*Make all first prototypes and samples. Sewing on premises.*
Markets:	*Womenswear, Menswear, Ready to Wear.*
Packages:	*Full service*
Minimums:	*Low*

QUICK FUSING INC.

260 West 36th Street
New York, NY 10018
Igor Goldenberg
(1) (212) 967 0311   Fax: (1) (212) 967 1432

E-Mail:	*quickfuse5@aol.com*
Web Site:	*www.apparelexpert.com*

Description:	Cut and sew contractor from start to finish. All done in the USA.
Year Est:	1987
Categories:	Patternmaking, Cutting/Fusing
Specialties:	Cutting, fusing, sponging, bonding fabrics & leather, patternmaking, sewing, samples. Full production small and large lots.
Markets:	Womenswear, Childrenswear, Accessories.
Packages:	Complete packages.
Minimums:	Small

RAINBOW STYLE

242 West 38th Street
New York, NY 10018

(1) (212) 290 0209

E-Mail:	info@rainbowpattern.com
Web Site:	www.rainbowpattern.com
Description:	One-stop service from concept to production. We can cover all types of fabric for knit, chiffon, jersey, netting, denim, wool, leather etc.
Categories:	Patternmaking, Sportswear/Knits
Markets:	Menswear, Womenswear, Childrenswear

ROBKO LLC

214 Oak Street
Nazareth, PA 18064
Arthur Rader
(1) (610) 746 4933   Fax: (1) (610) 746 5563

E-Mail:	art@customapparelzone.com
Web Site:	www.customapparelzone.com
Description:	Full service private label manufacturing. From pattern making, grading, markers, sample making, cut and sew.
Categories:	Patternmaking, Sample Grading/Marking Services
Specialties:	Specialize in t-shirts, sport shirts, oxfords, onesies, sweatshirts, camp shirts, rib t-shirts, sports specialty wear.
Markets:	Menswear, Womenswear, Childrenswear

ROYAL APPAREL INC.   See our ad on page 9, 113, 129

65 Commerce Street
Hauppauge, NY 11788
Morey Mayeri
(1) (631) 213 8299   Fax: (1) (631) 922 8438

E-Mail:	sales@royalapparel.net
Web Site:	www.royalapparel.net
Description:	Manufacturer & private label contractor.
Year Est:	1993
Exporting Since:	1993
Categories:	Tee Shirts, Sportswear-Knits, Activewear/Athleticwear, Embroidery, Cutting/Fusing
Specialties:	Create patterns & make samples according to customers requirements. We produce organic blanks and products.
Markets:	Menswear, Womenswear & Childrenswear.
Packages:	Full service, complete packages.

Export to:	*Canada & Europe*
Minimums:	*100 dozen per size/per color*

S. KANOUNI DESIGN & PATTERN STUDIO

824 Los Angeles Street
Los Angeles, CA 90014
Soad
(1) (213) 627 2281

E-Mail:	*skfashion@att.net*
Description:	*Patterns, samples, duplicates & small production lots.*
Categories:	*Patternmaking, Sample Rooms/Small Production.*
Specialties:	*In-house cut & sew. One stop service.*
Markets:	*Menswear, Womenswear & Childrenswear.*
Packages:	*CMT packages available.*
Minimums:	*None*
Factory Locals:	*Second address: 7171 Grandoaks Dr., Stanton, CA 90680*
	Cell: 213-880-0515

SEW PRECISE COMPANY

3212 N. Kilpatrick Avenue
Chicago, IL 60641

(1) (773) 481 1400   Fax: (1) (773) 481 1335

E-Mail:	*info@sewprecise.com*
Web Site:	*www.sewprecise.com*
Description:	*Full service cutting and sewing contractor of all types of apparel.*
Categories:	*Grading/Marking, Childrenswear*
Specialties:	*Grading/marker, pressing/finishing, embroidery.*
Markets:	*Menswear, Womenswear, Childrenswear.*
Machinery:	*80 machines of all types including fusing machines, pressing equipment, and 2 40ft. cutting tables.*

SEWN PRODUCT SERVICES

111 S. Lander Street
Seattle, WA 98134
Kristine Carlton/Jenny Mae Miller
(1) (206) 467 5459   Fax: (1) (206) 467 5459

E-Mail:	*contact@sewnproductservices.com*
Web Site:	*www.sewnproductservices.com*
Description:	*Design consultation, patternmaking, sample sewing, raw goods sourcing, grading & marking, fit assesments, tech pack development.*
Categories:	*Athletic/Activewear, Lingerie/Intimate Apparel, Sleepwear, Leather Apparel, Swimwear, Costuming, Dancewear, Soft Goods Accessories*
Specialties:	*We offer a full menu of services supporting sewn product development including production management & small run production.*
Markets:	*Menswear, Womenswear & Childrenswear.*

SHEHU

333 S. 20th Street
Philadelphia, PA 19148
Bela Shehu
(1) (267) 496 5208

E-Mail:	*bela@shehu.net*
Web Site:	*www.shehu.net*
Description:	*Full service design & development company. We specialize in pattern & sample making. Contractor of small production lots.*
Year Est:	*2007*
Categories:	*Patternmaking*
Specialties:	*All types of women & girls apparel. Dresses, bottoms, tops, sleepwear, uniforms, sportswear, scarves/shawls.*
Markets:	*Womenswear & Girlswear.*
Machinery:	*5 Straight Stitch, 4 Marrow, 1 Cover Stitch, 1 Pearl Stitch, 2 Zigzag.*
Packages:	*CMT & Samples*
Production Capacity:	*500 pcs/month*

SKY BLUE SEWING

960 Mission Street
San Fransicso, CA 94103
Steven
(1) (415) 777 9978   Fax: (1) (415) 777 9938

E-Mail:	*skyblueswg@sbcglobal.net*
Description:	*Private label manufacturer. Provides CMT, sample making, hand pressing, tagging, poly bagging and packing.*
Year Est:	*1988*
Categories:	*Jeans/Denimwear*
Specialties:	*Specialize in the cutting and sewing of denim, and other medium and heavy weight woven fabrics.*
Markets:	*Menswear, Womenswear & Childrenswear.*
Machinery:	*Electric cutting knife, keyhole, automatic belt loop, hemming, side seam serger, open seam press.*
Packages:	*CMT & private label.*
Production Capacity:	*20,000-30,000 units/month (basic five pocket jeans)*

SOLID STONE FABRICS

26 Fayette Street
Martinsville, VA 24112
David Stone
(1) (276) 634 0115   Fax: (1) (276) 632 8986

E-Mail:	*dstone@solidstonefabrics.com*
Web Site:	*www.solidstonefabrics.com*
Description:	*Cut and sew contractor of dancewear and clothing for athletes such as gymnasts.*
Categories:	*Athleticwear, Dancewear*
Specialties:	*Small production lots.*
Markets:	*Menswear & Womenswear.*
Minimums:	*Small*

SOMIYA INC.

307 West 38th Street
New York, NY 10018
Leo and Liz
(1) (212) 302 3089   Fax: (1) (212) 302 3089

E-Mail: *somiyainc@yahoo.com*
Description: *Patternmaking, samples, small production is done in New York City,*
bulk production capabilities at sister factory overseas.
Categories: *Patternmaking*
Specialties: *Specialize in pattern and samples.*
Markets: *All markets.*
Minimums: *None*

SPOILED ROTTEN U.S.A.

605 East 132nd Street
Bronx, NY 10454
Eric Beroff
(1) (718) 993 7006   Fax: (1) (718) 993 6314

E-Mail: *eberoff@yahoo.com*
Description: *Cut and sew contractor of knit & wovens for womenswear.*
All types of tops and bottoms.
Specialties: *We can also source your fabric.*
Minimums: *Very low*

STUDIO NTK LLC

2946 Welcome Way
Greenwood, IN 46143
Nataliya Kitic
(1) (317) 886 7327

E-Mail: *studiontk@gmail.com*
Web Site: *www.studiontk.com*
Description: *Apparel design and manufacturing. Our services are for start up &*
small companies to leading brands.
Year Est: *2011*
Categories: *Patternmaking*
Specialties: *Consulting, concept ideas to detailed sketches, specks, production*
samples, patternmaking, cut and sew, quality control.
Markets: *Womenswear, Accessories*
Packages: *CMT & Samples*
Minimums: *None*
Production Capacity: *1,000 pcs*

STUDIO ONE LEATHER DESIGN INC.

270 West 39th Street
New York, NY 10018
Arthur Cohen
(1) (212) 760 1701   Fax: (1) (212) 760 1702

E-Mail: *arthur@studio1leather.com*
Description: *A full service sample room working in the development of men's and*
women's sportswear and outerwear.
Categories: *Patternmaking, Production Sourcing, Leather/Suede*

Specialties:	*Specialize in leather and suede.*
Markets:	*Menswear, Womenswear*
Machinery:	*5 sewing machines, buttonhole, fur sewing machine and merrow.*
Minimums:	*25 pcs/style (leather garments, woven)*
Factory Locals:	*All work in done in the USA.*
Production Capacity:	*800-1,000 units/month*

STYLE SOURCE INC.

913 Orange Street
Wilmington, NC 28401
Geoffrey Krasnov
(1) (910) 399 2288   Fax: (1) (910) 399 2289

E-Mail:	*geoff@style-source.com*
Web Site:	*www.style-source.com*
Description:	*Full range of pattern making services to the trade. Manufacturing & sourcing, fabric sales, pre-patterned apparel & private label apparel.*
Year Est:	*2002*
Categories:	*Patternmaking Services*
Specialties:	*Devise first patterns from conceptual drawings & produce first samples & specs, sourcing & manufacturing both domestic & overseas.*
Markets:	*Womenswear, Childrenswear, Accessories.*
Factory Locals:	*All work is done in North Carolina*
Production Capacity:	*5,000 dozen/monthly*

SUPERIOR PATTERN SERVICES

1095 East 15th Street
Hialeah, FLorida 33010
Jeff Trieb, President
(1) (305) 805 1540

E-Mail:	*superior_patterns@yahoo.com*
Web Site:	*www.superiorpatterns.com*
Description:	*Sample room and small production runs of up to 100 pieces.*
Year Est:	*1997*
Categories:	*Grading/Marking, Production Sourcing, Patternmaking*
Specialties:	*All pattern services for woven & knit apparel. Specialize in assisting new designers create their collection.*
Markets:	*Menswear, Womenswear, Childrenswear*
Machinery:	*Gerber Accumark System*
Packages:	*Full packages.*
Minimums:	*Vary*
Factory Locals:	*Factories in Dominican Republic & Guatemala.*

TESTFABRICS, INC.

PO Box 3026
West Pittston, PA 18643
Tom Klaas
(1) (570) 603 0432   Fax: (1) (570) 603 0433

E-Mail:	*info@testfabrics.com*
Web Site:	*www.testfabrics.com*
Description:	*Custom sourcing/manufacturing including small lot dyeing, we also provide cutting & slitting services & special textile services.*

Specialties:	*Sewing including overcast merrow stitching, custom assembly of composite test specimens, samples, ""mock"" garments, etc.*
Minimums:	*One Linear Meter*

TRUE MEASURE INC.
1042 S. Gerhart Avenue
City of Commerce, CA 90022

(1) (323) 213 3184

E-Mail:	*melida@truemeasureinc.com*
Web Site:	*www.truemeasureinc.com*
Description:	*Fashion design, pattern making services, samples, full scale manufacturing in the USA and overseas.*
Categories:	*Patternmaking Services*
Specialties:	*Specialize in menswear, womens formal & casual wear, swimwear, & intimate apparel. We cater to start-ups as well as established brands.*
Markets:	*Menswear & Womenswear.*

V.A. PRIVATE LABEL
3237 Amber Street
Philadelphia, PA 19134
Sarah
(1) (215) 496 0408   Fax: (1) (215) 496 0925

E-Mail:	*info@vaprivatelabel.com*
Web Site:	*www.vaprivatelabel.com*
Description:	*Full service garment production in wovens & knits. Production samples, grading & marking, cutting, sewing, trim, pressing and packing.*
Categories:	*Sportswear/knits, Sportswear/Wovens*
Specialties:	*Custom silk screen printing and embroidery.*
Markets:	*Menswear & Womenswear*

Z.W. DESIGNS, INC.
443 Flint Hill Court
Lawrenceville, GA 30044
Z. Arthur
(1) (770) 513 0906

E-Mail:	*zwd@zwdesigns.com*
Web Site:	*www.zwdesigns.com*
Description:	*Expert apparel & product development, specifications, digital patterns, grading, markers; plotting, samples, small lot manufacturing.*
Year Est:	*1983*
Categories:	*Patternmaking, Grading & Marking Services, CAD/CAM Software Marketing*
Specialties:	*CAD/CAM patternmaking, technical design, design sketching/flats; choir robes, uniforms, government contractor certified (WOSP,SDB).*
Markets:	*Womenswear, Menswear, Childrenswear.*
Production Capacity:	*Small lots, but varies*

A PROMOS USA DBA THE IMAGEMAKER & AARROW PROMOTIONS

143 East Merrick Road
Freeport, NY 11520
Mindy Younger
(1) (516) 377 0186   Fax: (1) (516) 377 0198

E-Mail:	*sales@imagemakerus.com*
Web Site:	*www.apromosusa.com*
Description:	*Screenprinted custom t-shirts, embroidery and promotional items.*
	All work done in-house.
Year Est:	*1990*
Categories:	*Embroidery*
Specialties:	*Embroidery on polo shirts, golf shirts, t-shirts, sweaters, hats/caps.*
	Oversized printing, specialty inks, 3D embroidery.
Markets:	*Menswear, Womenswear, Childrenswear.*
Machinery:	*Automated presses*
Production Capacity:	*T-shirts: 15,000/day*

ABSTRACT GRAPHICS

214 Oak Street
Nazareth, PA 18064
Arthur Rader
(1) (610) 746 4933   Fax: (1) (610) 746 5563

E-Mail:	*art@customapparelzone.com*
Web Site:	*www.customapparelzone.com*
Description:	*Provide full service screen printing from creating the logo to*
	imprinting it with a wide variety of specialty inks.
Specialties:	*Complete embroidery services from digitizing the logo to the*
	finished sewn out logo on any apparel or accessory desired.
Markets:	*Menswear, Womenswear, Childrenswear*

AIR WAVES, INC.

7787 Graphics Way
Lewis Center, OH 43035

(1) (740) 548 1200   Fax: (1) (740) 548 1212

E-Mail:	*cs@airwavesinc.com*
Web Site:	*www.airwavesstore.com*
Description:	*Toll Free #1-800 468 7335. Contract screenprinting*
	& heat transfers on finished garments or pieces.
Year Est:	*1983*
Specialties:	*Thousands of stock designs with custom design capabilities.*
	Puff, spot, 4-color process & 4-color process puff printing.
Machinery:	*Full line of heat press machines: manual, automatic &*
	specialty.
Export to:	*Over 120 countries*
Minimums:	*Vary*
Production Capacity:	*100,000-500,000 doz/month*

ALL U, INC.

9 Interstate Avenue
Albany, NY 12205
Tina Benson
(1) (518) 438 2558   Fax: (1) (518) 438 7282

E-Mail:	*sales@allu.com*
Web Site:	*www.allu.com*
Description:	*Quality custom screenprinting and embroidery.*
Year Est:	*1986*
Categories:	*Embroidery*
Specialties:	*Our in-house digitizing allows us to reproduce even the most demanding designs quickly and accurately.*
Machinery:	*8 color and two 12 color automatic presses, and 6 color and 2 color manual presses for screenprinting.*

AMERICAN ICON SCREEN PRINTING

392 N. Montgomery Street
Newburgh, NY 12550
Katrina Pulichene
(1) (845) 561 1299   Fax: (1) (845) 913 9067

E-Mail:	*katrina@americaniconmerch.com*
Web Site:	*www.americaniconshirts.com*
Description:	*Screenprinting, discharge printing, process printing, over-zipper printing, tag - less printing/neck labels.*
Year Est:	*2005*
Specialties:	*Full service apparel screen printing on all types of tees, sweatshirts, pullover hoods, crewneck sweatshirts, totes bags, caps etc.*
Markets:	*Menswear, Womenswear, Childrens, Accessories.*
Minimums:	*Low but vary depending on process*
Production Capacity:	*50,000 prints/monthly*

APPAREL PRINTING DIV OF KENMAR SHIRTS

1578 White Plains Road
Bronx, NY 10462
Karen Greene
(1) (718) 824 3880   Fax: (1) (718) 823 4233

E-Mail:	*kareng@apparelprinting.com*
Web Site:	*www.apparelprinting.com*
Description:	*Screen printing contractor. Multi-color, high density, glitter, 4CP lites/darks, puff, gel, suede, metallic, crystalline & soft hand printing.*
Year Est:	*1950*
Specialties:	*Can also provide label change, tagging, automatic folding and hanging, drop shipping. Phthalate free inks.*
Markets:	*All markets.*
Machinery:	*2 M&R Challenger 14 color, 1 Precision oval 8 color, 2 Challenger, 1 Folding, 1 Sealing, 1 Oval.*
Minimums:	*12 dozen*
Production Capacity:	*150,000 units/month*

BERGEN SCREEN PRINTING

255 West Broadway
Paterson, NJ 07522
Uday Patel
(1) (973) 595 1222   Fax: (1) (973) 595 5707

E-Mail:	*uday@bergenscreen.com*
Web Site:	*www.bergenscreen.com*
Description:	*One point source. Cotton, linen, silk, spandex, nylon, polyester roll-to-roll textile printing.*
Categories:	*Digital Textile Printing/Screenprinting*
Specialties:	*Specialize in digital textile printing - short run & commercial production.*
Markets:	*All apparel, accessory & home markets.*
Machinery:	*1 - Kornit Allegro Digital Textile Printer*
	4 - M&R Screen Printers
Production Capacity:	*5,000 yards/monthly*

BIG PRINTING T-SHIRT COMPANY

2110 Adams Avenue
San Leandro, CA 94577
Dawaud Muhammad
(1) (510) 638 2782   Fax: (1) (510) 638 2783

E-Mail:	*bigprinting@gmail.com*
Web Site:	*www.bigprintingtshirts.com*
Description:	*Experts in t-shirt printing, embroidery, digital printing & heat transfers.*
Year Est:	*2002*
Specialties:	*Full service apparel manufacturer including screenprinting, embroidery, cut n sew, applique embellishment & custom packaging.*

CALIFORNIA RAIN

1213 E. 14th Street
Los Angeles, CA 90021

(1) (213) 623 6061   Fax: (1) (213) 627 5703

E-Mail:	*info@californiarainla.com*
Web Site:	*www.californiarainla.com*
Description:	*Vertically integrated manufacturing facility. Custom design and manufacture all types of garments to your specs, size, scale & color.*
Year Est:	*1988*
Categories:	*Tee Shirts/Sweat Shirts*
Specialties:	*Screenprint or embroider on any type of material. Also, application of rhinestones, nailheading and transfers. Hangtag & polybag.*
Markets:	*Menswear, Womenswear & Childrenswear.*
Packages:	*Complete package programs*
Minimums:	*Small*
Factory Locals:	*U.S.A., Latin American, Asia*

COLORSTAR CORP.

6464 Ruch Road
Bethlehem, PA 18017
Ali Ismail
(1) (610) 837 2400   Fax: (1) (610) 837 8114

E-Mail:	*colorstar@aol.com*
Web Site:	*www.colorstaronline.com*
Description:	*Factory Direct custom heat seal transfers including: plastisol, white-backing/litho, shimmer, glitter, glow in the dark, foil, hot-peel, etc.*
Year Est:	*1950*
Categories:	*Screenprinting/Heat Transfers*
Specialties:	*Application & finishing provided on site. Provide superior silkscreen products, iron on letters, jersey numbers, stock designs.*
Markets:	*Womens, Mens & Childrens.*

DELUXE SCREEN PRINTING

1358 E 15th Street
Los Angeles, CA 90021
Elsie Acevedo
(1) (213) 765 0838   Fax: (1) (213) 765 8199

E-Mail:	*deluxe@deluxescreenprinting.net*
Web Site:	*www.deluxescreenprinting.net*
Description:	*Provide screenprinted samples & small runs for market week, trade shows, independent clothing lines.*
Year Est:	*2007*
Specialties:	*Specialize in waterbase, discharge inks, plastisol, foils, heat transfer lamination & novelty techniques. Work on cut pieces & finished garments.*
Markets:	*Contemporary, mens, juniors, kids.*
Minimums:	*None*
Production Capacity:	*5,000 units weekly*

DYE FX

544 Park Avenue
Brooklyn, NY 11205
Carol Perri
(1) 718 596 4611   Fax: (1) 718 596 5646

E-Mail:	*carolperri@verizon.net*
Description:	*Silk screen printing contractor on cut pieces or finished garments.*
Year Est:	*2005*
Specialties:	*Silk screen printing, flocking, foil, beads, sequins, tie dye, dip dye, heat transfer application, nail head & rhinestone application.*
Markets:	*Menswear, Womenswear, Children, Accessories, Home.*
Machinery:	*Printing, heat transfer, folding and more.*
Minimums:	*None*
Production Capacity:	*Machine & tie dye: 222,500 doz/month*

EMBROIDERY ONE CORPORATION

1359 Channing Street
Los Angeles, CA 90021

(1) (213) 572 0280   Fax: (1) (213) 572 0283
E-Mail: *emb1@pacbell.net*
Web Site: *www.embroidery-one.com*
Description: *Embroidery and screenprinting contractor.*
Specialties: *Fast turnaround, high quality, reliable and committed to excellence.*

ESTEPHANIAN ORIGINALS INC.

2666 East Huntington Drive
Duarte, CA 91010
Mark Estephanian
(1) (626) 358 7265   Fax: (1) (626) 358 4286
E-Mail: *mark@eodye.com*
Web Site: *www.eodye.com*
Description: *Garment dyed and screen printed looks on nylon, silk, cotton, rayon*
finished garments in a variety of dip dye and tie-dye looks.
Year Est: *1976*
Categories: *Dyeing*
Specialties: *Specialize in tie dye, dip dye, airbrush, contracting services,*
discharge prints, burnouts. All work done in-house.
Markets: *Womenswear & Girlswear.*
Machinery: *Custom machinery*

EXPLOSION SPORTSWEAR/ IMAGE SOURCE

4814 South 35th Street
Phoenix, AZ 85040

(1) (602) 243 2728   Fax: (1) (602) 276 4315
E-Mail: *info@explosionsportswear.com*
Web Site: *www.explosionsportswear.com*
Year Est: *1998*
Categories: *Embroidery*
Specialties: *One stop shop for all apparel, screenprint, embroidery and*
promotional needs.
Markets: *Menswear, Womenswear, Childrenswear, Infants, Accessories.*
Machinery: *90+ Tajima & Brother machines in factory; plus subcontract and*
overseas. Also, embroidery, laundering, washing, printing &
screenprinting equipment.
Packages: *CMT & sewing, finishing & packing.*
Minimums: *36 pieces/style*

FANTASY DESIGNS

23136 Arroyo Vista
Rancho Santa Margarita, CA 92688
David Gleckman
(1) (949) 635 9591   Fax: (1) (949) 635 9592
E-Mail: *dgleck@fantasydesigns.net*
Web Site: *www.fantasydesigns.net*

Description:	*Custom screenprinting, embroidery, graphic design & digitizing on apparel, team uniforms, promo products and catalogs.*
Year Est:	*1994*
Specialties:	*Specialize in low minimums.*
Machinery:	*12 color auto, manual press, numbering machine. Embroidery - 14 heads plus two single heads for small work & personalization.*
Production Capacity:	*60,000 units/monthly*

FINE PRODUCTS/FP SERVICES INC.
90 North Main Street
Florida, NY 10921
Jay Feinberg
(1) (845) 651 4020   Fax: (1) (845) 651 4182

E-Mail:	*jay@fineproducts.net*
Web Site:	*www.fpservicesapparel.com*
Description:	*Custom screen printing, sublimated made in the USA apparel.*
Specialties:	*Made in USA apparel; poly/spandex blanks/all over sublimation poly/blend apparel.*
Markets:	*Menswear, Womenswear, Childrenswear.*
Packages:	*Cut & Sew, design, Ecommerce, production packages.*
Production Capacity:	*60,000-80,000 units/month*

GIMASPORT
241 Ledyard Street
Hartford, CT 06114
Roberto S. Giansiracusa
(1) (860) 296 4441   Fax: (1) (860) 296 8423

E-Mail:	*sales@gimasport.com*
Web Site:	*www.gimasport.com*
Description:	*Custom screenprinting on hats, jackets, tee shirts, polos, bags etc. Fulfillment services.*
Year Est:	*1992*
Categories:	*Embroidery*
Specialties:	*Quality, delivery and attention to detail are our specialties.*
Machinery:	*55 Barudan Embroidery Multi-head.*
Packages:	*All work done in house.*
Factory Locals:	*25,000 sq. ft. building in Hartford, CT.*
Production Capacity:	*75,000 pcs/month*

HENDERSON ADVERTIZING
2508 East Cook Street
Springfield, IL 62703
Leon Henderson
(1) (217) 544 9419   Fax: (1) (217) 522 8155

E-Mail:	*hendersonart@ameritech.net*
Web Site:	*www.henderson-advertising.com*
Description:	*We provide a variety of custom embroidery, embossing, or silk-screening to help you create your product.*
Categories:	*Embroidery*
Specialties:	*A large selection of promotional products. Custom shirts, hats, jackets, sportswear, aprons.*

Markets: *Menswear, Womenswear, Childrens & Accessories.*

LATITUDES
2425 NE Riverside Way
Portland, OR 97211

(1) (503) 248 2060   Fax: (1) (503) 248 2134

E-Mail:	*info@latitudespdx.com*
Web Site:	*www.latitudespdx.com*
Description:	*Custom screen printing, embroidery, design, promotional products. We can accommodate all your design needs from concept to production.*
Categories:	*Embroidery*
Specialties:	*Other services provided - tagging, UPC bar coding, folding, poly-bagging, boxing, palletizing, full service shipping worldwide.*
Markets:	*Menswear, Womenswear, Childrens, Accessories.*
Machinery:	*Embroidery: 15 head Tajima, 6 head Tajima, 1 head Melco*
Packages:	*Full Package Programs including private label product.*
Factory Locals:	*In-house*
Production Capacity:	*150,000 prints/weekly*

LIBERTY GRAPHICS
44 Main Street
Liberty, ME 04949

(1) (207) 589 4596   Fax: (1) (207) 589 4415

E-Mail:	*sales@lgtees.com*
Web Site:	*www.lgtees.com*
Description:	*Toll free#: 1-800-338-0015. Contract screen printer. Screen print on sportswear, outerwear & tees.*
Year Est:	*Special handling, folding, tagging & bagging.*
Specialties:	*Nature-oriented tee shirt design & production, with 100% water based ink. Cotton or cool-max substrates.*
Markets:	*Menswear, Womenswear.*
Machinery:	*2 automatic screen print presses for textiles, 1 hand screen print press & full pre-press dept & separationists.*
Minimums:	*50 units per ink color*

MOONLITE GRAPHICS CO., INC.
951 Broadway
Fall River, MA 02724
Bill Boudreau
(1) (508) 676 6674   Fax: (1) (508) 679 8128

E-Mail:	*moonlite79@verizon.net*
Description:	*Wholesale/contract screenprinting.*
Year Est:	*1979*
Categories:	*Embroidery*
Specialties:	*In-house graphics. Four-color process, cut part printing, familiar with hi-tech fabrics & large volume.*
Markets:	*All apparel markets & all price points.*
Machinery:	*2 automatics & 6 manuals*
Factory Locals:	*14,000 sq. ft. facility*

OREGON SCREEN IMPRESSIONS

3580 NE Broadway
Portland, OR 97232

(1) (503) 231 0181   Fax: (1) (503) 231 9756

E-Mail:	*tiffanyf@oregonscreen.com*
Web Site:	*www.oregonscreen.com*
Description:	*Excellence in screenprinting and embroidery. We offer a broad range of garments - tees, sweats, polos, dress shirts, jackets & bags.*
Categories:	*Embroidery*
Specialties:	*We also provide the following services: labeling, hang tags, packaging, fulfillment services, shipping.*
Markets:	*Menswear, Womenswear, Childrens, Accessories.*
Minimums:	*Screen Printing 24 pcs, Embroidery 12 pcs.*
Factory Locals:	*Our factory is in Oregon but we assist customers throughout the US*

PRIMAL SCREEN

1021 Mason Avenue
Kent, OH 44240
Catie Kuchenbecker
(1) (330) 677 1766   Fax: (1) (330) 677 4299

E-Mail:	*catie@primalscreenprinting.com*
Web Site:	*www.primalscreenprinting.com*
Description:	*Design and print t-shirts, sweatshirts, and other printed apparel.*
Year Est:	*1995*
Specialties:	*Full graphic design and art service, embroidery and other promotions.*
Markets:	*Menswear, Womenswear, Childrens*

QUINTIN CO.

2630 Humboldt Street
Los Angeles, CA 90031

(1) (323) 221 9202   Fax: (1) (323) 221 7304

E-Mail:	*info@quintinco.com*
Web Site:	*www.quintinco.com*
Description:	*Silk Screening specialists. Can produce machine printed & hand printed garments. Samples available.*
Categories:	*Accessories, Embroidery*
Specialties:	*Plastisol based, water based, simulated 4-color process, ink-jet garment printing, burnout/washout, foil, heat transfer pressing etc.*
Markets:	*Menswear & Womenswear, Childrenswear, Infants*
Machinery:	*Large plant with wide variety of machinery.*
Minimums:	*None*

ROYAL APPAREL INC.

See our ad on page 9, 113, 129

65 Commerce Street
Hauppauge, NY 11788
Morey Mayeri
(1) (631) 213 8299   Fax: (1) (631) 922 8438

E-Mail:	*sales@royalapparel.net*

Web Site:	*www.royalapparel.net*
Description:	*Embroidery & screen printing contract work.*
Year Est:	*1993*
Exporting Since:	*1993*
Categories:	*Tee Shirts, Sportswear-Knits, Activewear/Athleticwear,*
	Embroidery, Cutting/Fusing, Childrenswear
Specialties:	*Simple text or complex multi-color artwork.*
Markets:	*Menswear, Womenswear & Childrenswear.*
Packages:	*Full service, complete packages.*
Export to:	*Canada & Europe*
Minimums:	*100 dozen per size/per color*

SEMEL'S EMBROIDERY, INC.

1078 Route 46 West
Clifton, NJ 07013
Dolly Semel
(1) (973) 473 3959   Fax: (1) (973) 473 8895

E-Mail:	*embroideri@aol.com*
Web Site:	*www.semelsembroidery.com*
Description:	*Screenprinting, chainstitch, chenille & vintage embroidery*
	contract work.
Year Est:	*1935*
Exporting Since:	*1990*
Categories:	*Embroidery, Screenprinting Contractors.*
Specialties:	*Same day samples & on-demand delivery. Screen*
	printing, emblems & applique.
Minimums:	*Low. small & large runs okay. Also, do samples.*

SQUEEGEE PRINTERS

4067 VT Route 102
Canaan, VT 05903
Pat Beauregard
(1) (802) 266 3426   Fax: (1) (802) 266 3654

E-Mail:	*squeegee@together.net*
Description:	*Toll-free: 1-800-962-0252. Cater to corporate,*
	special events, advertising specialties & resortwear.
Year Est:	*1984*
Categories:	*Embroidery, Screenprinting Contractors*
Specialties:	*Full service contract screen printing. 4-color*
	process printing.
Machinery:	*M & R Challenger 8-color & M & R Gauntlet II 10-color.*
	2 Automatic press, 1 14-head embroidery machine.
Minimums:	*12 dozen*
Production Capacity:	*Screenprinting: 350 units/hour, Embroidery: Varies*

STYLE COUNCIL, THE

242 West 36th Street
New York, NY 10018
Marissa Porskievies
(1) (212) 564 9380   Fax: (1) (212) 594 2315

E-Mail:	*marissa@stylecouncil.com*

Web Site:	*www.stylecouncil.com*
Description:	*Digital fabric printing for a last minute print for a photo shoot, sales presentation, runway show or short run production domestically in NYC.*
Specialties:	*Colorfast, non-colorfast, dye sublimation and screenprinting.*

SUNDOG PRODUCTIONS

3850 Jermantown Road
Fairfax, VA 22030
John
(1) (703) 978 0041   Fax: (1) (703) 978 0043

E-Mail:	*j.sague@sunpup.com*
Web Site:	*www.sunpup.com*
Description:	*Custom dye work, design work or screenprinting on tee shirts.*
Categories:	*Dyeing contractors*
Specialties:	*Proprietary printing process using seaweed instead of plastisol or traditional water based inks. It has no phalyet PVC's resins or binders.*

UNIQUE SCREEN PRINTING, INC.

10-16 McKinley Street
Linden, NJ 07036
Jose Agrajeda
(1) (908) 925 3773   Fax: (1) (908) 925 3087

E-Mail:	*Jose@uniquescreenprinting.com*
Web Site:	*www.uniquescreenprintings.com*
Description:	*Full range fashion screen printer.*
Specialties:	*Printing & dyeing on cut parts as well as whole garments. Specialize in fashion novelties.*
Markets:	*Menswear, Womenswear & Childrenswear.*
Packages:	*Full packages*
Minimums:	*100 dozen*
Factory Locals:	*Linden, N.J. & Puebla, Mexico*

AMERICAN TEXTILE & APPAREL INC.

10408 W State Road 84
Davie, FL 33324
Luis Mejia
(1) (954) 734 9988   Fax: (1) (954) 734 9966

E-Mail:	*luis.mejia@ata-usa.com*
Web Site:	*www.ata-usa.com*
Description:	*Contractor of knits & woven athletic sportswear, tee shirts, polo shirts and ladies underwear.*
Year Est:	*2002*
Specialties:	*Specialize in private label manufacturing in both knits and woven apparel.*
Markets:	*Menswear, Womenswear, Childrenswear.*
Packages:	*CMT & Full Packages*
Factory Locals:	*Davie Florida plus a network of the best apparel and textile manufacturers from both hemispheres.*
Production Capacity:	*T-Shirts 50,000 doz/month, Polo Shirts 35,000 doz/month, Sportwear 10,000 doz/month, Underwear 100,000 doz/month*

APPAREL PRODUCTION INC.

270 West 39th
New York, NY 10018
Teddy Sadaka
(1) (212) 278 8362   Fax: (1) (212) 278 8357

E-Mail:	*teddyapparelprod@aol.com*
Web Site:	*www.apparelproductionny.com*
Description:	*Manufacture any type of top or bottom from pattern to production.*
Year Est:	*1993*
Categories:	*Pants/shorts/skirts*
Markets:	*Menswear, Womenswear, Boyswear, Girlswear.*
Packages:	*Full service, CMT & Complete.*
Factory Locals:	*Hangzhou China, most patterns however are made in our pattern facility in New York City.*

CALIFORNIA APPAREL SERVICE

2109 S. Standard Avenue
Santa Ana, CA 92707
Tom Lo/Helen Lo
(1) (714) 222 1970   Fax: (1) (714) 442 2788

E-Mail:	*tom@californiaapparelservice.com*
Web Site:	*www.californiaapparelservice.com*
Description:	*Knit & woven tops. Complete T-shirt program. One-stop shop solution for your apparel ideas---tops, bottoms, skirts, dresses.*
Year Est:	*2003*
Categories:	*T-Shirts, Pants/Shorts/Skirts, Childrenswear, Dresses/Blouses, Sportswear*
Specialties:	*Full service apparel manufacturing from design, patterns and grading to cutting, sewing and finishing. From concept through to completion.*
Markets:	*All markets.*
Packages:	*Full package services & private label programs.*

Minimums:	*100 pieces/style*
Factory Locals:	*Work done in-house.*
	http://www.youtube.com/caapparel
Production Capacity:	*2500 - 3000/month - various styles*

CATAWBA CREATIONS

PO Box 1159
Hildebran, NC 28637
Doris Houston
(1) (828) 397 7088   Fax: (1) (828) 397 2357

E-Mail:	*catawbacreations@msn.com*
Description:	*Cut and sew family-owned business specializing in knit tops and bottoms for men, women and children.*
Categories:	*Pants/Shorts/Skirts*
Minimums:	*Will do small quantities*

CRAIG INDUSTRIES

213 Pearl Street
Lamar, SC 29069
Larry Crolley
(1) (843) 326 5561   Fax: (1) (843) 326 1234

E-Mail:	*craig.ind@craigindustries.net*
Categories:	*Shirts/Tops, Tee Shirts.*
Specialties:	*Placket & sport shirts.*
Markets:	*Menswear, Womenswear, Boyswear.*
Machinery:	*Hemmers, pocket setters, placket fusing, serger & embroidery. Also, marking, grading & cutting equipment.*
Packages:	*Complete & CMT.*
Minimums:	*100 dozen/style*
Factory Locals:	*Plants in Lamar & Dalzell, SC.*

DARWOOD MANUFACTURING CO.

620 West Railroad Street
Pelham, GA 31779
Allen Burford, President
(1) (229) 294 4932   Fax: (1) (229) 294 9323

E-Mail:	*darwood@bellsouth.net*
Web Site:	*www.darwoodmfg.com*
Description:	*Cut & sew shirt & garment contractor. Grading/marking, patternmaking, sample making, washing & more.*
Year Est:	*1960*
Categories:	*Grading/Marking, Patternmaking, Sample Rooms, Washing, Embroidery*
Specialties:	*Expertise with all kinds of shirts, tops, pants, shorts, skirts, uniforms & outerwear.*
Markets:	*Menswear, Womenswear, Boyswear & Accessories.*
Packages:	*CMT & complete packages available.*
Minimums:	*5 dozen/style*
Factory Locals:	*Pelham, GA*

DYNOTEX INC.
236 Greenpoint Avenue
Brooklyn, NY 11222
Annie Kwan
(1) (917) 532 9068

E-Mail:	*dynotexinc@gmail.com*
Web Site:	*www.dynotex.com*
Description:	*Manufacture ladies and mens woven & knit bottoms, tops and outerwear. More than just cut & sew services. Quality conscious.*
Year Est:	*1999*
Specialties:	*We can provide patternmaking services, cutting room in-house, sample making, grading & marking, 100% inspection,*
Markets:	*Menswear & Womenswear*
Machinery:	*18 Single Needle, 8 Merrow, 1 Double Needle, 2 Blind Stitch, 2 Double Needle Cover Stitch, 1 Zig Zag, 2 Purl Stitch, 2 Button, 1 Button Hole Straight, 1 Button Hole Keyhole, 2 Snap Machines, 3 Thread Trimmer, 1 Fabric Steamer, 2 Cutting Tables and more.*
Packages:	*Comprehensive technical knowledge of fabrics.*
Minimums:	*None*
Factory Locals:	*All work is done in-house.*
Production Capacity:	*Knitwear: 15,000 units/month, Pants: 10,000 units/month, Blouses: 10,000 units/month, Blazers: 5,000 units/month.*

FIDUCCIA CUSTOM SHIRTS
433 Lincoln Street
Carlstadt, NJ 07072
Walter Quiroga
(1) (201) 507 0644

E-Mail:	*walter@fiducciacustomshirts.com*
Web Site:	*www.fiducciacustomshirts.com*
Description:	*Custom made dress and sport shirt specialists. Specialize in wovens. Samples available.*
Year Est:	*1968*
Specialties:	*Small or large lots.*
Markets:	*Menswear & Boyswear.*

GEMBA GROUP, INC.
501 N Bridge Street
Hidalgo, TX 78557
Jorge Avila Trevino
(1) (956) 607 0890

E-Mail:	*joavila@gembagroup.com*
Description:	*Contract manufacturer of fire retardant garments & Arc Flash Suits up to HRC4.*
Categories:	*Pants, Uniforms*
Specialties:	*Coveralls, hoods, bibs, jackets, pants & lab coats out of FR fabrics like Nomex, Westex Indura/Ultrasoft, Milliken Amplitude, Itex & Keviar fabrics.*
Factory Locals:	*Mexico tel#899 132-6161*

GRECO APPAREL

420 North Spring Garden St.
Ambler, PA 19002

(1) (215) 628 2557   Fax: (1) (215) 352 0464

E-Mail:	*joe@grecoapparel.com*
Web Site:	*www.grecoapparel.com*
Description:	*Contract to order - full package or CMT - from product development to delivery duty paid.*
Year Est:	*1951*
Categories:	*Suits/Tailored Garments, Outerwear, Uniforms, Pants/Shorts/Skirts.*
Specialties:	*Specialize in pants (dress, work & casual), jeans, tailored clothing, shirts (woven & knit), skirts, dresses, outerwear, flame retardant.*
Markets:	*Menswear, Womenswear & Childrenswear.*
Packages:	*Full packages*
Factory Locals:	*USA (Berry Amendment Compliant for US Government), Dominican Republic, Central America, Far East.*
Production Capacity:	*125,000 units/week*

H.T.T. HEADWEAR LTD.

41185 Raintree Court
Murrieta, CA 92562

(1) (951) 304 0400   Fax: (1) (951) 304 0420

E-Mail:	*contact@httapparel.com*
Web Site:	*www.httapparel.com*
Description:	*Manufacturer & contractor of polo shirts.*
Categories:	*Accessories, Outerwear*
Specialties:	*Our factories offer the latest technology such as stain resistant and organic materials along with cutting edge embellishments.*
Markets:	*Womenswear & Menswear.*
Packages:	*All packages.*
Export to:	*United Kingdom & Australia*
Factory Locals:	*Have own domestic plants & can import through Taiwan, China & Pakistan.*
Production Capacity:	*Hats: 5,000 dozen/month & Shirts: 120,00 units/month*

HAGINS INDUSTRIES, INC.

2128 Marion Stage Road
Fairmont, NC 28340
Johnnie Hagins
(1) (910) 628 6777   Fax: (1) (910) 628 5160

E-Mail:	*haginsinds@bellsouth.net*
Description:	*Contractor specializing in knit shirts, tops, golf shirts and polo shirts.*
Year Est:	*1989*
Categories:	*Activewear, Rework/Inspection*
Specialties:	*All type of rework and re-labeling capabilities.*
Markets:	*Menswear, Womenswear & Childrenswear.*
Machinery:	*Overlock & flatlock machines. Full cutting room.*

Packages:	CMT & complete packages available.
Minimums:	None
Production Capacity:	4800 pcs/month

IN.STYLE EXCHANGE™

See our ad on page 75

1844 W. Division Street
Arlington, TX 76012
Sales Manager
(1) (817) 886 9222

E-Mail:	info@instyleexchange.com
Web Site:	www.instyleexchange.com
Description:	Full service, 'one-stop-shop' for shirts & tops, including design, patterns, grading/marking, samples & small run production.
Categories:	Sample Rooms/Small Production, Production Sourcing, Patternmaking, Childrens Wear, Dresses & Blouses, Lingerie, Sleepwear & Robes.
Packages:	Private label & full packages.
Minimums:	50 pieces per color per style
Production Capacity:	50,000 pcs/month

JADE APPAREL

1017 Race Street
Philadelphia, PA 19107
Anh Thai
(1) (215) 922 3953   Fax: (1) (215) 922 7231

E-Mail:	jadey989@aol.com
Description:	Cut and sew moderate size lot contractor.
Year Est:	1995
Categories:	Dresses/Blouses
Specialties:	Specialize in better knits & woven tops, blouses, dresses and men's button down shirts, pants.
Markets:	Menswear, Womenswear & Childrenswear.
Machinery:	40 single needle, 4 double needle coverstitch, zig zag, pearl stitch, safety stitch, blind stitch & bar tack machines, welt pocket machine, smocking.
Packages:	CMT
Minimums:	200 unit per style.
Factory Locals:	Philadelphia, PA
Production Capacity:	30,000 pieces

M.S.R. CUSTOM MADE SHIRTS

600 Broad Avenue
Ridgefield, NJ 07657
Mike/Robert
(1) (201) 941 7970   Fax: (1) (201) 941 7994

E-Mail:	msrcostumshirt@verizon.net
Web Site:	www.msrcustomshirtmakers.com
Description:	Samples & patterns for sport, stretch & dress shirts, costumes & shirt-waist dresses. Custom shirts & blouses made to order.
Year Est:	1990
Categories:	Sample Rooms/Small Production, Costumes
Specialties:	Expert with cowboy, dress & tuxedo shirt styling. Costume design.

Hand packing available.

Markets:	*Menswear & Womenswear*
Machinery:	*Patternmaking, sewing, cutting & grading all in house.*
	10 Single Needle, 5 Irons, 1 Button Hole, 2 Cutting
Packages:	*Full service contractor, all packages available.*
Minimums:	*Vary*
Factory Locals:	*Manufacturing done in-house.*
Production Capacity:	*1,000 pcs/month*

MIAMI STYLE INC.

7480 NW 52nd Street
Miami, FL 33166
Amnon Bensimon/Sofia Rincon
(1) (305) 805 1168   Fax: (1) (305) 805 0075

E-Mail:	*sofia@miamistyle.com*
Web Site:	*www.miamistyle.com*
Description:	*Sourcing agent for all types of active wear, bottoms, tops, tee shirts, knit sportswear, beachwear, sports bras, basics and children's wear.*
Year Est:	*1997*
Categories:	*Active/Athletic Wear, Pants/Shorts/Skirts, Tee Shirts/Sweat Shirts*
Specialties:	*Production services: Private label, sewing, cutting, patternmaking, printing, embroidery, screenprinting, samplemaking, dyeing, beading & more.*
Markets:	*Menswear, Womenswear, Boyswear, Girlswear.*
Factory Locals:	*Bangladesh and China*
Production Capacity:	*3 million pcs per month*

MONALISA FASHIONS INC.

650 East Green Street
Allentown, PA 18109
Mereille Najm
(1) (610) 770 0806   Fax: (1) (610) 770 0823

E-Mail:	*monalisamfg@gmail.com*
Web Site:	*www.monalisamfg.com*
Description:	*Family-owned CMT contractor. The 15,000SF facility includes cutting, sewing, trimming, shipping/storage.*
Year Est:	*1984*
Categories:	*Active & Athletic wear, Childrens Wear, Shirts & Tops, Swimwear, T-Shirts, Sportswear-knits, Sample Rooms/Small Production.*
Specialties:	*Garment dye, organic, contemporary knitwear, infantwear.*
Markets:	*Menswear, Womenswear, Childrens*
Machinery:	*Over-lock, safety, 2-ndl and 3-ndl cover stitch, straight stitch, single needle, neck tape, double needle, metal snaps, elastic cover stitch, binding, button hole, button sewer, picot machine, flatlock, heat press, fusing.*
Packages:	*CMT, Sewing*
Export to:	*Canada, Europe, Asia*
Minimums:	*200 units/style*
Production Capacity:	*50,000 pcs/month*

ROYAL APPAREL INC.

65 Commerce Street
Hauppauge, NY 11788
Morey Mayeri
(1) (631) 213 8299   Fax: (1) (631) 922 8438

See our ad on page 9, 113, 129

E-Mail:	*sales@royalapparel.net*
Web Site:	*www.royalapparel.net*
Description:	*Manufacturer & private label contractor/converter of premium knit apparel. Made to order custom programs.*
Year Est:	*1993*
Exporting Since:	*1993*
Categories:	*Tee Shirts, Sportswear-Knits, Activewear/Athleticwear, Embroidery, Cutting/Fusing*
Specialties:	*Specialize in all kinds of shirts and tops. We produce organic blanks and products.*
Markets:	*Menswear, Womenswear & Childrenswear.*
Packages:	*Full service, complete packages.*
Export to:	*Canada & Europe*
Minimums:	*100 dozen per size/per color*

WELLS HOSIERY MILLS, INC.

1758 South Fayetteville Street
Asheboro, NC 27205

(1) (336) 633 4881   Fax: (1) (336) 633 4862

E-Mail:	*info@wellshosiery.com*
Web Site:	*www.wellshosiery.com*
Description:	*Cut and sew operations specializing in womens high end knit tops.*
Categories:	*Accessories*
Specialties:	*Ladies hosiery. Brand name & private label products. Seamless lines.*
Markets:	*Womenswear.*

Notes

info@fashiondex.com © The Fashiondex, Inc.

COTTON & ELSE INC.
2921 N.W. 28th Street
Lauderdale Lakes, FL 33311

(1) (954) 677 8010   Fax: (1) (954) 677 0270
E-Mail:	*cottonet@bellsouth.net*
Web Site:	*www.cottonandelse.net*
Year Est:	*1992*
Categories:	*Dyeing, Active/Athletic Wear*
Specialties:	*Specialize in knitting, dyeing and sewing of cotton knitted garments. We offer a wide range of Tee-Shirts.*
Markets:	*Menswear, Womenswear & Childrenswear.*
Export to:	*Canada, Europe, Middle East, South America*
Factory Locals:	*Florida*
Production Capacity:	*10,000 doz/week (garments)*

HEMINGWAY APPAREL MFG., INC.
Highway 41 North, P.O. Box 459
Hemingway, SC 29554
Jack Marsh
(1) (843) 558 3482   Fax: (1) (843) 558 9530
E-Mail:	*jmarsh@hemingwayapparel.com*
Web Site:	*www.hemingwayapparel.com*
Description:	*Sewing contractor of ladies sleepwear & lingerie.*
Year Est:	*1978*
Specialties:	*Service for product development.*
Markets:	*Womenswear*
Machinery:	*200 overlock, 20 zig-zag, 80 coverstitch, single needle, double needle, multi-needle, all types of hemmers & more.*
Packages:	*Sewing & CMT. Cutting room on premises.*
Minimums:	*500 dozen/style*
Production Capacity:	*32,000 dozen/month*

IN.STYLE EXCHANGE™   See our ad on page 75
1844 W. Division Street
Arlington, TX 76012
Sales Manager
(1) (817) 886 9222
E-Mail:	*info@instyleexchange.com*
Web Site:	*www.instyleexchange.com*
Description:	*Full service, 'one-stop-shop' for sleepwear & robes, including design, patterns, grading/marking, samples & small run production.*
Categories:	*Sample Rooms/Small Production, Production Sourcing, Shirts & Tops, Childrens Wear, Dresses & Blouses, Lingerie, Patternmaking.*
Packages:	*Private label & full packages.*
Minimums:	*50 pieces per color per style*
Production Capacity:	*50,000 pcs/month*

NEW ICM, LP
220 Sam Bishkin Road
El Campo, TX 77437
R. C. Whitson, Projects Coordinator
(1) (979) 578 0543   Fax: (1) (979) 578 0503

E-Mail:	*rcwhitson@newicm.com*
Web Site:	*www.newicm.com*
Description:	*Manufacturer, designer & contractor of children's sleepwear, slips & panties.*
Year Est:	*1948*
Specialties:	*Flame resistant children's sleepwear, undergarments & slips.*
Markets:	*Childrenswear*
Machinery:	*Over 400 serger, safety stitch, double & triple needle, cover stitch, single needle, zig-zag & numerous other special-operations machines.*
Export to:	*Piece goods & trims for various programs exported to countries in Latin America & Asia.*
Minimums:	*Domestic - none, overseas - negotiable.*
Factory Locals:	*El Campo, TX. Also affiliated with factories in Mexico, Dominican Republic, China & Southeast Asia.*
Production Capacity:	*4,000 units/day for domestic. Virtually unlimited for overseas.*

www.royalapparel.**net**

Manufacturer of Premium Knit Apparel

T-shirts / Blanks
*Private Label / Full Package

Toll Free: 866-769-2517
Fax: 631-922-8438
www.RoyalApparel.net

BRIARCLIFF APPAREL TECHNOLOGIES LTD.

246 West 38th Street
New York, NY 10018
Edward Kostyra, President
(1) (212) 840 7666   Fax: (1) (212) 840 7168

E-Mail:	*fashionprofessor@hotmail.com*
Description:	*Full package sewing contractor of all styles of cut & sew knits & wovens.*
Year Est:	*1994*
Categories:	*Active/Athleticwear, Knit Sportswear, Woven Sportswear, Outerwear, Tee Shirts, Dresses/Suits, Robes/Sleepwear.*
Markets:	*Menswear, Womenswear, Childrens & Infantwear.*
Packages:	*Full, CMT, Samples, Patterns & all production services.*
Minimums:	*Flexible*
Factory Locals:	*New York, NY & throughout tri-state area.*
Production Capacity:	*No limit*

FASHIONS UNLIMITED, INC.

1100 Wicomico Street
Baltimore, MD 21230
Mary Murphy
(1) (410) 783 1584

E-Mail:	*fashionsu@verizon.net*
Web Site:	*www.fashionsu.net*
Description:	*Contractor of knit sportswear, layered ski wear & bodywear. Patternmaker & sample room on premises.*
Year Est:	*1976*
Categories:	*Active/Athleticwear, Lingerie/Intimate Apparel, Sportswear-Knits, Swimwear/Dancewear.*
Specialties:	*We specialize in seamless development. We have seamless knitting capabilities on Santoni Machines. Bras, tops, pants, underwear, swim.*
Markets:	*Womenswear, Childrenswear*
Machinery:	*Overlock, single needle, coverstitch (1 and 2 needle) zig zag, walking foot machines, flat locks.*
Packages:	*Full service, CMT & complete packages.*
Minimums:	*None*
Factory Locals:	*Baltimore MD, Hellam PA, Charlotte NC (Seamless)*
Production Capacity:	*Swim: 1,000 units/week, Activewear: 1,500 units/week, Dance: 1,500 units/week, Sportswear: 1,000 units/week*

GRANITE KNITWEAR/DBA CAL CRU

805 S Salisbury Avenue
Granite Quarry, NC 28072
Mike Jones, President
(1) (704) 279 5526   Fax: (1) (704) 279 8205

E-Mail:	*calcru@mindspring.com*
Web Site:	*www.calcru.com*
Description:	*1-800-476-9944. Contractor & manufacturer of knit apparel & tee shirts using Coolmax & Dri-Release performance knit fabrics.*
Year Est:	*1968*
Exporting Since:	*1980*

Categories:	Active/Athletic Wear, Tee Shirts
Specialties:	Private labeling, custom design & manufacturing, stock inventory & final packaging.
Markets:	Menswear, Womenswear, Children/Infantwear.
Machinery:	1 flatlock, 30 overedger, 4 coverseam, 4 covertape, 4 single needle, 1 button hole, 1 snap machine, 1 pocket, 1 shirring.
Packages:	Full package, screenprinting, embroidery, pattern making.
Export to:	Japan
Minimums:	60 dozen/color/style
Production Capacity:	2,000 doz/month

L.I. CUTTING

2523 Merrick Road
Bellmore, NY 11710
Peter Romeo
(1) (516) 826 6138   Fax: (1) (516) 826 6148

E-Mail:	info@licutting.com
Web Site:	www.licutting.com
Description:	Private label contractor of all types of ladies sportswear knits. Pattern through production.
Categories:	Sample Rooms/Small Production, Swimwear, Uniforms
Specialties:	All work done in-house. Screenprinting & sublimation on site.
Markets:	Womens & childrens markets.
Packages:	CMT, Patternmaking, Samplemaking & Grading.
Minimums:	None

L.S.W. CUTTING & SEWING SERVICE

670 Ninth Street
Oakland, CA 94607
Lana Wong
(1) (510) 891 9246

E-Mail:	lswcuttingandsewing@hotmail.com
Description:	Contractor of cut & sew knit sportswear for all markets.
Specialties:	Complete patternmaking services.
Markets:	Menswear, Womenswear, Chldrenswear.
Packages:	Full service, CMT & complete packages.
Minimums:	300 units/style
Production Capacity:	30,000 pcs/month

MONALISA FASHIONS INC.

650 East Green Street
Allentown, Pennsylvania 18109
Mereille Najm
(1) (610) 770 0806   Fax: (1) (610) 770 0823

E-Mail:	monalisamfg@gmail.com
Web Site:	www.monalisamfg.com
Description:	Family-owned CMT contractor. The 15,000SF facility includes cutting, sewing, trimming, shipping/storage.
Year Est:	1984
Categories:	Active & Athletic wear, Childrens Wear, Shirts & Tops, Swimwear, T-Shirts, Sportswear-knits, Sample Rooms/Small Production.

Specialties:	*Garment dye, organic, contemporary knitwear, infantwear.*
Markets:	*Menswear, Womenswear, Childrens*
Machinery:	*Over-lock, safety, 2-ndl and 3-ndl cover stitch, straight stitch, single needle, neck tape, double needle, metal snaps, elastic cover stitch, binding, button hole, button sewer, picot machine, flatlock, heat press, fusing.*
Packages:	*CMT, Sewing*
Export to:	*Canada, Europe, Asia*
Minimums:	*200 units/style*
Production Capacity:	*50,000 pcs/month*

RAINBOW STYLE

242 West 38th Street
New York, NY 10018

(1) (212) 290 0209

E-Mail:	*info@rainbowpattern.com*
Web Site:	*www.rainbowpattern.com*
Description:	*One-stop service from concept to production. We can cover all types of fabric for knit, chiffon, jersey, netting, denim, wool, leather etc.*
Categories:	*Patternmaking, Samples/Small Production*
Markets:	*Menswear, Womenswear, Childrenswear*

ROYAL APPAREL INC.

See our ad on page 9, 113, 129

65 Commerce Street
Hauppauge, NY 11788
Morey Mayeri
(1) (631) 213 8299   Fax: (1) (631) 922 8438

E-Mail:	*sales@royalapparel.net*
Web Site:	*www.royalapparel.net*
Description:	*Manufacturer & private label contractor/converter of premium knit apparel. Made to order custom programs.*
Year Est:	*1993*
Exporting Since:	*1993*
Categories:	*Tee Shirts, Sample Room, Activewear/Athleticwear, Embroidery, Cutting/Fusing*
Specialties:	*Active sportswear styles in knit jersey, ribs, cotton blends. We produce organic blanks and products.*
Markets:	*Menswear, Womenswear & Childrenswear.*
Packages:	*Full service, complete packages.*
Export to:	*Canada & Europe*
Minimums:	*100 dozen per size/per color*

SARAH LYNN SPORTSWEAR, INC.

431 N. Jordan Street
Allentown, PA 18102
Richard Koury
(1) (610) 770 1702   Fax: (1) (610) 770 1785

E-Mail:	*rkoury@slsportswear.com*
Web Site:	*www.slsportswear.com*

Description:	*Contractor of all types of knit sportswear.*
Year Est:	*1985*
Categories:	*Active/Athletic Wear, Sportswear-Knits, Childrenswear, Tee-Shirts*
Specialties:	*Experience with stretch fabrics & all types of knits. All work done in-house. Also, patternmaking, sample making & rework/inspection.*
Markets:	*Menswear, Womenswear & Childrenswear.*
Machinery:	*20 overlock, 20 safety, 8 coverstitch, 4 button, 4 binding, 9 flat-seam and more.*
Packages:	*Sewing only, Complete & CMT packages.*
Production Capacity:	*75,000 pcs/month*

SILK CITY SALES INTERNATIONAL

108 West 39th Street
New York, NY 10018
Maureen Kwiat
(1) (212) 382 2235   Fax: (1) (212) 382 0923

E-Mail:	*maureen@silkcitysales.com*
Description:	*Fine quality novelty yarns from Italy, Uruguay & classic cashmere from China. Custom handknit garment programs from South America.*
Specialties:	*Cashmere machine knits, natural fiber digital printed knits & woven scarves from China. Sourcing & development for volume knitting in China.*
Markets:	*Menswear & Womenswear.*

SUNCOAST TRENDS CORP.

2860 21st Avenue North
St. Petersburg, FL 33713
Rosanna Carl
(1) (727) 321 4948   Fax: (1) (727) 321 4320

Description:	*Cut & sew contractor of all types of casual knit & woven sportswear.*
Categories:	*Sportswear/Wovens, Accessories*
Markets:	*Menswear, Womenswear, Childrens, Accessories.*
Minimums:	*12 dozen*

SWEENIE MANUFACTURING CORPORATION

34 Sedgwick Avenue
Yonkers, NY 10705
Diane Walker
(1) (646) 825 5027   Fax: (1) (646) 825 5027

E-Mail:	*diane@sweeniemanufacturing.com*
Web Site:	*www.sweeniemanufacturing.com*
Description:	*Branded manufacturer. Specialize in design/merchandising, sourcing and production of activewear, swimwear and cut/sew knits.*
Specialties:	*Specialize in swimwear, activewear, tee-shirts, knit & woven sportswear, sportsbags, gym bags, cosmetic bags. Printed & logo trims.*
Markets:	*Menswear, Womenswear, Childrenswear.*
Machinery:	*Flat bed, button holer, spaghetti strap*
Packages:	*Full package or CMT only*
Factory Locals:	*Domestic & Overseas Production Capabilities.*

V.A. PRIVATE LABEL

3237 Amber Street
Philadelphia, PA 19134
Sarah
(1) (215) 496 0408   Fax: (1) (215) 496 0925

E-Mail:	*info@vaprivatelabel.com*
Web Site:	*www.vaprivatelabel.com*
Description:	*Full service garment production in wovens & knits. Production samples, grading & marking, cutting, sewing, trim, pressing and packing.*
Categories:	*Sportswear/Wovens, Samples/Small Production*
Specialties:	*Custom silk screen printing and embroidery.*
Markets:	*Menswear & Womenswear*

BOULDER PATH DESIGNS

110 E. 2nd Street
The Dalles, OR 97058
Luise Langheinrich
(1) (541) 296 4470   Fax: (1) (541) 298 5067

E-Mail:	*info@boulderpathdesigns.com*
Web Site:	*www.boulderpathdesigns.com*
Description:	*Full service contractor. Product development, specifications, patterns, CAD service, grading, marker making, samples, production runs.*
Categories:	*Patternmaking, Samples/Small Production, Activewear.*
Specialties:	*Problem solving. Experience in work wear, sportswear, hospital gowns, active wear, and more. Can do all styles of tops, bottoms and jackets.*
Markets:	*Menswear, Womenswear & Childrenswear.*
Packages:	*Full service, prototype, development, samplemaking*
Minimums:	*None*
Factory Locals:	*Oregon, USA*

BRIARCLIFF APPAREL TECHNOLOGIES LTD.

246 West 38th Street
New York, NY 10018
Edward Kostyra, President
(1) (212) 840 7666   Fax: (1) (212) 840 7168

E-Mail:	*fashionprofessor@hotmail.com*
Description:	*Full package sewing contractor of all styles of cut & sew knits & wovens.*
Year Est:	*1994*
Categories:	*Active/Athleticwear, Knit Sportswear, Woven Sportswear, Outerwear, Tee Shirts, Dresses/Suits, Robes/Sleepwear.*
Markets:	*Menswear, Womenswear, Childrens & Infantwear.*
Packages:	*Full, CMT, Samples, Patterns & all production services.*
Minimums:	*Flexible*
Factory Locals:	*New York, NY & throughout tri-state area.*
Production Capacity:	*No limit*

MCBEE MANUFACTURING COMPANY

347 West Cypress Avenue
McBee, SC 29101
John/Tom Campolong
(1) (843) 335 8234   Fax: (1) (843) 335 8236

E-Mail:	*vinci@shtc.net*
Web Site:	*www.vinciclothiers.com*
Description:	*Contractor of ladies woven sportswear, tops, bottoms, jackets, pants & skirts.*
Year Est:	*1960*
Categories:	*Sportswear-Wovens, Coats/Jackets, Pants/Shorts/ Skirts.*
Markets:	*Womenswear*
Machinery:	*Complete range of machinery.*
Packages:	*CMT & Full packages available.*
Minimums:	*Vary*
Factory Locals:	*McBee & Camden, South Carolina*

SUNCOAST TRENDS CORP.

2860 21st Avenue North
St. Petersburg, FL 33713
Rosanna Carl
(1) (727) 321 4948   Fax: (1) (727) 321 4320

Description:	*Cut & sew contractor of all types of casual knit & woven sportswear.*
Categories:	*Sportswear/Knits, Accessories*
Markets:	*Menswear, Womenswear, Childrens, Accessories.*
Minimums:	*12 dozen*

SWEENIE MANUFACTURING CORPORATION

34 Sedgwick Avenue
Yonkers, NY 10705
Diane Walker
(1) (646) 825 5027   Fax: (1) (646) 825 5027

E-Mail:	*diane@sweeniemanufacturing.com*
Web Site:	*www.sweeniemanufacturing.com*
Description:	*Branded manufacturer. Specialize in design/merchandising, sourcing and production of activewear, swimwear and cut/sew knits.*
Specialties:	*Specialize in swimwear, activewear, tee-shirts, knit & woven sportswear, sportsbags, gym bags, cosmetic bags. Printed & logo trims.*
Markets:	*Menswear, Womenswear, Childrenswear.*
Machinery:	*Flat bed, button holer, spaghetti strap*
Packages:	*Full package or CMT only*
Factory Locals:	*Domestic & Overseas Production Capabilities.*

V.A. PRIVATE LABEL

3237 Amber Street
Philadelphia, PA 19134
Sarah
(1) (215) 496 0408   Fax: (1) (215) 496 0925

E-Mail:	*info@vaprivatelabel.com*
Web Site:	*www.vaprivatelabel.com*
Description:	*Full service garment production in wovens & knits. Production samples, grading & marking, cutting, sewing, trim, pressing and packing.*
Categories:	*Sportswear/Knits, Samples/Small Production*
Specialties:	*Custom silk screen printing and embroidery.*
Markets:	*Menswear & Womenswear*

CANDILEJAS CLOTHING CO.

742 South Hill Street
Los Angeles, CA 90014
Angelina Munoz
(1) (213) 489 2855   Fax: (1) (213) 489 1845

Description:	*Full service contractor.*
Categories:	*Coats/Jackets, Suits/Tailored Apparel.*
Specialties:	*Women's jackets, pants, skirts, skorts in all fabrics.*
Markets:	*Womenswear.*
Packages:	*CMT & complete packages. Sample room on premises.*
Minimums:	*None*

GRECO APPAREL

420 North Spring Garden St.
Ambler, PA 19002

(1) (215) 628 2557   Fax: (1) (215) 352 0464

E-Mail:	*joe@grecoapparel.com*
Web Site:	*www.grecoapparel.com*
Description:	*Contract to order - full package or CMT - from product development to delivery duty paid.*
Year Est:	*1951*
Categories:	*Shirts/Tops, Outerwear, Uniforms, Pants/Shorts/Skirts.*
Specialties:	*Specialize in pants (dress, work & casual), jeans, tailored clothing, shirts (woven & knit), skirts, dresses, outerwear, flame retardant.*
Markets:	*Menswear, Womenswear & Childrenswear.*
Packages:	*Full packages*
Factory Locals:	*USA (Berry Amendment Compliant for US Government), Dominican Republic, Central America, Far East.*
Production Capacity:	*125,000 units/week*

IN STYLE USA, INC.

307 West 36th Street
New York, NY 10018
James Mallon
(1) (212) 631 0278   Fax: (1) (212) 631 0279

E-Mail:	*instyleusa@instyleusa.net*
Description:	*Contractor & private label manufacturer.*
Categories:	*Dresses/Blouses, Patternmaking, Sample Room/Small Production*
Specialties:	*Expert with women's suits, dresses, blouses, tailored garments. On-time delivery.*
Markets:	*Womenswear*
Machinery:	*Over 100 new machines.*
Packages:	*All*
Minimums:	*None*
Factory Locals:	*New York City.*
Production Capacity:	*12,000 to 20,000 pcs/month*

LEONORA FASHIONS, INC.

1095 East 15th Street
Hialeah, FL 33010
Michael Fiorilli
(1) (305) 885 8148   Fax: (1) (305) 885 8148

E-Mail:	*mike@leonorafashions.com*
Web Site:	*www.leonorafashions.com*
Description:	*Contractor specialized in tailored suits, uniforms, tuxedos, vests & lined jackets & sportcoats.*
Categories:	*Coats/Jackets, Active Outerwear, Uniforms, Suits/Formal*
Specialties:	*Designing, pattern making and grading.*
Markets:	*Menswear, Womenswear.*
Machinery:	*State-of-the-art machinery.*
Packages:	*Full package.*
Factory Locals:	*20,000 sq. ft. factory with warehouse in Hialeah, FL.*
Production Capacity:	*5,000 pieces/week*

ANDARI FASHION INC.

9626 Telstar Avenue
El Monte, CA 91731

(1) (626) 575 2759   Fax: (1) (626) 575 3629

E-Mail:	*info@andari.com*
Web Site:	*www.andari.com*
Description:	*Full service sweater and knits manufacturer.*
Year Est:	*1991*
Specialties:	*Fast turnaround on sampling and production.*
Machinery:	*Wide range of Stoll and Shima Seiki computerized flat-bed knitting machines.*
Factory Locals:	*Domestic manufacturing capabilities plus facilities in China to offer customers more options.*

ARTEX KNITTING MILLS INC.

300 Harvard Avenue
Westville, NJ 08093
Jill Ann Bal
(1) (856) 456 2800   Fax: (1) (856) 456 4111

E-Mail:	*sales@artexknit.com*
Web Site:	*www.artexknit.com*
Description:	*Knitting contractor of hats, leg warmers, gloves, men's ties and more.*
Year Est:	*1926*
Categories:	*Accessories, Embroidery*
Specialties:	*Specialize in custom knitted accessories, embroidery and custom color.*
Machinery:	*Knitting, embroidery and sewing machines. Production done in-house.*
Minimums:	*None*
Factory Locals:	*Above*
Production Capacity:	*100,000 doz/month*

AVITEX

461 Frelinghuysen Avenue
Newark, NJ 07114
Avi
(1) (973) 242 2410   Fax: (1) (973) 242 7258

E-Mail:	*avi@avitex.com*
Web Site:	*www.celioavitex.com*
Description:	*Knitting contractor catering to outerwear, athletic, sportswear, uniform & military markets.*
Specialties:	*Full-fashion sweaters in course & fine gauge knit.*
Markets:	*Menswear, Womenswear, Children/Infantwear.*
Packages:	*Full packages available*

BLANKET BOSS

87 Windermere Avenue
Greenwood Lake, NY 10925
Barney Lopilato
(1) (845) 477 4774

E-Mail:	*blanketboss@aol.com*

Web Site:	*www.theblanketboss.com*
Description:	*Specialize in making patterns & samples of knit sweaters & cards for production knitting machines.*
Categories:	*Sample Rooms/Small Production, Embroidery*
Specialties:	*Personalized photo blankets & pillows and unique scarves. Sublimation - print high quality photos on apparel & shoulder bags.*
Markets:	*Mens, womens & childrens sweater makers.*
Machinery:	*Knitting machines: Stoll 7 gg, Stoll 10 gg, Shima 7 gg, Shima 10 gg.*
Production Capacity:	*1,000 units/month*

FAIR TRADE KNITTERS

12 Brooklawn Drive
East Windsor, NJ 08520
Meredith Kubicki
(1) (609) 610 4018   Fax: (1) (609) 426 9266

E-Mail:	*sales@fairtradeknitters.com*
Web Site:	*www.fairtradeknitters.com*
Description:	*We can knit anything that's handknitted, from garments to accessories to home decor, costumes, jewelry. Create samples for knitwear designers.*
Specialties:	*Hand knit; embroidery, intarsia, cables, stitch patterns, lace color changes, fair isle knitting, crochet.*
Markets:	*Menswear, Womenswear, Children, Accessories, Home.*
Export to:	*Canada, Europe, Australia*
Minimums:	*Production knitting on both a small & large scale.*
Production Capacity:	*250/300 adult sweaters/month*

J.B.'S PRIVATE LABEL

1031 South Broadway
Los Angeles, CA 90015
Jackie Bender
(1) (213) 747 1922   Fax: (1) (213) 747 1963

E-Mail:	*jackiembender@aol.com*
Web Site:	*www.dunadesigns.com*
Year Est:	*1980*
Categories:	*Sweaters/Knitwear*
Specialties:	*Hand-loomed knitwear.*
Markets:	*Womenswear.*
Machinery:	*Flatbed machinery in house, no industrial machines.*
Minimums:	*Low*

LEAHPATRA KNITTING

7543 Trask Avenue
Los Angeles, CA 90293
Leah Walton
(1) 310 951 9095

E-Mail:	*leahpatra@leahpatra.com*
Web Site:	*www.leahpatra.com*
Description:	*Domestic knitting contractor. Design, sample making services, small & large production capabilities. By appointment only.*
Categories:	*Sample Room/Small Production*

Specialties:	Specialty is cashmere & high end novelty knitwear, scarves, handbags, sweaters.
Minimums:	None
Production Capacity:	1500 units/month

SILK CITY FIBERS
155 Oxford Street
Paterson, NJ 07522
Mady Fechner
(1) 800 899 7455   Fax: (1) 888 899 6737

E-Mail:	scfserv@aol.com
Web Site:	www.silkcityfibers.com
Description:	Knit projects from design sketch to samples to offshore production, whether for small or large runs.
Specialties:	Crochet, embroidery, hand knitting also offered.

SWEATER BRAND INC.
401 Park Avenue
Brooklyn, NY 11205
Moshie Rosenberg
(1) (718) 797 0505   Fax: (1) (718) 875 8028

E-Mail:	info@sweaterbrand.com
Description:	Sweater contracting & private label manufacturing.
Year Est:	1983
Exporting Since:	1983
Markets:	All
Machinery:	75 computer & 150 finishing machines.
Packages:	All types of programs & private label import packages.
Export to:	Canada 10%
Minimums:	50 dozen/style
Production Capacity:	15,000 dozen/month

FASHIONS UNLIMITED, INC.

1100 Wicomico Street
Baltimore, MD 21230
Mary Murphy
(1) (410) 783 1584

E-Mail:	*fashionsu@verizon.net*
Web Site:	*www.fashionsu.net*
Description:	*Contractor of swimwear, bodywear & costumes. Patternmaker & sample room on premises.*
Year Est:	*1976*
Categories:	*Active/Athleticwear, Lingerie/Intimate Apparel, Sportswear-Knits, Swimwear/Dancewear.*
Specialties:	*We specialize in seamless development. We have seamless knitting capabilities on Santoni Machines. Bras, tops, pants, underwear, swim.*
Markets:	*Womenswear, Childrenswear*
Machinery:	*Overlock, single needle, coverstitch (1 and 2 needle) zig zag, walking foot machines, flat locks.*
Packages:	*Full service, CMT & complete packages.*
Minimums:	*None*
Factory Locals:	*Baltimore MD, Hellam PA, Charlotte NC (Seamless)*
Production Capacity:	*Swim: 1,000 units/week, Activewear: 1,500 units/week, Dance: 1,500 units/week, Sportswear: 1,000 units/week*

HARDRIVE PRODUCTIONS, INC.

4605 L.B. McLeod Road
Orlando, FL 32811
Michael
(1) (407) 872 3030   Fax: (1) (407) 872 1474

E-Mail:	*hdrivemike@aol.com*
Web Site:	*www.hardriveinc.com*
Description:	*Sewing contract work.*
Specialties:	*Expertise with theatrical costumes, dancewear, show choirs & various other apparel types.*
Markets:	*Womenswear, Childrenswear.*
Packages:	*Patternmaking, samples & small production sewing.*

HEIDI-HO, INC.

8322 George Washington Hwy
Keysville, VA 23947

(1) (434) 736 8763   Fax: (1) (434) 736 0646

E-Mail:	*heidiho@kinex.net*
Description:	*Cut, sew and finish contractor since 1976. Dance costumes, swimwear, kids clothes woven and knit.*
Markets:	*Womenswear, Girlswear, Infantwear.*

L.I. CUTTING
2523 Merrick Road
Bellmore, NY 11710
Peter Romeo
(1) (516) 826 6138   Fax: (1) (516) 826 6148

E-Mail:	*info@licutting.com*
Web Site:	*www.licutting.com*
Description:	*Private label contractor of all types of ladies swimwear.* *Pattern through production.*
Categories:	*Sample Rooms/Small Production, Uniforms, Sportswear/Knits*
Specialties:	*All work done in-house. Screenprinting & sublimation on site.*
Markets:	*Womens & childrens markets.*
Packages:	*CMT, Patternmaking, Samplemaking & Grading.*
Minimums:	*None*

SOLID STONE FABRICS
26 Fayette Street
Martinsville, VA 24112
David Stone
(1) (276) 634 0115   Fax: (1) (276) 632 8986

E-Mail:	*dstone@solidstonefabrics.com*
Web Site:	*www.solidstonefabrics.com*
Description:	*Cut and sew contractor of dancewear and clothing for athletes such as gymnasts.*
Categories:	*Athleticwear, Small Production*
Specialties:	*Small production lots.*
Markets:	*Menswear & Womenswear.*
Minimums:	*Small*

SWEENIE MANUFACTURING CORPORATION
34 Sedgwick Avenue
Yonkers, NY 10705
Diane Walker
(1) (646) 825 5027   Fax: (1) (646) 825 5027

E-Mail:	*diane@sweeniemanufacturing.com*
Web Site:	*www.sweeniemanufacturing.com*
Description:	*Branded manufacturer. Specialize in design/merchandising, sourcing and production of activewear, swimwear and cut/sew knits.*
Specialties:	*Specialize in swimwear, activewear, tee-shirts, knit & woven sportswear, sportsbags, gym bags, cosmetic bags. Printed & logo trims.*
Markets:	*Menswear, Womenswear, Childrenswear.*
Machinery:	*Flat bed, button holer, spaghetti strap*
Packages:	*Full package or CMT only*
Factory Locals:	*Domestic & Overseas Production Capabilities.*

www.royalapparel.**net**

Manufacturer of
Premium Knit Apparel
T-shirts / Blanks
*Private Label / Full Package

Toll Free: 866-769-2517
Fax: 631-922-8438
www.RoyalApparel.net

BIG PRINTING T-SHIRT COMPANY

2110 Adams Avenue
San Leandro, CA 94577
Dawaud Muhammad
(1) (510) 638 2782   Fax: (1) (510) 638 2783

E-Mail:	*bigprinting@gmail.com*
Web Site:	*www.bigprintingtshirts.com*
Description:	*Experts in t-shirt printing, embroidery, digital printing &*
	heat transfers.
Year Est:	*2002*
Specialties:	*Full service apparel manufacturer including screenprinting,*
	embroidery, cut n sew, applique embellishment & custom packaging.

CALIFORNIA APPAREL SERVICE

2109 S. Standard Avenue
Santa Ana, CA 92707
Tom Lo/Helen Lo
(1) (714) 222 1970   Fax: (1) (714) 442 2788

E-Mail:	*tom@californiaapparelservice.com*
Web Site:	*www.californiaapparelservice.com*
Description:	*Complete T-shirt program. From concept through to completion,*
	1-stop shop solution for your t-shirt ideas.
Year Est:	*2003*
Categories:	*Shirts/Tops, Pants/Shorts/Skirts, Childrenswear,*
	Dresses/Blouses, Sportswear
Specialties:	*Full service apparel manufacturing from design, patterns and grading*
	to cutting, sewing and finishing.
Markets:	*All markets.*
Packages:	*Full package services & private label programs.*
Minimums:	*100 pieces/style*
Factory Locals:	*Work done in-house.*
	http://www.youtube.com/caapparel
Production Capacity:	*2500 - 3000/month - various styles*

CALIFORNIA RAIN

1213 E. 14th Street
Los Angeles, CA 90021

(1) (213) 623 6061   Fax: (1) (213) 627 5703

E-Mail:	*info@californiarainla.com*

Web Site:	*www.californiarainla.com*
Description:	*Vertically integrated manufacturing facility. Custom design and manufacture all types of garments to your specs, size, scale & color.*
Year Est:	*1988*
Categories:	*Screenprinting*
Specialties:	*Screenprint or embroider on any type of material. Also, application of rhinestones, nailheading and transfers. Hangtag & polybag.*
Markets:	*Menswear, Womenswear & Childrenswear.*
Packages:	*Complete package programs*
Minimums:	*Small*
Factory Locals:	*U.S.A., Latin American, Asia*

CRAIG INDUSTRIES

213 Pearl Street
Lamar, SC 29069
Larry Crolley
(1) (843) 326 5561   Fax: (1) (843) 326 1234

E-Mail:	*craig.ind@craigindustries.net*
Categories:	*Shirts/Tops, Tee Shirts.*
Specialties:	*Tee shirts & placket shirts.*
Markets:	*Menswear, Womenswear, Boyswear.*
Machinery:	*Hemmers, pocket setters, placket fusing, serger & embroidery. Also, marking, grading & cutting equipment.*
Packages:	*Complete & CMT.*
Minimums:	*100 dozen/style*
Factory Locals:	*Plants in Lamar & Dalzell, SC.*

FINE PRODUCTS/FP SERVICES INC.

90 North Main Street
Florida, NY 10921
Jay Feinberg
(1) (845) 651 4020   Fax: (1) (845) 651 4182

E-Mail:	*jay@fineproducts.net*
Web Site:	*www.fpservicesapparel.com*
Description:	*From tees to jackets to uniforms and more, we are the source for everything custom. Private Label programs available.*
Categories:	*Screenprinting, Uniforms*
Specialties:	*Made in USA apparel; poly/spandex blanks/all over sublimation poly/blend apparel.*
Markets:	*Menswear, Womenswear, Childrenswear.*
Packages:	*Cut & Sew, design, Ecommerce, production packages.*
Production Capacity:	*60,000-80,000 units/month*

GRANITE KNITWEAR/DBA CAL CRU

805 S Salisbury Avenue
Granite Quarry, NC 28072
Mike Jones, President
(1) (704) 279 5526   Fax: (1) (704) 279 8205

E-Mail:	*calcru@mindspring.com*
Web Site:	*www.calcru.com*
Description:	*1-800-476-9944. Contractor & manufacturer of knit apparel &*

tee shirts using Coolmax & Dri-Release performance knit fabrics.

Year Est:	*1968*
Exporting Since:	*1980*
Categories:	*Sportswear-Knits, Active/Athletic Wear*
Specialties:	*Private labeling, custom design & manufacturing, stock inventory & final packaging.*
Markets:	*Menswear, Womenswear, Children/Infantwear.*
Machinery:	*1 flatlock, 30 overedger, 4 coverseam, 4 covertape, 4 single needle, 1 button hole, 1 snap machine, 1 pocket, 1 shirring.*
Packages:	*Full package, screenprinting, embroidery, pattern making.*
Export to:	*Japan*
Minimums:	*60 dozen/color/style*
Production Capacity:	*2,000 doz/month*

HARPER INDUSTRIES, INC.

29 Hillcrest Road
Berkeley, CA 94705
Tom Friedland
(1) (510) 655 5143   Fax: (1) (510) 923 9542

E-Mail:	*tsf@harcrest.com*
Web Site:	*www.harcrest.com*
Description:	*Contractor & manufacturer of tee shirts, sport team uniforms, medical scrubs, smocks.*
Categories:	*Production Sourcing/Factory Agent*
Markets:	*Menswear, Womenswear, Unisex.*
Packages:	*CMT, Sewing & Full Packages.*
Factory Locals:	*Yucatan Peninsula Mexico*
Production Capacity:	*1,000,000 pcs/month*

HEMINGWAY APPAREL MFG., INC.

Highway 41 North, P.O. Box 459
Hemingway, SC 29554
Jack Marsh
(1) (843) 558 3482   Fax: (1) (843) 558 9530

E-Mail:	*jmarsh@hemingwayapparel.com*
Web Site:	*www.hemingwayapparel.com*
Description:	*Sewing contractor of ladies tee shirts.*
Year Est:	*1978*
Categories:	*Tee Shirts, Lingerie/Intimate Apparel, Sleepwear/Robes.*
Specialties:	*Service for product development.*
Markets:	*Womenswear*
Machinery:	*200 overlock, 20 zig-zag, 80 coverstitch, single needle, double needle, multi-needle, all types of hemmers & more.*
Packages:	*Sewing & CMT. Cutting room on premises.*
Minimums:	*1,000 dozen/style*
Production Capacity:	*32,000 dozen/month*

MIAMI STYLE INC.
7480 NW 52nd Street
Miami, FL 33166
Amnon Bensimon/Sofia Rincon
(1) (305) 805 1168   Fax: (1) (305) 805 0075

E-Mail:	*sofia@miamistyle.com*
Web Site:	*www.miamistyle.com*
Description:	*Sourcing agent for all types of active wear, bottoms, tops, tee shirts, knit sportswear, beachwear, sports bras, basics and children's wear.*
Year Est:	*1997*
Categories:	*Active/Athletic Wear, Pants/Shorts/Skirts, Shirts/Tops*
Specialties:	*Production services: Private label, sewing, cutting, patternmaking, printing, embroidery, screenprinting, samplemaking, dyeing, beading & more.*
Markets:	*Menswear, Womenswear, Boyswear, Girlswear.*
Factory Locals:	*Bangladesh and China*
Production Capacity:	*3 million pcs per month*

MONALISA FASHIONS INC.
650 East Green Street
Allentown, PA 18109
Mereille Najm
(1) (610) 770 0806   Fax: (1) (610) 770 0823

E-Mail:	*monalisamfg@gmail.com*
Web Site:	*www.monalisamfg.com*
Description:	*Family-owned CMT contractor. The 15,000SF facility includes cutting, sewing, trimming, shipping/storage.*
Year Est:	*1984*
Categories:	*Active & Athletic wear, Childrens Wear, Shirts & Tops, Swimwear, T-Shirts, Sportswear-knits, Sample Rooms/Small Production.*
Specialties:	*Garment dye, organic, contemporary knitwear, infantwear.*
Markets:	*Menswear, Womenswear, Childrens*
Machinery:	*Over-lock, safety, 2-ndl and 3-ndl cover stitch, straight stitch, single needle, neck tape, double needle, metal snaps, elastic cover stitch, binding, button hole, button sewer, picot machine, flatlock, heat press, fusing.*
Packages:	*CMT, Sewing*
Export to:	*Canada, Europe, Asia*
Minimums:	*200 units/style*
Production Capacity:	*50,000 pcs/month*

PARAMOUNT APPAREL INTERNATIONAL
1 Paramount Drive
Bourbon, MO 65441

(1) (573) 732 4411   Fax: (1) (573) 732 5211

E-Mail:	*sales@paramountapparel.com*
Web Site:	*www.paramountapparel.com*
Description:	*Custom screenprinted t-shirts.*
Specialties:	*Fashion knit headwear & fedoras. Cap & Tee combos. .Cutting edge designs.*

Markets:	*Menswear, Womenswear, Boyswear, Girlswear.*	
Packages:	*Full service including embroidery & silk-screening.*	
Minimums:	*Vary*	

ROOCHI TRADERS INC.

6393 East Washington Blvd
City of Commerce, CA 90040
Mickey Sachdeva
(1) (323) 722 5592   Fax: (1) (323) 724 0045

E-Mail:	*mickey@roochi.com*
Web Site:	*www.cottonheritage.com*
Description:	*Over 25+ years of sportswear and activewear sourcing for men, women and children, also junior knits.*
Categories:	*Production Sourcing/Factory Agent, Jeans/Denimwear, Outerwear, Polo Shirts*
Specialties:	*We stock blank inventory in our DC's NJ, FL and CA for at once delivery.*
Markets:	*Menswear, Womenswear & Childrenswear.*
Export to:	*Europe, Mexico, Central America, Canada*
Production Capacity:	*100,000 doz/month + per category*

ROYAL APPAREL INC.

See our ad on page 9, 113, 129

65 Commerce Street
Hauppauge, NY 11788
Morey Mayeri
(1) (631) 213 8299   Fax: (1) (631) 922 8438

E-Mail:	*sales@royalapparel.net*
Web Site:	*www.royalapparel.net*
Description:	*Manufacturer & private label contractor/converter of all tee shirt styles. Made to order custom programs.*
Year Est:	*1993*
Exporting Since:	*1993*
Categories:	*Sample Rooms, Sportswear-Knits, Activewear/Athleticwear, Embroidery, Cutting/Fusing*
Specialties:	*Active sportswear styles in knit jersey, ribs, cotton blends. We produce organic blanks and products.*
Markets:	*Menswear, Womenswear & Childrenswear.*
Packages:	*Full service, complete packages.*
Export to:	*Canada & Europe*
Minimums:	*100 dozen per size/per color*

SARAH LYNN SPORTSWEAR, INC.

431 N. Jordan Street
Allentown, PA 18102
Richard Koury
(1) (610) 770 1702   Fax: (1) (610) 770 1785

E-Mail:	*rkoury@slsportswear.com*
Web Site:	*www.slsportswear.com*
Description:	*Contractor of all types of tee shirts.*
Year Est:	*1985*
Categories:	*Active/Athletic Wear, Sportswear-Knits, Childrenswear*

Specialties:	*Experience with stretch fabrics & all types of knits. All work done in-house. Also, patternmaking, sample making & rework/inspection.*
Markets:	*Menswear, Womenswear & Childrenswear.*
Machinery:	*20 overlock, 20 safety, 8 coverstitch, 4 button, 4 binding, 9 flat-seam and more.*
Packages:	*Sewing only, Complete & CMT packages.*
Production Capacity:	*75,000 pcs/month*

SWEENIE MANUFACTURING CORPORATION

34 Sedgwick Avenue
Yonkers, NY 10705
Diane Walker
(1) (646) 825 5027   Fax: (1) (646) 825 5027

E-Mail:	*diane@sweeniemanufacturing.com*
Web Site:	*www.sweeniemanufacturing.com*
Description:	*Branded manufacturer. Specialize in design/merchandising, sourcing and production of activewear, swimwear and cut/sew knits.*
Specialties:	*Specialize in swimwear, activewear, tee-shirts, knit & woven sportswear, sportsbags, gym bags, cosmetic bags. Printed & logo trims.*
Markets:	*Menswear, Womenswear, Childrenswear.*
Machinery:	*Flat bed, button holer, spaghetti strap*
Packages:	*Full package or CMT only*
Factory Locals:	*Domestic & Overseas Production Capabilities.*

AA WORLD CLASS EMBROIDERY & EMBELLISHMENT CO.

450 Murray Hill Parkway
East Rutherford, NJ 07073
Ben Amoruso
(1) (201) 313 0022   Fax: (1) (201) 313 0044

E-Mail:	*bena@aaworld.com*
Web Site:	*www.aaworld.com*
Description:	*Toll-free: 1-800-526-0411. Contractor expert*
	types of heat seal embroidery & embellishments.
Year Est:	*1986*
Exporting Since:	*1990*
Specialties:	*Embroidered, applique, emblems, transfers, novelty self trims,*
	& many exciting processes. Any design can be made.
Markets:	*Menswear, Womenswear, Childrenswear, Accessories.*
Export to:	*Worldwide*
Minimums:	*250-1,000/style per size*
Production Capacity:	*Unlimited*

ADVANCE PLEATING & BUTTON CO.

750 Florida Street
San Francisco, CA 94110
Greg Cruz, Manager
(1) (415) 648 3111   Fax: (1) (415) 648 7284

Description:	*Contractor of textile trimmings. Custom trimming and covered*
	buttons for apparel and accessories.
Specialties:	*Specialized trimmings: bias, cord edge, spaghetti,*
	piping, looping, strapping, ruffling, fringe & more.
Minimums:	*$25.00/order*

FLEXSYSTEMS USA INC.

727 West Main Street
El Cajon, CA 92020
Gary Smith
(1) (619) 401 1858   Fax: (1) (619) 401 1848

E-Mail:	*sales@flexsystems.com*
Web Site:	*www.flexsystems.com*
Description:	*Manufacturer of custom PVC, corn plastic labels, zip pulls,*
	promotional products.
Year Est:	*1994*
Categories:	*Small Production*
Specialties:	*Sourcing, assembly, fulfillment, custom R&D, sewing, warehousing*
	and packaging.
Markets:	*Menswear, Womenswear, Children, Accessories, Home.*
Export to:	*Canada 8%, Mexico 2%*
Minimums:	*None*

FORMART CORPORATION

312 Fifth Avenue
New York, NY 10001
Sheung Mei Liu
(1) (212) 819 1819   Fax: (1) (212) 921 1992

E-Mail:	*bellini_formart@hotmail.com*
Web Site:	*www.formartcorp.com*
Description:	*Beading, stone setting contractor for jewelry, accessories and garments.*
Year Est:	*1988*
Specialties:	*Hot-Fix crystal stones onto all kinds of fabric, leather, garments and accessories.*
Minimums:	*None*
Production Capacity:	*5,000 sets/month*

HICKORY BRANDS INC.

P.O. Box 429
Hickory, NC 28603
Josh Higgins
(1) (828) 322 2600   Fax: (1) (828) 328 1700

E-Mail:	*josh@hickorybrands.com*
Web Site:	*www.tenseconds.com*
Description:	*Custom fabric trims, drawcords, lanyards, shoe laces, insoles & more.*
Year Est:	*1923*
Specialties:	*Open line of childrens designs & can do any custom design.*
Markets:	*Casual & activewear markets & all price points.*
Minimums:	*2500 yds.*

JUST JEN

23510 Telo Avenue
Torrance, CA 90505
Lawrence Smith/Jennifer Smith
(1) 310 539 6000   Fax: (1) 323 903 0308

E-Mail:	*jennifer@justjen.com*
Web Site:	*www.justjen.com*
Description:	*Rhinestone setter with great service & fast turnaround times on all designs. Great designs on t-shirts made with Swarovski crystal.*
Categories:	*Embroidery*
Specialties:	*Wholesale rhinestone t-shirt orders from retailers, organizations and individuals. We also do embroidery decoration.*
Markets:	*Menswear, Womenswear, Childrens/Infantwear.*
Minimums:	*None*

KEMESTRY

1221 Stirling Road
Dania Beach, FL 33004
Fred Kinigsberg
(1) (954) 922 2802   Fax: (1) (954) 922 2012

E-Mail:	*elj1978@aol.com*
Web Site:	*www.kemestryonline.com*
Description:	*Nailhead, rhinestone, eyeletting, rivetting, laminating*

& stud work.

Specialties:	*Application on any type of garment or fabric.*
Markets:	*Middle to high-end.*
Minimums:	*None*

LAMCOM, INC.
224 West 35th Street
New York, NY 10001
Kit Wong
(1) (212) 868 6910   Fax: (1) (212) 868 4050

E-Mail:	*lamcom1@aol.com*
Web Site:	*www.lamcominc.com*
Description:	*Contractor & reliable manufacturing supplier of all types of buttons, zippers, drawcords, patches, snaps & more.*
Specialties:	*All products meet ASTM standards. Customer designs welcome.*
Minimums:	*Sample, small & large size lots workable.*
Factory Locals:	*Factories in China & Taiwan for worldwide distribution.*

METRO TRIMMING CORP.
327 West 36th Street
New York, NY 10018

(1) (212) 564 7966   Fax: (1) (212) 564 6262

E-Mail:	*metrotrimming@gmail.com*
Web Site:	*www.metrotrimmingcorp.com*
Description:	*On prem manufacturer of dress trimmings & bias binding products.*
Year Est:	*1955*
Specialties:	*Spaghetti straps, braiding, bias in all sizes, belt loops, frogs, ruffles, cordedge, baby hemming, fabric flowers, straight & cross cutting.*
Markets:	*All womens markets.*
Factory Locals:	*New York, NY*

NEW CONCEPTS OF NEW YORK LLC
313 West 37th Street
New York, NY 10018
Mel Weiss
(1) (212) 695 4999   Fax: (1) (212) 695 4513

E-Mail:	*sales@newconceptsllc.com*
Web Site:	*www.newconceptsllc.com*
Description:	*Nailhead & rhinestone design work on belts, hats & any type of apparel.*
Categories:	*Accessories, Trim Application*
Minimums:	*None*

SNAPCO MANUFACTURING CORPORATION
140 Central Avenue
Hillside, NJ 07205
Ray
(1) (973) 282 0300   Fax: (1) (973) 282 7627

E-Mail:	*ray.snapco@gmail.com*

Web Site:	*www.snapco.com*
Description:	*Applications of stud, snap, eyelet & nailhead contract work.*
Year Est:	*1946*
Minimums:	*None*

AETNA SHIRT/ON CALL MEDICAL COATS

620 Franklin Avenue
Baltimore, MD 21221
Dan Kohn
(1) (410) 574 2657   Fax: (1) (410) 574 6307

E-Mail:	*customerservice@medicalcoats.com*
Web Site:	*www.medicalcoats.com*
Description:	*CMT contractors of high quality medical coats. Offer state of the art embroidery of names & logos.*
Year Est:	*1916*
Categories:	*Accessories*
Specialties:	*Big & tall shirts, ladies blouses, medical coats & more. Can do custom collars, cuffs & tucking.*
Markets:	*Menswear, Womenswear*
Machinery:	*Over 50 sewing machines: single needle, felling, embroidery, formal shirt pleating & more.*
Packages:	*Sewing, CMT & Complete packages available.*
Export to:	*Japan*
Agent:	*Dan or Wayne. Tel: 877-355-2898.*
Minimums:	*None*
Factory Locals:	*Baltimore, MD*
Production Capacity:	*250 labcoats/week, 1500-2000 woven shirts/week*

AMERICAN SEWING DYNAMICS, INC.

2441 Vermont Avenue #154
Blue Island, IL 60406
Bob Choi
(1) (773) 394 9544   Fax: (1) (773) 394 9610

E-Mail:	*sales@americansewingdynamics.com*
Web Site:	*www.americansewingdynamics.com*
Description:	*Sewing, cutting & assembly services for military & commercial uniforms, casual wear, shoe uppers, leather goods, home & specialty.*
Categories:	*Leather Accessories, Coats/Jackets, Casual Wear*
Specialties:	*Specialize in coveralls, pants, combat uniforms, casual shirts, sportswear, leather & military shoe & boot uppers, leather goods.*
Markets:	*Menswear, Womenswear, Accessories.*
Machinery:	*Multiple - Single needle, double needle, walking, cylinder, felling, pattern tacker, riveting, grommeting, eyeletting, snap, splitting, skiving, button hole, button sewing, bartacker, die cutting, table cutting, puritan, autobarr, zigzag, web cutting, folding, trimming.*
Minimums:	*Vary*
Factory Locals:	*Chicago, IL*
Production Capacity:	*500 - 25,000 units/month depending on material & design.*

BIG FRONT UNIFORMS

4535 Huntington Drive S.
Los Angeles, CA 90032

(1) (323) 227 4222   Fax: (1) (323) 227 4111

E-Mail:	*info@bigfront.com*
Web Site:	*www.bigfrontuniforms.com*

Description:	Our designers will help you to create custom uniforms. Personalized embroidery available. All work done in our on-site factory.
Year Est:	1977
Markets:	Menswear & Womenswear.
Minimums:	2 dozen
Factory Locals:	Domestic 1-800-234-8383

BLOOM FASHION USA

5589-B Guinea Road
Fairfax, VA 22032

(1) (703) 323 6793   Fax: (1) (703) 323 6795

E-Mail:	sales@bloomfashionusa.com
Web Site:	www.bloomfashionusa.com
Description:	Sewing contractor of school, work, athletic & customer uniforms.
Categories:	Childrens Wear, Pants/Shorts/Skirts
Specialties:	We can help you start your new business. 100% of our products are made in the USA.
Markets:	Menswear, Womenswear, Childrenswear.
Minimums:	Low Minimums

CHATHAM KNITTING MILLS, INC.

P.O. Box 152
Chatham, VA 24531
Matt Harris
(1) (434) 432 4701 x11   Fax: (1) (434) 432 3742

E-Mail:	mattharris2006@gmail.com
Description:	Contract sewing of men's & women's outerwear. Also, uniforms & work coats.
Year Est:	1951
Categories:	Coats/Jackets, Uniforms.
Packages:	Sewing only & complete packages.
Minimums:	None

CREATIVE OUTLET, INC.

1600 Bridges Street
Moorhead City, NC 28557
Jim Garner
(1) (252) 808 3898   Fax: (1) (252) 808 2188

E-Mail:	sscrubs@yahoo.com
Web Site:	www.creativeoutlet.info
Description:	Contractor for healthcare apparel & related textile products.
Specialties:	Specialize in hospital uniforms & hospital pajamas.
Machinery:	Digitized embroidery system on site.
Minimums:	None

E.T. MANUFACTURING CO.
192 E. Athens Street
Winder, GA 30680

(1) (770) 867 8152   Fax: (1) (770) 867 0025
E-Mail:	*info@etmanufacturing.com*
Web Site:	*www.etmanufacturing.com*
Description:	*We work with start-ups and apparel/uniform manufacturers by designing & developing your product from concept to production.*
Year Est:	*1990*
Specialties:	*Specialize in industrial uniforms. Aprons, vests, smocks, lab coats, bias binding and tote bags.*
Machinery:	*Our cutting room is equipped with a manual spreader & cutter & can manage fabrics as wide as 60 inches. Our sewing room is equipped with multiple range of singe needle, serger, bar-tack, button-hole & more.*
Packages:	*CMT*

FINE PRODUCTS/FP SERVICES INC.
90 North Main Street
Florida, NY 10921
Jay Feinberg
(1) (845) 651 4020   Fax: (1) (845) 651 4182
E-Mail:	*jay@fineproducts.net*
Web Site:	*www.fpservicesapparel.com*
Description:	*From tees to jackets to uniforms for restaurants & schools, we are the source for everything custom. Private Label programs available.*
Categories:	*Screenprinting, Tee-shirts*
Specialties:	*Made in USA apparel; poly/spandex blanks/all over sublimation poly/blend apparel.*
Markets:	*Menswear, Womenswear, Childrenswear.*
Packages:	*Cut & Sew, design, Ecommerce, production packages.*
Production Capacity:	*60,000-80,000 units/month*

GENESIS IMPORTS
2408 Royal Lytham Drive
Austin, TX 64500
Art Kimbel
(1) (512) 292 4000   Fax: (1) (512) 292 4515
E-Mail:	*akimbel@aol.com*
Web Site:	*www.genesismexico.com*
Description:	*Cut & sew contractors of work shirts, chef coats & coveralls.*
Year Est:	*1993*
Exporting Since:	*1995*
Categories:	*Accessories, Home Furnishings*
Specialties:	*Uniforms*
Machinery:	*160 sewing machines. Single needle, overlocking, double needle, bar tack, flat safety stitch, button, buttonholers & cutting knives, plus 2 20-ton die cut presses & 2 50-foot cutting tables.*
Export to:	*USA & Canada.*
Minimums:	*None*
Factory Locals:	*Promotora Genesis in Monterrey, Mexico. Two locations*

with over 30,000 sq ft. Registered with the FDA in USA.

GIL SEWING CORPORATION
3500 N. Kostner Avenue
Chicago, IL 60641

(1) (773) 545 0990   Fax: (1) (773) 545 0778

E-Mail:	*gilsewing@sbcglobal.net*
Web Site:	*www.gilsewing.com*
Description:	*Garment manufacturer. Pattern creation, cut, sew, quality control &*
	shipped according to client's specs.
Year Est:	*1993*
Specialties:	*Specialize in uniforms, tailored and work clothing.*
Markets:	*Womenswear & Menswear.*
Machinery:	*Gerber GTXL Computer Cutter*

GRECO APPAREL
420 North Spring Garden St.
Ambler, PA 19002

(1) (215) 628 2557   Fax: (1) (215) 352 0464

E-Mail:	*joe@grecoapparel.com*
Web Site:	*www.grecoapparel.com*
Description:	*Contract to order - full package or CMT - from product development*
	to delivery duty paid.
Year Est:	*1951*
Categories:	*Suits/Tailored Garments, Shirts/Tops, Outerwear*
	Pants/Shorts/Skirts.
Specialties:	*Specialize in pants (dress, work & casual), jeans, tailored clothing,*
	shirts (woven & knit), skirts, dresses, outerwear, flame retardant.
Markets:	*Menswear, Womenswear & Childrenswear.*
Packages:	*Full packages*
Factory Locals:	*USA (Berry Amendment Compliant for US Government),*
	Dominican Republic, Central America, Far East.
Production Capacity:	*125,000 units/week*

HARPER INDUSTRIES, INC.
29 Hillcrest Road
Berkeley, CA 94705
Tom Friedland
(1) (510) 655 5143   Fax: (1) (510) 923 9542

E-Mail:	*tsf@harcrest.com*
Web Site:	*www.harcrest.com*
Description:	*Contractor & manufacturer of tee shirts, sport team uniforms, medical*
	scrubs, smocks.
Categories:	*Tee Shirts/Sweat Shirts, Production Sourcing Agent*
Markets:	*Menswear, Womenswear, Unisex.*
Packages:	*CMT, Sewing & Full Packages.*
Factory Locals:	*Yucatan Peninsula Mexico*
Production Capacity:	*1,000,000 pcs/month*

INTEDGE INDUSTRIES INC.

1875 Chumley Road
Woodruff, SC 29388

(1) (864) 969 9601   Fax: (1) (864) 969 9604

E-Mail:	*sales@intedge.com*
Web Site:	*www.intedge.com*
Description:	*Contractor of men's & women's chef wear.*
Year Est:	*1914*
Categories:	*Uniforms, Home Furnishings.*
Markets:	*Mainly restaurant industry, but open to more.*
Machinery:	*3 overlock, 10 single needle, 1 double needle, 1 bartack, 2 buttonhole, & multi-needle quilting machinery.*
Packages:	*Sewing*
Export to:	*Canada 10%, Puerto Rico 2%*
Minimums:	*None*

JONCO INDUSTRIES INC.

2501 West Hampton Avenue
Milwaukee, WI 53209

(1) (414) 449 2000   Fax: (1) (414) 449 5200

E-Mail:	*tom.ryan@joncoind.com*
Web Site:	*www.joncoind.com*
Description:	*Industrial sewing contractor. Also provide packaging & complete warehousing.*
Year Est:	*1980*
Categories:	*Distribution/Warehouse, Accessories, Sample Rooms/Small Production.*
Specialties:	*Open for all your apparel sewing needs. All work done in-house.*
Markets:	*Menswear & Womenswear*
Machinery:	*5 Juki, 3 Consew, 3 Singer, 1 Melco Amaya, 1 Pegasus 2 Path Finder Cutters, 1 Kongsberg, 1 5' x 10' Laser.*
Minimums:	*None*
Production Capacity:	*Varies by Item*

L.I. CUTTING

2523 Merrick Road
Bellmore, NY 11710
Peter Romeo
(1) (516) 826 6138   Fax: (1) (516) 826 6148

E-Mail:	*info@licutting.com*
Web Site:	*www.licutting.com*
Description:	*Private label contractor of all types of uniforms. Pattern through production.*
Categories:	*Sample Rooms/Small Production, Swimwear, Sportswear/Knits*
Specialties:	*All work done in-house. Screenprinting & sublimation on site.*
Markets:	*Womens & childrens markets.*
Packages:	*CMT, Patternmaking, Samplemaking & Grading.*
Minimums:	*None*

LACORP/LEBANON APPAREL CORP.

70 Thornhill Drive
Lebanon, VA 24266
Jeoff Bodenhorst
(1) (276) 889 3656   Fax: (1) (276) 889 2830

E-Mail:	*jeoff@lacorpusa.com*
Web Site:	*www.lacorpusa.com*
Description:	*Contractor of all types of uniforms.*
Year Est:	*1968*
Categories:	*Pants/shorts/skirts, Childrenswear, Home Furnishings, Rework & Inspection Services.*
Specialties:	*Specialize in a large variety of medical & hospitalwear uniforms.*
Markets:	*Menswear, Womenswear, Childrenswear & Home.*
Machinery:	*Over 500 various sewing machines & electronic cutting, embroidery & besum pocket equipment on site.*
Packages:	*CMT, Sewing, Cutting, Sample Making & Embroidery.*
Minimums:	*Will adjust to fit your needs.*
Factory Locals:	*All work is done in-house.*

LEONORA FASHIONS, INC.

1095 East 15th Street
Hialeah, FL 33010
Michael Fiorilli
(1) (305) 885 8148   Fax: (1) (305) 885 8148

E-Mail:	*mike@leonorafashions.com*
Web Site:	*www.leonorafashions.com*
Description:	*Contractor specialized in tailored uniforms, military jackets & suits of all types.*
Categories:	*Coats/Jackets, Active Outerwear, Uniforms, Suits/Formal*
Specialties:	*Designing, pattern making and grading.*
Markets:	*Menswear, Womenswear.*
Machinery:	*State-of-the-art machinery.*
Packages:	*Full package.*
Factory Locals:	*20,000 sq. ft. factory with warehouse in Hialeah, FL.*
Production Capacity:	*5,000 pieces/week*

NEW ICM, LP

220 Sam Bishkin Road
El Campo, Texas 77437
R. C. Whitson, Projects Coordinator
(1) (979) 578 0543   Fax: (1) (979) 578 0503

E-Mail:	*rcwhitson@newicm.com*
Web Site:	*www.newicm.com*
Description:	*Manufacturer, designer & contractor.*
Year Est:	*1948*
Categories:	*Childrenswear, Activewear, Sleepwear/Robes*
Specialties:	*Industrial workwear coveralls & insulated jackets made of flame resistant fabrics. Nomex, 100% cotton & cotton & modacrylic blends.*
Markets:	*Menswear, Womenswear*
Machinery:	*Over 400 serger, safety stitch, double & triple needle, cover stitch, single needle, zig-zag & numerous other special-operations machines.*

Export to:	Piece goods & trims for various programs exported to countries in Latin America & Asia.
Minimums:	Domestic - none, overseas - negotiable.
Factory Locals:	El Campo, TX. Also affiliated with factories in Mexico, Dominican Republic, China & Southeast Asia.
Production Capacity:	4,000 units/day for domestic. Virtually unlimited for overseas.

PRIORITY MANUFACTURING
571 N.W. 29th Street
Miami, FL 33127
Richard Levy
(1) (305) 576 3000   Fax: (1) (305) 576 2672

E-Mail:	richard@customuniforms.com
Web Site:	www.customuniforms.com
Description:	Manufacturer & contractor of uniforms for restaurants, theme parks, cruise lines, resorts, industrial, chef apparel & more.
Year Est:	1972
Categories:	Uniforms
Specialties:	Custom embroidery & screen printing to any specifications. Toll free-1-800-835-5528
Markets:	Menswear & Womenswear
Packages:	Cutting & sewing, complete & CMT packages available.
Minimums:	36 pieces
Production Capacity:	2000 pcs/month

ROUND HOUSE MANUFACTURING
One American Way
Shawnee, OK 74801
Jim Antosh
(1) (405) 273 0510   Fax: (1) (405) 273 0511

E-Mail:	info@round-house.com
Web Site:	www.round-house.com
Description:	Contractor specializing in bib overalls.
Categories:	Jeans/Denimwear, Uniforms.
Specialties:	All work is produced in the USA.
Packages:	CMT & complete packages. Cutting room in house.
Minimums:	50 dozen/style

SOARING EAGLE OUTERWEAR, INC.
1916 20th Avenue S.E.
Minot, ND 58701
Austin Hall
(1) (701) 838 2110   Fax: (1) (701) 852 4941

E-Mail:	seagle@srt.com
Description:	Contractor of bib coveralls, labor outerwear, smocks & more.
Categories:	Coats/Jackets.
Machinery:	Sergers, cover stitch, multi-needle & pressing machinery.
Packages:	Sewing & CMT packages.
Minimums:	None. Can handle small & large production lots.

STERLINGWEAR OF BOSTON, INC.

175 McClellan Highway
East Boston, MA 02128
David Fredella
(1) (617) 567 6465   Fax: (1) (617) 567 6472

E-Mail:	*dfredella@sterlingwear.com*
Web Site:	*www.sterlingwear.com*
Description:	*Manufacturers of quality outerwear for men, women & children plus military outerwear clothing.*
Categories:	*Coats & Jackets*
Specialties:	*Will do contract work for private label uniforms.*
Minimums:	*Vary*

TOPPS SAFETY APPAREL INC.

2516 East State Road 14
Rochester, IN 46975

(1) (574) 223 4311   Fax: (1) (574) 223 8622

E-Mail:	*info@toppssafetyapparel.com*
Web Site:	*www.toppssafetyapparel.com*
Description:	*Contractor & manufacturer of flame resistant industrial uniforms & workclothes, such as: cover-alls & jumpsuits.*
Specialties:	*Specialize in safety apparel.*
Machinery:	*Automatic cutting & marking in house.*
Packages:	*CMT, Sewing & Complete.*
Minimums:	*25 dozen/style*
Factory Locals:	*3 factories in Kentucky*

TURFER ATHLETIC

240 Bald Hill Road
Warwick, RI 02886
Gary Goldberg
(1) (401) 427 1369   Fax: (1) (401) 633 7061

E-Mail:	*ggoldberg@turfer.com*
Web Site:	*www.turfer.com*
Description:	*We personalize & customize apparel, uniforms & accessory items for schools, teams, colleges and more.*
Minimums:	*None*

ACE BINDING CO.,INC.

3031 James Street
Baltimore, MD 21230
Larry Cohen
(1) (410) 525 0700   Fax: (1) (410) 525 0714

E-Mail:	*larry@acebinding.com*
Web Site:	*www.acebinding.com*
Description:	*Waist-band, binding, cutting & sewing services.*
Year Est:	*1942*
Specialties:	*Die cutting, table cutting, roll cutting (score, razor, hot knife, pinked), perforating and slotting. Fusing: 72"" capacity, roll to roll.*
Packages:	*807 & CBI Programs*
Minimums:	*Low*

APPAREL SOLUTIONS CORP.

249 West 34th Street
New York, NY 10001
John Harihar
(1) (212) 868 1700   Fax: (1) (212) 868 1701

E-Mail:	*john@usapparelsolutions.com*
Web Site:	*www.usapparelsolutions.com*
Description:	*Pleating, special stitching, cutting & finishing, embroidery, digitizing & trimming contractor.*
Year Est:	*1975*
Categories:	*Pleating/Tucking/Stitching, Cutting & Fusing, Finishing/Coating.*
Specialties:	*Experts in all kinds of cutting. Table, machine, sample, bias, laser & sonic. Also, pressing, labeling & packaging.*

EAST BAY GARMENT CUTTING & SEWING SERVICE

3315 Farnam Street
Oakland, CA 94601
Kelvin Lam
(1) (510) 261 6688   Fax: (1) (510) 261 6888

E-Mail:	*annielam6688@gmail.com*
Description:	*Cutting contract work for all fabric.*
Categories:	*Sample Rooms/Small Production Contractors, Cutting/Fusing Contractors.*
Specialties:	*Great with fabrics for shirts, outerwear, dresses, sportswear, lingerie, uniforms & vests.*
Markets:	*Menswear, Womenswear*
Minimums:	*None*

EXACTA

118 John F. Kennedy Drive North
Bloomfield, NJ 07003
Jeff Giberstein
(1) (973) 259 0104   Fax: (1) (973) 259 0107

E-Mail:	*contactus@exactagarment.com*
Web Site:	*www.exactagarment.com*
Description:	*Full service apparel & garment cutting contractor. Computerized cutting, grading, marking, fusing, piece goods warehousing and more.*

Year Est:	*1970*
Specialties:	*Local production lets you manufacture and ship the latest styles to retailers in two weeks or less. Great for in-season re-order business.*
Markets:	*All apparel markets.*

FINE LINE, INC.
12457 Gladstone Avenue
Sylmar, CA 91342
Michael Collier
(1) (818) 361 8103   Fax: (1) (818) 361 1194

E-Mail:	*info@finelineinc.com*
Web Site:	*www.finelineinc.com*
Description:	*Cutting & fusing service.*
Categories:	*Cutting/Fusing Contractors, Grading/Marking, Patternmaking.*
Specialties:	*Domestic production and sourcing solutions...all made in the USA.*
Markets:	*All*
Machinery:	*Fully automated cutting machines.*

POL SYSTEMS
236 Highway 79 South
Magnolia, AR 71753
Donna Keith
(1) 870 562 2901   Fax: (1) 877 479 7618

E-Mail:	*mdkeith@suddenlink.net*
Web Site:	*www.polsystems.net*
Description:	*Computerized conveyor cutting center with design & nesting capabilities. Complex patterns & materials are cut precisely including notches & holes.*
Year Est:	*2005*
Specialties:	*All work done in-house. We can process a wide variety of materials including fabrics, leather, foam, paper, plastic, films & more.*
Markets:	*All Apparel, Accessories, Home.*
Packages:	*Cutting only*

QUICK FUSING INC.
260 West 36th Street
New York, NY 10018
Igor Goldenberg
(1) (212) 967 0311   Fax: (1) (212) 967 1432

E-Mail:	*quickfuse5@aol.com*
Web Site:	*www.apparelexpert.com*
Description:	*Cut and sew contractor from start to finish. All done in the USA.*
Year Est:	*1987*
Categories:	*Patternmaking, Samples/Small Production*
Specialties:	*Cutting, fusing, sponging, bonding fabrics & leather, patternmaking, sewing, samples. Full production small and large lots.*
Markets:	*Womenswear, Childrenswear, Accessories.*
Packages:	*Complete packages.*
Minimums:	*Small*

RENATO'S CUTTING SERVICE

2193 East 14th Street
Los Angeles, CA 90021
Renato Molina
(1) (213) 489 0944   Fax: (1) (213) 489 0944

Description:	*Garment cutting service.*
Year Est:	*1984*
Specialties:	*Women's dresses, skirts, shorts & tops.*
Minimums:	*100-200 pieces. All size lots welcome.*

ROYAL APPAREL INC.

See our ad on page 9, 113, 129

65 Commerce Street
Hauppauge, NY 11788
Morey Mayeri
(1) (631) 213 8299   Fax: (1) (631) 922 8438

E-Mail:	*sales@royalapparel.net*
Web Site:	*www.royalapparel.net*
Description:	*Cutting and fusing services.*
Year Est:	*1993*
Exporting Since:	*1993*
Categories:	*Tee Shirts, Sportswear-Knits, Activewear/Athleticwear, Embroidery, Screenprinting, Childrenswear*
Markets:	*Menswear, Womenswear & Childrenswear.*
Packages:	*Full service, complete packages.*
Export to:	*Canada & Europe*
Minimums:	*100 dozen per size/per color*

TODD RUTKIN

5801 South Alameda Street
Los Angeles, CA 90001
Abe Garcia
(1) (323) 584 9225   Fax: (1) (323) 584 9295

E-Mail:	*jan@toddrutkin.com*
Web Site:	*www.toddrutkin.com*
Description:	*A complete source for cutting, fusing, grading, marking, slitting & embroidery.*
Categories:	*Grading & Marking, Embroidery*

ACCURATE SERVICES, INC.
951 Broadway
Fall River, MA 02724
Sue Teixeira
(1) (508) 674 5773   Fax: (1) (508) 674 5649
E-Mail:	*suetex@accurateservice.com*
Web Site:	*www.accurateservice.com*
Description:	*Warehousing & distribution for sewn products manufacturers.*
Year Est:	*1955*
Categories:	*Rework/Inspection Services*
Specialties:	*Full range of finishing services: alter, hem, fix patterns, press and steam. Also, label, re-label & package goods.*
Machinery:	*100,000+ sq. ft. of modern shelves, racks, overhead trolleys and conveyors.*

AMERICAN STITCHCO INC.
4662 Highway 62 West
Mountain Home, AR 72653

(1) 888 903 0049   Fax: (1) 870 425 4900
E-Mail:	*stitchco@stitchco.com*
Web Site:	*www.stitchco.com*
Description:	*Over 500,000 sq ft of floor space and 80 shipping docks for all your inbound & outbound shipping & warehousing needs.*
Specialties:	*Automated conveyors, climate controlled, organized racking systems.*

ARI SHIPPING CORP.
80 Sheridan Boulevard
Inwood, NY 10096
Ilan Fidler
(1) (516) 371 7770   Fax: (1) (516) 371 7757
E-Mail:	*ilan@arishipping.com*
Web Site:	*www.arishipping.com*
Description:	*Full service logistics company, air & ocean import/export consolidated services, customs clearance & compliance service.*
Year Est:	*1980*
Specialties:	*Bonded CFS, warehouse & distribution, crating & packing, complete supply-chain management.*

CHANGES/INT'L WAREHOUSING & DISTRIBUTION
5959 NW 37th Avenue
Miami, FL 33142

(1) (305) 828 6811   Fax: (1) (305) 828 6814
E-Mail:	*changes440@aol.com*
Description:	*Customized methods to receive, maintain & distribute inventory.*
Categories:	*Rework & Inspection*
Specialties:	*In-house transportation, bar code capabilities, short- & long-term storage, quality control inspection, return inspection & rework.*
Machinery:	*20 single needle, 20 zig zag, 3 button, 3 coverstitch*
Production Capacity:	*100,000 dz/month*

DEPENDABLE DISTRIBUTION CENTERS

2555 East Olympic Boulevard
Los Angeles, CA 90023
J.P. Durrer
(1) (323) 526 2200 ext. 2086   Fax: (1) (323) 526 2201

E-Mail:	*jp.durrer@dependableinc.com*
Web Site:	*www.godependable.com*
Description:	*Third-party warehousing throughout California.*
Year Est:	*1956*
Specialties:	*Distribution, automated GOH, racks, pick & pack, order fulfillment, cross docking, flat pack, short or long term storage, EDI.*
Markets:	*Menswear, Womenswear & Childrenswear.*
Factory Locals:	*1,350,000 sq. ft. of public warehouse.*

DEPENDABLE LOGISTICS SERVICES

2555 East Olympic Boulevard
Los Angeles, CA 90023
J.P. Durrer
(1) (323) 526 2200   Fax: (1) (323) 526 2252

E-Mail:	*jp.durrer@dependableinc.com*
Web Site:	*www.godependable.com*
Description:	*Complete distribution, warehouseing & freight forwarding service center.*
Year Est:	*1956*
Categories:	*Freight Forwarders/Customs Broker*
Specialties:	*Warehousing, trucking & repackaging under one roof.*
Markets:	*Menswear, Womenswear & Childrenswear.*
Factory Locals:	*1,350,000 sq. ft. of public warehouse.*

IDEA LLC.

6331 Fain Street
North Charleston, SC 29406
Tom DeMuth
(1) (843) 744 2727   Fax: (1) (843) 744 9993

E-Mail:	*tomdemuth@ideallc.com*
Web Site:	*www.ideallc.com*
Description:	*3PL, US materials and finished goods distributor, currently working with Wal-Mart, KMart, Target, Marshalls.*
Categories:	*Freight Forwarder/Customs Broker*
Specialties:	*LCL/FCL consolidation, door to door US to Honduras, El Salvador, Nicaragua and Guatemala.*
Factory Locals:	*Warehouses in San Pedro Sula Honduras, San Salvador El Salvador and Managua Nicaragua.*

INTERNATIONAL FULFILLMENT, INC.

7395 West 18th Lane
Hialeah, FL 33014
Tristan Cuadrado/Stuart Friedman
(1) (305) 825 1040   Fax: (1) (305) 825 1912

E-Mail:	*tristan@jessicainternational.com*
Web Site:	*www.jessicainternational.com*

Description:	*A complete solution enterprise dedicated to warehousing/distribution, fulfillment services and sales & marketing.*
Categories:	*Distribution/Warehouse Center*
Specialties:	*Assembly, packing, inspection, E-Commerce, returns center, government contracts, kitting, pick & pack, inventory control.*

JONCO INDUSTRIES INC.
2501 West Hampton Avenue
Milwaukee, WI 53209

(1) (414) 449 2000   Fax: (1) (414) 449 5200

E-Mail:	*tom.ryan@joncoind.com*
Web Site:	*www.joncoind.com*
Description:	*Industrial sewing contractor.*
	Also provide packaging & complete warehousing.
Year Est:	*1980*
Categories:	*Uniforms, Accessories, Sample Rooms/Small Production*
Specialties:	*Open for all your apparel sewing needs. All work done in-house.*
Markets:	*Menswear & Womenswear*
Machinery:	*5 Juki, 3 Consew, 3 Singer, 1 Melco Amaya, 1 Pegasus*
	2 Path Finder Cutters, 1 Kongsberg, 1 5' x 10' Laser.
Minimums:	*None*
Production Capacity:	*Varies by Item*

LOGISTICS ON THE WEST
102 Gracey Street
Edison, NJ 08817

(1) (732) 418 0800   Fax: (1) (732) 418 0840

E-Mail:	*info@logisticsonthewest.com*
Web Site:	*www.logisticsonthewest.com*
Description:	*Full service logistics solutions provider for your Pacific West Imports.*
Specialties:	*Warehousing, distribution, vendor compliance, drop ship, routing, palletizing, small parcel, interstate trucking, labeling, bar-coding etc.*

PRECISION WAREHOUSING & DISTRIBUTION
16055 Heron Avenue
La Mirada, CA 90638
Rob Boissevain
(1) (714) 690 9344   Fax: (1) (714) 690 9345

E-Mail:	*rob@precisioninc.com*
Web Site:	*www.precisioninc.com*
Description:	*Full line of supply chain services including container unloading, cross-docking, storage, shipping and the coordinating of pick ups & deliveries.*
Specialties:	*Southern California Warehousing and Distribution Center.*

QUETICO LOGISTICS LLC

5521 Schaefer Avenue
Chino, CA 91710
Nick
(1) (909) 628 6200   Fax: (1) (909) 628 8340

E-Mail:	nick@queticollc.com
Web Site:	www.queticollc.com
Description:	Custom-tailored warehousing services including the latest in distribution technology & computerization.
Specialties:	Pick & pack, product fulfillment, merchandise pallet display, kit assembly, design & manufacturing point of purchase display.
Factory Locals:	Partnerships in facilities in Texas, Canada & Mexico.

TAYLORED SERVICES INC.

231 Mill Road
Edison, NJ 08837
Chris Kearns
(1) (732) 248 7900   Fax: (1) (732) 248 7950

E-Mail:	ckearns@tpservices.com
Web Site:	www.tayloredservices.com
Description:	Warehousing, distribution & logistics. Reverse logistics pick & pack operation, blister & RF sealing, bar coding, labeling and more.
Specialties:	Real time visibility of inventory via TSI's custom website, narrow aisle system using wire-guided equipment.
Factory Locals:	Facilities in New Jersey, California (909-548-4048).

TOUCHDOWN FREIGHT COMPANY

20250 South Alameda Street
E. Compton, CA 90221

(1) (310) 973 7112   Fax: (1) (310) 973 7113

E-Mail:	touch@touchdownco.com
Description:	Air/ocean import & export, air/ocean consolidations, modern packing & crating, customs clearance, domestic/local trucking.
Specialties:	Staff members speak Chinese, Tagalog, Korean, Japanese, Portuguese, Spanish and English.

WAITEX INTERNATIONAL

135 West 36th Street
New York, NY 10018
Candice
(1) (212) 967 8100   Fax: (1) (212) 967 8266

E-Mail:	candice@waitex.com
Web Site:	www.waitex.com
Description:	Merchandise distribution, warehousing, garment refurbishing, label sewing & more.
Year Est:	1981
Machinery:	Pressing & sewing machinery. 1,200,00 square feet warehousing facility.
Factory Locals:	13 plants: North Bergen, Carlstadt, East Rutherford, Clifton & Secaucus, NJ. Rancho Cucamonga, CA., China

ALL AMERICAN WASH CO.

2932 East 11th Street
Los Angeles, CA 90023
Alex Kahen
(1) (323) 265 2626   Fax: (1) (323) 265 3307

E-Mail:	*alexkahen@allamericanwashco.com*
Description:	*Premimum denim wash and garment dyeing. All work is done in-house.*
Categories:	*Laundry/Wash Contractor, Small Production/Sample Room, Jeans/Denimwear*
Markets:	*Menswear, Womenswear, Childrenswear.*
Packages:	*Complete & CMT packaging available.*
Minimums:	*Low*

ALMORE DYE HOUSE, INC.

6850 North Tujunga Avenue
North Hollywood, CA 91605
Jamie Yonover
(1) (818) 506 5444   Fax: (1) (818) 762 3905

E-Mail:	*adh@almoredyehouse.com*
Web Site:	*www.almoredyehouse.com*
Description:	*Garment dyers.*
Year Est:	*1919*
Categories:	*Dyeing/Finishing Contractors.*
Specialties:	*Fiber reactive, disperse, acid, ballwash, pigment and sulphur dyeing. Specialize in cotton, rayon & tencel fabrics.*
Markets:	*All apparel markets.*
Machinery:	*30 washer/dyers*
Minimums:	*3 lbs.*
Production Capacity:	*100,000 to 200,000 pcs/month*

ALVARADO DYE & KNITTING MILL

30542 Union City Boulevard
Union City, CA 94587
Raymond Chan
(1) (510) 324 8892   Fax: (1) (510) 324 8704

E-Mail:	*sales@alvaradomills.com*
Web Site:	*www.alvaradomill.wix.com/oursdesign*
Description:	*Dyeing & finishing of knit sportswear, tee shirts & denim. Also, full pressing service.*
Specialties:	*Expertise with tencel processing.*
Machinery:	*23 paddle dye & 4 tumbler dye machines. Capacity from 40-600 lbs.*
Export to:	*Japan 20%*
Minimums:	*40 lbs./color*
Production Capacity:	*100,000 pcs/month*

BLUE CREATIONS OF CA INC.

22632 S. Avalon Boulevard
Carson, CA 90745
Oscar Quintero
(1) (310) 816 3100   Fax: (1) (310) 816 9388

E-Mail:	*info@bluecreationsinc.com*
Web Site:	*www.bluecreationsinc.com*
Description:	*Denim specialists. Easy washes, stone wash, enzyme wash plus destruction, sand blast, whiskers, tint and dyeing.*
Year Est:	*2005*
Categories:	*Laundry/Washing Contractor*
Specialties:	*Professional denim process & garment dye laundry specialist.*

CALEDONIAN DYE WORKS, INC.

3300 Emerald Street
Philadelphia, PA 19134
Richard Fitch
(1) (215) 739 2322   Fax: (1) (215) 739 6121

Description:	*Dyers of cotton, rayon, wool & polyester yarns.*
Year Est:	*1911*
Machinery:	*22 dyeing machines*
Minimums:	*50 lbs.*
Production Capacity:	*130,000 lbs/month*

CAROLINA COTTON WORKS, INC.

14 Commerce Drive
Gaffney, SC 29340
Bryan
(1) (864) 488 2824   Fax: (1) (864) 488 0488

E-Mail:	*bryan@carolinacotton.com*
Web Site:	*www.carolinacotton.com*
Description:	*Knit fabric dyeing & finishing. Jersey, rib, fleece, french terry, interlock, pique, thermal & herringbone.*
Categories:	*Dyeing/Finishing Contractors*
Machinery:	*State-of-the-art equipment yields excellent shrinkage control.*
Minimums:	*800 lbs.*

COLORWORKS INC.

161 Canal Street
Ellenville, NY 12428
Russ Damsky
(1) (845) 647 0300

E-Mail:	*dyestudio@colorworksalley.com*
Web Site:	*www.colorworksalley.com*
Description:	*Sample dyeing, piece dyeing, garment dyeing - single & multiple fabric garments.*
Year Est:	*1987*
Minimums:	*None*

COTTON & ELSE INC.

2921 N.W. 28th Street
Lauderdale Lakes, FL 33311

(1) (954) 677 8010   Fax: (1) (954) 677 0270
           E-Mail: *cottonet@bellsouth.net*
           Web Site: *www.cottonandelse.net*
           Year Est: *1992*
           Categories: *Sleepwear/Robes, Active/Athletic Wear*
           Specialties: *Specialize in knitting, dyeing and sewing of cotton knitted garments.*
                          We offer a wide range of Tee-Shirts.
           Markets: *Menswear, Womenswear & Childrenswear.*
           Export to: *Canada, Europe, Middle East, South America*
           Factory Locals: *Florida*
Production Capacity: *10,000 doz/week (garments)*

CUSTOM APPAREL PROCESSING

994 Jefferson Street
Fall River, MA 02721

(1) (508) 675 2962
           Description: *Textile dyeing and finishing.*
           Specialties: *Custom dyeing and tie-dyeing of apparel, including neon.*

DYE IT UP

1002 E. Pennsylvania Boulevard
Trevose, PA 19053
Mark
(1) (267) 288 5545   Fax: (1) (267) 288 5545
           E-Mail: *sales@dyeitup.com*
           Web Site: *www.dyeitup.com*
           Description: *Tie dye contractor of finished goods.*
           Markets: *Menswear, Womenswear, Children/Infantwear.*

DYEHOUSE, INC., THE

601 Harris Avenue
Quitman, MS 39355
Paul Brown
(1) (601) 776 3777   Fax: (1) (601) 776 5008
           E-Mail: *prb21439@aol.com*
           Description: *All types of garment dyeing.*
           Categories: *Laundry/Washing*
           Specialties: *Dyeing on any type of fabric or apparel.*
           Machinery: *Dye extract & testing machinery on premises.*
           Minimums: *None*

DYENAMIX INC.
151 Grand Street
New York, NY 10013
Raylene Marasco, President
(1) (212) 941 6642   Fax: (1) (212) 941 7407

E-Mail:	*info@dyenamix.com*
Web Site:	*www.dyenamix.com*
Description:	*Custom print development, original design collection, silkscreen & digital printing of sample & production yardage.*
Year Est:	*1991*
Specialties:	*Solid & specialty dyeing.*
Markets:	*Womenswear, Menswear, Accessories, Home.*
Minimums:	*None*
Production Capacity:	*Up to 350 yards/dye lots & 500 yds for printing.*

EAGLE DYERS
357 Flushing Avenue
Brooklyn, NY 11205
Lucretia/Shelley
(1) 212 947 2712   Fax: (1) 718 338 0848

E-Mail:	*vjsavta@aol.com*
Description:	*All types of dyeing for lace, trims & fabrics.*
Markets:	*All markets & all price points.*
Packages:	*Can do samples & large quantity runs.*
Minimums:	*$75.00 for dye charge.*

ESTEPHANIAN ORIGINALS INC.
2666 East Huntington Drive
Duarte, CA 91010
Mark Estephanian
(1) (626) 358 7265   Fax: (1) (626) 358 4286

E-Mail:	*mark@eodye.com*
Web Site:	*www.eodye.com*
Description:	*Garment dyed and screen printed looks on nylon, silk, cotton, rayon finished garments in a variety of dip dye and tie-dye looks.*
Year Est:	*1976*
Categories:	*Screenprinting*
Specialties:	*Specialize in tie dye, dip dye, airbrush, contracting services, discharge prints, burnouts. All work done in-house.*
Markets:	*Womenswear & Girlswear.*
Machinery:	*Custom machinery*

HANES DYE & FINISHING COMPANY
600 Northwest Boulevard
Winston-Salem, NC 27101

(1) (336) 725 1391   Fax: (1) (336) 722 0890

E-Mail:	*hfcsales@hanesindustries.com*
Web Site:	*www.hanesfinishing.com*
Description:	*Latest dyeing technology.*
Year Est:	*1924*

Specialties:	Pad, jigg & beam dyeing. Can dye cottons, polyesters, acrylics & poly blends.
Markets:	Home Furnishings, Apparel & Industrial Fabrics
Machinery:	Pressure beams 800,000 yds, jiggs 500,000 yds, coating range 1,700,000.
Export to:	Europe 10%, Asia 5%, Mexico 5%, Canada 5%
Factory Locals:	Butner, North Carolina and Winston-Salem, North Carolina. 877-453-9476
Production Capacity:	3,000,000 linear yards

METRO DYEING SERVICES, LTD

306 West 38th Street
New York, NY 10018
John
(1) 212 391 1001   Fax: (1) 646 219 7119

E-Mail:	cs@nyfashioncenter.com
Web Site:	www.metrodyeing.com
Description:	Premiere sample dyers for all fabrics, fibers & apparel.
Specialties:	Specialize in matching components for intimate apparel & sportswear. 24 hour service.
Markets:	All markets.
Minimums:	None

RED FISH BLUE FISH DYE WORKS INC.

145 Green Street
Somersworth, NH 03878
Jeff Basseches/David Bailey
(1) (603) 692 3900   Fax: (1) (603) 692 2733

E-Mail:	jeff@rfbfdyeworks.com
Web Site:	www.rfbfdyeworks.com
Description:	Full service garment dye house. Service on your garments or ours.
Year Est:	1994
Specialties:	Garment direct dyeing, including specialty dye effects. Tie-dyeing and heat transfer printing.
Markets:	Menswear, Womenswear & Childrenswear.

ROYAL BLUE INTERNATIONAL

9025 Wilshire Boulevard #301
Beverly Hills, CA 90211
Sami Kahen/Eli Kahen
(1) (310) 888 0156   Fax: (1) (310) 888 0157

E-Mail:	samikahen@aol.com
Description:	Dyeing contractor of all types of finished garments including tees, denimwear, uniforms, childrenswear, knits & activewear.
Year Est:	1986
Categories:	Laundry/Washing
Specialties:	All types of garment dye, tie-dye & garment washes. Direct, pigment, distress, dip-dye, crystal & crinkle. Mineral, silicone & enzyme wash.
Minimums:	Low
Factory Locals:	Los Angeles - Eli 323-750-9900

SUNBRITE DYE COMPANY

35 Eighth Street
Passaic, NJ 07055

(1) (973) 777 9830   Fax: (1) (973) 777 0678

E-Mail:	*info@sunbritedyeco.com*
Description:	*Complete dyeing, coating & finishing contractors.*
Year Est:	*1961*
Specialties:	*Complete urethane coatings, acrylic coatings, ciré & refinishing on widths up to 74"".*
Markets:	*All apparel, accessory & home markets.*
Machinery:	*New modern equipment to serve the industry.*
Packages:	*All*
Export to:	*Worldwide*
Minimums:	*Vary*
Factory Locals:	*Passaic, Industrial Park*
Production Capacity:	*No limit*

SUNDOG PRODUCTIONS

3850 Jermantown Road
Fairfax, VA 22030
John
(1) (703) 978 0041   Fax: (1) (703) 978 0043

E-Mail:	*j.sague@sunpup.com*
Web Site:	*www.sunpup.com*
Description:	*Custom dye work, design work or screenprinting on tee shirts.*
Categories:	*Screenprinting*
Specialties:	*Proprietary printing process using seaweed instead of plastisol or traditional water based inks. It has no phalyet PVC's resins or binders.*

SUPERTEX LIBERTY INDUSTRIES INC.

312 West Luther Avenue
Liberty, NC 27298

(1) (336) 622 1000

E-Mail:	*info@supertex-inc.com*
Web Site:	*www.supertex-inc.com*
Description:	*Dyeing, finishing and coating to widths up to 230 inches. We also do slitting and chopping.*
Year Est:	*1982*
Categories:	*Finishing/Coating Contractor*
Specialties:	*Fully integrated and vertical warp knitting mill.*
Packages:	*Full Package*
Factory Locals:	*All work is done in the North Carolina Facility. 1-800-790-1000*

SWAN DYEING

372 Stevens Street
Fall River, MA 02721
Mike Rodriques
(1) (508) 674 4611   Fax: (1) (508) 676 3730

E-Mail:	*swansales@swandyeandprint.com*
Web Site:	*www.swandyeandprint.com*
Description:	*Commission dyeing & printing on all types of fabrics. Domestic.*
Categories:	*Finishing/Coating Contractor*
Specialties:	*Finishing services include brushing/sanding & napping, sanforization, laundering, calendaring, embossing & more.*
Minimums:	*1,500 yds/color*

CO2 TEXTILES
88 Greenwich Street
New York, NY 07075
Melody Levy
(1) (212) 269 2222   Fax: (1) (212) 269 2203
E-Mail: *melodylevy@co2textiles.com*
Description: *Textile lamination and fabric finishing.*
Specialties: *Laminating, coating, waterproofing, sponging & more.*
All domestically produced. R&D on site.
Markets: *Menswear, Womenswear.*

DURO INDUSTRIES
110 Chace Street
Fall River, MA 02724
Bryan Boulis
(1) (508) 675 0101   Fax: (1) (508) 677 6791
E-Mail: *boulis_bryan@durolink.com*
Web Site: *www.duroindustries.com*
Description: *Nylon, polyesters, coated fabrics, flame retard fabrics, military*
fabrics, exclusive commercial distributor of Multicam® camo.
Year Est: *1948*
Specialties: *Full service lab testing.*
Minimums: *Varies on each fabric*

EAST COAST EMBOSSING
35 Eighth Street
Passaic, NJ 07055

(1) (973) 777 9830   Fax: (1) (973) 777 0678
E-Mail: *info@sunbritedyeco.com*
Description: *Contractors specializing in ciré finishing & complete*
embossing.
Year Est: *1961*
Specialties: *Complete urethane coatings, acrylic coatings, ciré &*
other sophisticated & fashion coating finishes.
Markets: *Apparel, home furnishing & industrial markets.*
Machinery: *New modern equipment to serve the industry.*
Packages: *All*
Export to: *Worldwide*
Minimums: *Vary*
Factory Locals: *Passaic, Industrial Park*
Production Capacity: *No limit*

GELTMAN INDUSTRIES
1914 Bay Street
Los Angeles, CA 90021
Shari Rezai
(1) (213) 622 2015   Fax: (1) (213) 622 4572
E-Mail: *info@geltman.com*
Web Site: *www.geltman.com*
Description: *All types of textile finishing serving the specialized needs*

of the apparel & home furnishing industry.

Year Est:	*1931*
Categories:	*Finishing/Coating Contractors, Laundry/Washing Contractors.*
Specialties:	*Heat-sealing, bonding, sponging, resin finishes, framing, natural crinkling, odor & smoke elimination & more.*
Markets:	*All apparel, accessory & home markets.*
Minimums:	*None*

HARODITE INDUSTRIES, INC.

2 Henderson Court
Travelers Rest, SC 29690
Tommy Bridges
(1) (864) 834 9066   Fax: (1) (864) 834 9089

E-Mail:	*tbridges@harodite.com*
Web Site:	*www.harodite.com*
Description:	*Custom finishing, coating, laminating, sheeting & die cutting of woven & non-woven textiles.*
Year Est:	*1910*
Categories:	*Finishing/coating*
Specialties:	*Specialize in shirt interlinings.*
Factory Locals:	*Taunton, Massachusetts and Travelers Rest, South Carolina in USA, plus, Aguascalientes, Mexico & Olocuilta, El Salvador.*

JORO, INC.

296 Fayette Drive
Winder, GA 30680
John Robinson
(1) (770) 867 7364   Fax: (1) (770) 867 5834

E-Mail:	*joro@joroinc.comcastbiz.net*
Description:	*Press, trim & inspect goods, apply hangtags/pocket flashers. Curing oven resin, waterproofing, wrinklefree, desize, enzyme & stone washes.*
Year Est:	*1987*
Categories:	*Washing/Laundry*
Specialties:	*Handsand/destruct denim & other fabrics. Dyeing & specialty finishes. All work done in-house.*
Markets:	*Menswear & Womenswear.*
Minimums:	*None*
Factory Locals:	*58 West May Street, Winder, Ga 30680*
Production Capacity:	*70,000 pcs per month*

LACOA INC

34 Waite Street
Paterson, NJ 07524
Hector E Baralt, President
(1) (973) 754 1000   Fax: (1) (973) 754 1015

E-Mail:	*hector@lacoa.com*
Web Site:	*www.lacoa.com*
Description:	*Contract laminating, embossing, coating, waterproofing, & other finishing processes.*
Year Est:	*1948*

Specialties:	*Mylar & holographic laminating & transfer paper laminating.*
Minimums:	*200-300 yards*
Factory Locals:	*30,000 sq. foot factory in Clifton, NJ*

SUPERTEX LIBERTY INDUSTRIES INC.

312 West Luther Avenue
Liberty, NC 27298

(1) (336) 622 1000

E-Mail:	info@supertex-inc.com
Web Site:	www.supertex-inc.com
Description:	*Dyeing, finishing and coating to widths up to 230 inches. We also do slitting and chopping.*
Year Est:	*1982*
Categories:	*Dyeing Contractor*
Specialties:	*Fully integrated and vertical warp knitting mill.*
Packages:	*Full Package*
Factory Locals:	*All work is done in the North Carolina Facility.* 1-800-790-1000

SWAN DYEING

372 Stevens Street
Fall River, MA 02721
Mike Rodriques
(1) (508) 674 4611   Fax: (1) (508) 676 3730

E-Mail:	swansales@swandyeandprint.com
Web Site:	www.swandyeandprint.com
Description:	*Commission dyeing & printing on all types of fabrics. Domestic.*
Categories:	*Dyeing Contractor*
Specialties:	*Finishing services include brushing/sanding & napping, sanforization, laundering, calendaring, embossing & more.*
Minimums:	*1,500 yds/color*

TEX PRINT USA, LLC

20-21 Wagaraw Road
Fair Lawn, NJ 07410
Ginetta Marino
(1) (201) 773 6531   Fax: (1) (201) 773 6535

E-Mail:	ginettam@texprintusa.com
Web Site:	www.texprintusa.com
Description:	*Manufacturer of textile products for the apparel & home trade. We are an evironmentally conscious facility. All work is done in the USA.*
Specialties:	*Heat Transfer, AirDye™, Pigment Printing, Crush, Broomstick, Cire, Foil, Glitter, Deluster, Puff, Bonding, Lamination & more.*

TRANN TECHNOLOGIES INC.

12526 U.S. Highway 90
Mossy Head, FL 32434
Samuel A. Goldstein
(1) (888) 668 6700   Fax: (1) (888) 308 7266

E-Mail:	*sales@tranntech.com*
Web Site:	*www.tranntech.com*
Description:	*Over 50 years of fabric coating and raw material processing.*
Specialties:	*Specialize in applications to nylon, Lycra/Spandex, cotton and other knit fabrics and nonwovens.*
Machinery:	*Unwinding systems, padding, laminating and vertical coating, paralell tenter entry with overfeeding capability, on-frame knife coater, levitator tenter dryer system and more.*
Packages:	*Full service.*

ALLIED TRANSPORT SYSTEM

One Cross Island Plaza
Rosedale, NY 11422

(1) (718) 977 9448   Fax: (1) (718) 276 7780

E-Mail:	*teresa@atsnyc.com*
Web Site:	*www.atsnyc.com*
Description:	*All service freight forwarder. All types of ocean and air cargo from the Far East to the USA.*
Specialties:	*US Custom Clearance, Warehousing and Delivery.*

ANTILLEAN MARINE SHIPPING CORP.

3038 Teofilo Babun Drive
Miami, FL 33142

(1) (305) 633 6361   Fax: (1) (305) 638 0579

E-Mail:	*antillean@antillean.com*
Web Site:	*www.antillean.com*
Description:	*Marine transport, logistics, trucking and intermodal services, warehousing & cargo consolidation.*
Year Est:	*1963*

ARI SHIPPING CORP.

80 Sheridan Boulevard
Inwood, NY 10096
Ilan Fidler
(1) (516) 371 7770   Fax: (1) (516) 371 7757

E-Mail:	*ilan@arishipping.com*
Web Site:	*www.arishipping.com*
Description:	*Full service logistics company, air & ocean import/export consolidated services, customs clearance & compliance service.*
Year Est:	*1980*
Specialties:	*Bonded CFS, warehouse & distribution, crating & packing, complete supply-chain management.*

CARMICHAEL INTERNATIONAL SERVICE

533 Glendale Boulevard
Los Angeles, CA 90026
Khim Lim
(1) (213) 353 0800   Fax: (1) (213) 975 0057

E-Mail:	*sales@carmnet.com*
Web Site:	*www.carmnet.com*
Description:	*Full-service, independent and privately owned customs broker and freight forwarder plus warehousing and distribution.*
Year Est:	*1961*
Specialties:	*Operate in the ports of LA/Long Beach, New York, Chicago, Seattle, San Francisco, Miami, Boston, Baltimore, Atlanta, Savannah, Memphis.*

DEPENDABLE GLOBAL EXPRESS

19201 Susana Road
Rancho Dominguez, CA 90221
Brad Dechter
(1) (310) 669 8888   Fax: (1) (310) 537 3291

E-Mail:	*brad.dechter@dhx.com*
Web Site:	*www.dgxglobal.com*
Description:	*An International shipping & logistics company. Your single source for reliable, cost-effective shipment of goods worldwide & here at home.*
Specialties:	*We ship to virtually all global and domestic points - both ocean and air.*
Machinery:	*Both box trucks and tractor/container combinations*

DEPENDABLE LOGISTICS SERVICES

2555 East Olympic Boulevard
Los Angeles, California 90023
J.P. Durrer
(1) (323) 526 2200   Fax: (1) (323) 526 2252

E-Mail:	*jp.durrer@dependableinc.com*
Web Site:	*www.godependable.com*
Description:	*Complete distribution, warehouseing & freight forwarding service center.*
Year Est:	*1956*
Categories:	*Distribution/Warehouse Center*
Specialties:	*Warehousing, trucking & repackaging under one roof.*
Markets:	*Menswear, Womenswear & Childrenswear.*
Factory Locals:	*1,350,000 sq. ft. of public warehouse.*

IDEA LLC.

6331 Fain Street
North Charleston, SC 29406
Tom DeMuth
(1) (843) 744 2727   Fax: (1) (843) 744 9993

E-Mail:	*tomdemuth@ideallc.com*
Web Site:	*www.ideallc.com*
Description:	*3PL, US materials and finished goods distributor, currently working with Wal-Mart, KMart, Target, Marshalls.*
Categories:	*Distribution/Warehouse*
Specialties:	*LCL/FCL consolidation, door to door US to Honduras, El Salvador, Nicaragua and Guatemala.*
Factory Locals:	*Warehouses in San Pedro Sula Honduras, San Salvador El Salvador and Managua Nicaragua.*

MERIDIAN SHIPPING CO. INC.

147-20 181st Street
Jamaica, NY 11413
Kenneth Blum
(1) (718) 995 3598   Fax: (1) (718) 244 0874

E-Mail:	*mershico@cs.com*
Description:	*A.B.I. certified customhouse broker, international freight forwarder & import/export.*

Year Est:	1975
Exporting Since:	1975
Specialties:	Offices throughout the world.

NETWORK BROKERS INTERNATIONAL
100 N. Centre Avenue
Rockville Centre, NY 11570
Judy Kearney
(1) (516) 825 6623   Fax: (1) (516) 825 3942

E-Mail:	info@networkbrokers.com
Web Site:	www.networkbrokers.com
Description:	Custom house brokers.
Year Est:	1981
Specialties:	Export forwarding, domestic distribution and warehousing.

OCASA
12-12 33rd Avenue
Long Island City, NY 11106

(1) (212) 758 0101   Fax: (1) (212) 758 1286

E-Mail:	customer.service@ocasa.com
Web Site:	www.ocasa.com
Description:	Freight Forwarders and Logistics.
Specialties:	Courier, biological, shipping and distribution, warehousing, loading, file storage, check mail and management.

OCEAN AIR LOGISTICS
1800 NW 133rd Avenue
Miami, FL 33182

(1) (305) 599 0966   Fax: (1) (305) 599 0766

E-Mail:	sales@oceanairlogistics.com
Web Site:	www.oceanairlogistics.com
Description:	International & domestic freight forwarder & freight consolidator serving Latin America. Air freight, air cargo, ocean cargo.
Specialties:	Customs clearance & transport services, packing & crating, warehouse & distribution. Consulting on all imports.

STILE ASSOCIATES LTD
181 South Franklin Avenue
Valley Stream, NY 11581
Isaac
(1) (516) 394 2166   Fax: (1) (516) 394 2195

E-Mail:	isaacg@stileintl.com
Web Site:	www.stileintl.com
Description:	Full service logistics company. Air/ocean, import/export, consolidated services, customs clearance and compliance service.
Year Est:	1972
Specialties:	Large roster of licensed customs brokers at our Atlantic & Pacific port offices. Ability to obtain advance clearance & remote location filing.

TOUCHDOWN FREIGHT COMPANY

20250 South Alameda Street
E. Compton, CA 90221

(1) (310) 973 7112   Fax: (1) (310) 973 7113

E-Mail:	*touch@touchdownco.com*
Description:	*Air/ocean import & export, air/ocean consolidations, modern packing & crating, customs clearance, domestic/local trucking.*
Specialties:	*Staff members speak Chinese, Tagalog, Korean, Japanese, Portuguese, Spanish and English.*

WORLD CLASS SHIPPING

210 Sunrise Highway
Valley Stream, NY 11581
Billy Shaw
(1) (516) 568 8861   Fax: (1) (516) 872 5017

E-Mail:	*billjr@worldclassshipping.com*
Web Site:	*www.worldclassshipping.com*
Description:	*International freight forwarder and customs broker*
Year Est:	*1987*
Specialties:	*Knowledge, expertise & resources for your in-house logistic solutions. Network of over 450 agents worldwide.*

AAA PATTERNS & MARKING SERVICES

233 Cypress Lane
Ozark, AL 36360
Michael Smith
(1) (334) 445 4870   Fax: (1) (334) 445 3910

E-Mail:	*patterns@aaapatternsmarking.com*
Web Site:	*www.aaapatternsmarking.com*
Description:	*Accurate & cost-effective grading, marking & plotting service.*
Year Est:	*2001*
Categories:	*Pattern Making, Grading/Marking*
Markets:	*All markets, all sizes & all styles.*

APPAREL MARK SERVICES

7117 Orizaba Avenue
El Paso, TX 79912
Barbara Bean
(1) (915) 833 2643

E-Mail:	*barbbctx@yahoo.com*
Description:	*Pattern grading and marking services.*
Markets:	*Womenswear, Menswear.*

B.M.A.C.

248 West 35th Street
New York, NY 10001
Mark Krieger
(1) (212) 736 5380   Fax: (1) (212) 629 3943

E-Mail:	*bmacservice@aol.com*
Web Site:	*www.bmacnewyork.com*
Description:	*Computerized grading & marking service.*
Specialties:	*Specialize in specs engineering, pattern scanning, pattern grading, marking, paper cutting, printing and pattern conversion.*
Markets:	*All markets.*
Machinery:	*Pattern scanners, Gerber plotters, Pattern cutters*
Production Capacity:	*100 styles per week*

BIANCA GROUP LTD

244 West 39th Street
New York, NY 10018
Richard Garcia
(1) (212) 768 3011   Fax: (1) (212) 768 1657

E-Mail:	*biancainc@aol.com*
Description:	*Computerized capabilities. Gerber system, pattern grading & marking for the men's, women's, children's, spec & inf. sheet.*
Specialties:	*24 hour turn-around. Instant overseas delivery available by modem.*
Markets:	*All markets.*

C.R.C. DESIGN SERVICES

19 Buena Vista Avenue
Asonet, MA 02702
Carlos Custodio/Lucy
(1) (508) 644 3166   Fax: (1) (508) 644 3166

E-Mail:	*carlos.c@comcast.net*
Description:	*Pattern grading & marking for the apparel industry.*
	Affordable, up-to-the-minute computerized capabilities.
Specialties:	*Experience in maximum fabric utilization. Exceptional*
	marker quality. Easy pattern changes.
Markets:	*All*
Machinery:	*Gerber system.*

CREATE-A-MARKER, INC.

254 West 35th Street
New York, NY 10001
Sadat Mamirova
(1) (212) 730 5615   Fax: (1) (212) 730 5616

E-Mail:	*cad@createamarkernyc.com*
Web Site:	*www.createamarkernyc.com*
Description:	*Digitizing, grading, marker making, emailing patterns, plotting paterns,*
	cutting patterns on oak tag, scanning patterns & copying markers.
Year Est:	*1993*
Exporting Since:	*1999*
Categories:	*Patternmaking Services*
Specialties:	*Cutting edge digital cutting system for samples & patterns.*
	Optimum fabric utilization & cost effectiveness.
Markets:	*Womens, Mens, Kids, Bride/Evening, Swimwear, Intimate, Leather/Fur*
Machinery:	*State-of-the-art equipment. 7 plotters, 2 digertizers, 2 scanners,*
	5 graders, 8 marker makers, 1 computer cutter,
	1 photo copier machines (amonia type).
Export to:	*China, Italy, Vietnam, Canada, Japan, Turkey,*
	Taiwan, India, Pakistan, Sri Lanka, Guatemala, SDomingo
Minimums:	*None*
Production Capacity:	*160 patterns/month*

CREATIVE PATTERN AND SAMPLE

112 West 9th Street
Los Angeles, CA 90015
Isabel Martinez
(1) (213) 233 0253   Fax: (1) (213) 233 4857

E-Mail:	*contact@creativepatternandsample.com*
Web Site:	*www.creativepatternandsample.com*
Description:	*Grades & marker, showroom samples, mock ups, sewing, sample*
	making, design consultation, prototypes, fittings.
Categories:	*Swimwear, jeans, dresses, suits, lingerie*
Specialties:	*Quality crafted patterns,1st patterns, production patterns,*
	spec sheets, pattern corrections. By appointment only.
Markets:	*Womenswear*

DARWOOD MANUFACTURING CO.

620 West Railroad Street
Pelham, GA 31779
Allen Burford, President
(1) (229) 294 4932   Fax: (1) (229) 294 9323

E-Mail:	*darwood@bellsouth.net*
Web Site:	*www.darwoodmfg.com*
Description:	*Cut & sew shirt & garment contractor. Grading/marking, patternmaking, sample making, washing & more.*
Year Est:	*1960*
Categories:	*Shirts/Tops*
Specialties:	*Expertise with all kinds of shirts, tops, pants, shorts, skirts, uniforms & outerwear.*
Markets:	*Menswear, Womenswear, Boyswear & Accessories.*
Packages:	*CMT & complete packages available.*
Minimums:	*5 dozen/style*
Factory Locals:	*Pelham, GA*

EXACTA

118 John F. Kennedy Drive North
Bloomfield, NJ 07003
Jeff Giberstein
(1) (973) 259 0104   Fax: (1) (973) 259 0107

E-Mail:	*contactus@exactagarment.com*
Web Site:	*www.exactagarment.com*
Description:	*Full service apparel & garment cutting contractor. Computerized cutting, grading, marking, fusing, piece goods warehousing and more.*
Year Est:	*1970*
Categories:	*Cutting & Fusing Contractor*
Specialties:	*Local production lets you manufacture and ship the latest styles to retailers in two weeks or less. Great for in-season re-order business.*
Markets:	*All apparel markets.*

FINE LINE, INC.

12457 Gladstone Avenue
Sylmar, CA 91342
Michael Collier
(1) (818) 361 8103   Fax: (1) (818) 361 1194

E-Mail:	*info@finelineinc.com*
Web Site:	*www.finelineinc.com*
Description:	*Grading & marking services.*
Categories:	*Cutting/Fusing Contractors, Grading/Marking, Patternmaking.*
Specialties:	*Domestic production and sourcing solutions...all made in the USA.*
Markets:	*All*
Machinery:	*Fully automated cutting machines.*

FRENCH CURVE DESIGNS
906 West McDermott Drive
Allen, TX 75013
Heather Madrid
(1) 972 571 1196   Fax: (1) 972 534 1218

E-Mail:	*hmadrid@frenchcurvedesigns.com*
Web Site:	*www.frenchcurvedesigns.com*
Description:	*Expert grading & marking. In-house Gerber Accumark Pattern & Grading System & Infinity Gerber Plotting System.*
Categories:	*Patternmaking*
Specialties:	*Tech design, spec writing, patternmaking, grading/marking.*
Markets:	*Menswear, Womenswear & Childrenswear.*

G & M SERVICES
2807 Satsuma Drive
Dallas, TX 75229

(1) (214) 358 0041   Fax: (1) (214) 358 0042

E-Mail:	*gary@gmser.com*
Web Site:	*www.gmser.com*
Description:	*Grading, marking & copy service.*
Year Est:	*1992*
Specialties:	*Samples & patternmaking with Pattern Maker onsite.*
Markets:	*Menswear, Womenswear & Childrenswear.*
Machinery:	*Infinity I Plotter, Infinity II Plotter, Gerber Accumark System, Lectra System, Microdynamics System.*

LANDZEG INC.
8025 Grenfell Street
Kew Gardens, NY 11415
Jonathan Lee
(1) (212) 575 0746   Fax: (1) (212) 575 0746

E-Mail:	*landzeg@gmail.com*
Description:	*Pattern grading & marking.*
Year Est:	*1941*
Markets:	*Womenswear*

LEFT IN STITCHES INC.
55 Ericson Court
Arcata, CA 95521

(1) (707) 822 3041   Fax: (1) (707) 822 3042

E-Mail:	*info@leftinstitches.com*
Web Site:	*www.leftinstitches.com*
Description:	*Over 29 years of patternmaking, grading and sewing. Samples, prototypes. Work with knits and wovens.*
Categories:	*Patternmaking, Dresses/Blouses, Samples/Small Production*
Specialties:	*Creative design and development from concept to production. Specialize in working with small and startup companies.*
Markets:	*Menswear, Womenswear & Childrenswear.*

MARK D.A., INC.

247 West 37th Street
New York, NY 10018

(1) 212 868 3081   Fax: (1) 866 475 0743

E-Mail:	*pbartual@msn.com*
Description:	*Expert grading & marking service.*
Markets:	*All*
Minimums:	*None*
Production Capacity:	*Minimum capacity: 100 styles per week.*

MARKER EXPRESS INC.

2773 Napa Valley Corporate Drive
Napa, CA 94558
Mary Ann Parker
(1) (707) 259 5201   Fax: (1) (707) 259 5205

E-Mail:	*maryann@markerxpress.com*
Web Site:	*www.markerxpress.com*
Description:	*Full grading & marking service. Computerized Gerber AccuMark, PAD, OptiTex, and MicroMark software systems.*
Categories:	*Grading/Marking*
Specialties:	*Offer grading, marker making, plotting & remote data support to CAD users.*
Markets:	*All markets.*

MICHAEL CALDERONE, INC.

265 West 37th Street
New York, NY 10018
Michael
(1) (212) 465 1093   Fax: (1) (212) 868 0628

E-Mail:	*mcpatterns@aol.com*
Description:	*Expert grading & marking. Computer & manual.*
Categories:	*Sample Room/Small Production, Patternmaking.*
Specialties:	*Specialize in plaids, stripes & cemetric type of prints.*
Markets:	*All.*

PATTERN DESIGN UNLIMITED, INC.

See our ad on page 73

550 West Rt. 897
Reinholds, PA 17569
Pamela Urban
(1) (717) 336 0500   Fax: (1) (717) 336 0309

E-Mail:	*pdu@patterndesign.com*
Web Site:	*www.patterndesign.com*
Description:	*20+year product development company; designing, patterns, grading, marking & samples.*
Year Est:	*1987*
Categories:	*Patternmaking, Sample Rooms/Small Production*
Specialties:	*On contract with GGT, Gerber Garment Technology to insure up-to-date technology. Expertise with mens, womens & kids markets.*
Markets:	*Menswear, Womenswear & Childrenswear.*
Packages:	*Complete & CMT packages.*

Minimums: *None*

PATTERN GRADING & MARKER SERVICES

3650 S.W. 141 Avenue
Miramar, FL 33027
Regina Gottlieb, Owner
(1) (954) 441 4432   Fax: (1) (954) 441 4344

E-Mail:	*regina@pattern-maker.com*
Web Site:	*www.pattern-maker.com*
Description:	*Technical consulting services and expert patternmaking, and grading & marking.*
Year Est:	*1999*
Categories:	*Patternmaking*
Specialties:	*Make patterns from an existing garment, a customer defined speck or sketch. Grading & marking specific to your specs and fabric.*
Machinery:	*10 machines*
Export to:	*Dominican Republic*
Minimums:	*Low: 1 to 200 units/style*

PATTERN GRADING & MARKING BY ANDREW GLONINGER

5 Roberts Road
Newtown Square, PA 19073
Andrew Gloninger
(1) (610) 356 1777   Fax: (1) (610) 356 1193

E-Mail:	*andrew@gradingandmarking.com*
Web Site:	*www.gradingandmarking.com*
Description:	*An experienced professional who provides pattern grading and marking services employing hardware and software from Lectra Systems.*
Specialties:	*Over thirty years experience in the apparel industry.*

POPULAR PATTERN CO.

340 West 39th Street
New York, NY 10018
Stephen or Ian
(1) (212) 947 2902   Fax: (1) (212) 947 2716

E-Mail:	*ssinger1@aol.com*
Description:	*Computer grading & marking, plus marker photocopies, mini markers, spec sheet grading & plotting.*
Categories:	*Patternmaking, Grading/Marking*
Specialties:	*Fast service, affordable prices, instant overseas delivery available by modem.*
Markets:	*Menswear, Womenswear, Children/Infantwear.*
Machinery:	*25 Accumark*
Export to:	*China, Vietnam, Domican Republic*
Production Capacity:	*400 graded patterns/monthly*

ROBKO LLC

214 Oak Street
Nazareth, PA 18064
Arthur Rader
(1) (610) 746 4933   Fax: (1) (610) 746 5563

E-Mail:	*art@customapparelzone.com*
Web Site:	*www.customapparelzone.com*
Description:	*Full service private label manufacturing. From pattern making, grading, markers, sample making, cut and sew.*
Categories:	*Patternmaking, Sample Room/Small Production*
Specialties:	*Specialize in t-shirts, sport shirts, oxfords, onesies, sweatshirts, camp shirts, rib t-shirts, sports specialty wear.*
Markets:	*Menswear, Womenswear, Childrenswear*

SEW PRECISE COMPANY

3212 N. Kilpatrick Avenue
Chicago, IL 60641

(1) (773) 481 1400   Fax: (1) (773) 481 1335

E-Mail:	*info@sewprecise.com*
Web Site:	*www.sewprecise.com*
Description:	*Full service cutting and sewing contractor of all types of apparel.*
Exporting Since:	*Small Production, Childrenswear*
Specialties:	*Grading/marker, pressing/finishing, embroidery.*
Markets:	*Menswear, Womenswear, Childrenswear.*
Machinery:	*80 machines of all types including fusing machines, pressing equipment, and 2 40ft. cutting tables.*

SEWN PRODUCT SERVICES

111 S. Lander Street
Seattle, WA 98134
Kristine Carlton/Jenny Mae Miller
(1) (206) 467 5459   Fax: (1) (206) 467 5459

E-Mail:	*contact@sewnproductservices.com*
Web Site:	*www.sewnproductservices.com*
Description:	*Design consultation, patternmaking, sample sewing, raw goods sourcing, grading & marking, fit assesments, tech pack development.*
Categories:	*Athletic/Activewear, Lingerie/Intimate Apparel, Sleepwear, Leather Apparel, Swimwear, Costuming, Dancewear, Soft Goods Accessories*
Specialties:	*We offer a full menu of services supporting sewn product development including production management & small run production.*
Markets:	*Menswear, Womenswear & Childrenswear.*

SUPERIOR PATTERN SERVICES

1095 East 15th Street
Hialeah, FLorida 33010
Jeff Trieb, President
(1) (305) 805 1540

E-Mail:	*superior_patterns@yahoo.com*
Web Site:	*www.superiorpatterns.com*
Description:	*We work with companys all over the world. We send either zip files*

	or cut files to our customers.
Year Est:	1997
Categories:	*Patternmaking, Production Sourcing, Sample Room/Small Production.*
Specialties:	*Grading, marking & pattern services for woven & knit apparel.*
	Specialize in assisting new designers create their collection.
Markets:	*Menswear, Womenswear, Childrenswear*
Machinery:	*Gerber Accumark System*
Packages:	*Full packages.*
Minimums:	*Vary*
Factory Locals:	*Factories in Dominican Republic & Guatemala.*

TAG STUDIO PATTERN DESIGN SERVICE

519 Lincoln Way #2
San Francisco, CA 94122
Monica Houlihan, Owner
(1) (415) 664 2408

E-Mail:	*tagpatrn@gmail.com*
Web Site:	*www.tagstudio.biz*
Description:	*Expert pattern design service. Computer patterns, product development consulting services, grading & marking.*
Year Est:	1993
Categories:	*Patternmaking Services, Grading/Marking, Sample Making*
Specialties:	*Experience in a wide range of garment & sewn product categories.*
Markets:	*All markets.*
Machinery:	*Computer-aided design PAD software. Gerber converter software.*

TODD RUTKIN

5801 South Alameda Street
Los Angeles, CA 90001
Abe Garcia
(1) (323) 584 9225   Fax: (1) (323) 584 9295

E-Mail:	*jan@toddrutkin.com*
Web Site:	*www.toddrutkin.com*
Description:	*A complete source for cutting, fusing, grading, marking, slitting & embroidery.*
Categories:	*Cutting & Fusing, Embroidery*
Machinery:	*Gerber Accumark machinery*

Z.W. DESIGNS, INC.

443 Flint Hill Court
Lawrenceville, GA 30044
Z. Arthur
(1) (770) 513 0906

E-Mail:	*zwd@zwdesigns.com*
Web Site:	*www.zwdesigns.com*
Description:	*Expert apparel & product development, specifications, digital patterns, grading, markers; plotting, samples, small lot manufacturing.*
Year Est:	1983

Categories:	Patternmaking, Sample Rooms/Small Production, CAD/CAM Software Marketing
Specialties:	CAD/CAM patternmaking, technical design, design sketching/flats; choir robes, uniforms, government contractor certified (WOSP, SDB).
Markets:	Womenswear, Menswear, Childrenswear.
Production Capacity:	Small lots, but varies

A+ LAUNDRY

224 Lawrence Avenue
Lawrence, NY 11559
Tommy Gregoretti
(1) (516) 371 2100   Fax: (1) (516) 371 5649

E-Mail:	*linens@aol.com*
Description:	*Commercial garment laundering, bleaching, pressing.*
Year Est:	*1976*
Markets:	*Menswear, Womenswear, Childrenswear*
Machinery:	*6 industrial washers capable of producing 3600 garments per hour as well as the necessary finishing equipment.*
Factory Locals:	*We are just 5 minutes south of Kennedy Airport*
Production Capacity:	*200,000 sets/month, 20,000 garments per day.*

ALL AMERICAN WASH CO.

2932 East 11th Street
Los Angeles, CA 90023
Alex Kahen
(1) (323) 265 2626   Fax: (1) (323) 265 3307

E-Mail:	*alexkahen@allamericanwashco.com*
Description:	*Premium denim wash and garment dyeing. All work is done in-house.*
Categories:	*Dyeing Contractor, Small Production/Sample Room, Jeans/Denimwear*
Markets:	*Menswear, Womenswear, Childrenswear.*
Packages:	*Complete & CMT packaging available.*
Minimums:	*Low*

AMERICA'S BEST CLEANERS

107 Koch Road
Corte Madera, CA 94925
Christopher White
(1) (415) 857 2378

E-Mail:	*chriswhite@americasbestcleaners.com*
Web Site:	*www.americasbestcleaners.com*
Description:	*Independent certification organization for the dry cleaning industry. Certify individual business with different equipment and process times.*
Specialties:	*Certification is focused on delivering the best quality to our partners in manufacturing, retail and the end consumer. Cell: 561-301-0431.*
Markets:	*Menswear & Womenswear*

BLUE CREATIONS OF CA INC.

22632 S. Avalon Boulevard
Carson, CA 90745
Oscar Quintero
(1) (310) 816 3100   Fax: (1) (310) 816 9388

E-Mail:	*info@bluecreationsinc.com*
Web Site:	*www.bluecreationsinc.com*
Description:	*Denim specialists. Easy washes, stone wash, enzyme wash plus destruction, sand blast, whiskers, tint and dyeing.*
Year Est:	*2005*
Categories:	*Dyeing contractor*

Specialties: *Professional denim process & garment dye laundry specialist.*

COLLECTIVE APPAREL

750 East Gage Avenue
Los Angeles, CA 90001
Don Valenzuela
(1) 310 770 1093　　　　　　　　　　　　　　Fax: (1) 323 750 5010

E-Mail:	*contact@collectiveapparel.us*
Web Site:	*www.collectiveapparel.us*
Description:	*One stop. We design, sketch, prepare patterns, do samples and production.*
Year Est:	*2009*
Categories:	*Jeans/Denimwear, Pants/Shorts/Skirts*
Specialties:	*We specialize in new and innovative wash techniques as well as organic wash and dye processes.*
Markets:	*Menswear, Womenswear, Childrenswear.*
Packages:	*Full packages - premium denim, tops & knits.*
Production Capacity:	*48,000 pcs/month*

DYEHOUSE, INC., THE

601 Harris Avenue
Quitman, MS 39355
Paul Brown
(1) (601) 776 3777　　　　　　　　　　　　Fax: (1) (601) 776 5008

E-Mail:	*prb21439@aol.com*
Description:	*Denim garment washing on premises.*
Categories:	*Dyeing Contractors*
Specialties:	*Dyeing on any type of fabric or apparel.*
Machinery:	*Dye extract & testing machinery on premises.*
Minimums:	*None*

FABRICLEAN

1139 50th Avenue
Long Island City, NY 11101
Walter Pepper
(1) (888) 692 2532

E-Mail:	*info@nycclean.com*
Web Site:	*www.nycclean.com*
Year Est:	*1988*
Specialties:	*Highly specialized dry cleaning, laundry, commercial washing & pressing service.*
Markets:	*All apparel & textile markets.*
Machinery:	*Large variety & assorted sizes of dry cleaning & laundering equipment.*
Production Capacity:	*1,500 pounds/hour*

FRSTEAM BY WEST COVINA CLEANERS

537 South Glendora Avenue
West Covina, CA 91790

(1) (626) 960 1911   Fax: (1) (626) 960 0132

E-Mail:	*westcovina@frsteam.com*
Web Site:	*www.frsteamwc.com*
Description:	*Restoration dry cleaning institution. Restoration of couture and specialty garments, leathers, furs etc.*
Year Est:	*1969*
Specialties:	*Smoke & odor restoration & dry cleaning. Specialists in rescuing garments considered a "total loss" because of smoke, water or odor damage.*
Markets:	*All Markets*
Factory Locals:	*California*
Production Capacity:	*Largest restoration dry cleaner in the western US with 4 plants, 150 employees.*

GELTMAN INDUSTRIES

1914 Bay Street
Los Angeles, CA 90021
Shari Rezai

(1) (213) 622 2015   Fax: (1) (213) 622 4572

E-Mail:	*info@geltman.com*
Web Site:	*www.geltman.com*
Description:	*All types of textile laundry processes.*
Year Est:	*1931*
Categories:	*Finishing/Coating Contractors, Laundry/Washing Contractors.*
Specialties:	*Laundry, sponging, scouring, pre-shrinking, wash down, soft-wash, bleaching & more.*
Markets:	*All apparel, accessory & home markets.*
Minimums:	*None*

JORO, INC.

296 Fayette Drive
Winder, GA 30680
John Robinson
(1) (770) 867 7364   Fax: (1) (770) 867 5834

E-Mail:	*joro@joroinc.comcastbiz.net*
Description:	*Press, trim & inspect goods, apply hangtags/pocket flashers. Curing oven resin, waterproofing, wrinklefree, desize, enzyme & stone washes.*
Year Est:	*1987*
Categories:	*Finishing*
Specialties:	*Handsand/destruct denim & other fabrics. Dyeing & specialty finishes. All work done in-house.*
Markets:	*Menswear & Womenswear.*
Minimums:	*None*
Factory Locals:	*58 West May Street, Winder, Ga 30680*
Production Capacity:	*70,000 pcs per month*

LAUNDRY SPECIALTIES LLC

431 N. Jordan Street
Allentown, PA 18102
Richard Koury
(1) (610) 351 3860   Fax: (1) (610) 770 1785

E-Mail:	*richard@laundryspecialties.com*
Web Site:	*www.laundryspecialties.com*
Description:	*Garment washing, bleaching & specialty washing.*
	We can also handle sewing repairs.
Year Est:	*2000*
Specialties:	*Unpacking & repacking of "finished" garments. Pressing, folding,*
	hanging, pre-ticketing, baging and drop-shipping.
Production Capacity:	*100,000 units/month*

MARGARET'S CLEANERS

5150 Convoy Street
San Diego, CA 92111
Scott Horst
(1) (858) 454 2375   Fax: (1) (858) 454 4303

E-Mail:	*generalmail@margarets.com*
Web Site:	*www.margarets.com*
Description:	*Premier dry & wet professional cleaner.*
Year Est:	*1953*
Specialties:	*Handbag cleaning & restoration, bridal cleaning, drapery/blind cleaning,*
	leather & suede cleaning, garment & knit repairs, vintage restoration.
Markets:	*All markets.*
Factory Locals:	*La Jolla, Del Mar, Newport Beach, Los Angeles California*
Production Capacity:	*150+ employees, multiple "green cleaning" technologies, including*
	Green Earth and System K4. Environmentally friendly.

NU YALE

6300 Highway 62
Jeffersonville, IN 47130
Mike Maloney
(1) (812) 285 7400   Fax: (1) (812) 285 7421

E-Mail:	*mike@nuyale.com*
Web Site:	*www.nuyale.com*
Description:	*Inspectors of import garments. Rework, inspections,*
	washing, pressing, dry cleaning & warehousing.
Year Est:	*1950*
Categories:	*Rework/Inspection Services, Laundry/Washing Contractors,*
	Restoration.
Specialties:	*Wet processing & washing of blue jeans, stone washing,*
	bleaching, pre-washing and restoration of any garment.
Markets:	*All apparel & accessory markets.*
Machinery:	*4 600-lb. washers, 2 900-lb. washers, 3 900-lb. dryers,*
	1 600-lb. dryer.
Minimums:	*None*
Production Capacity:	*10,000 dozen/month*

PRO WASH

9117 South Main Street
Los Angeles, CA 90003
Steve Koo
(1) (323) 756 6000   Fax: (1) (323) 756 8370

E-Mail:	*ykoo@aol.com*
Description:	*All types of washing & bleaching of garments & piece goods.*
Specialties:	*Stone, acid, chemical power & vintage washing & bleaching. Plus sand blasting, potassium processing & dyeing.*

ROYAL BLUE INTERNATIONAL

9025 Wilshire Boulevard #301
Beverly Hills, CA 90211
Sami Kahen/Eli Kahen
(1) (310) 888 0156   Fax: (1) (310) 888 0157

E-Mail:	*samikahen@aol.com*
Description:	*Washing/laundry contractor of all types of finished garments including denim.*
Year Est:	*1986*
Categories:	*Dyeing Contractor*
Specialties:	*All types of garment dye, tie-dye & garment washes. Direct, pigment, distress, dip-dye, crystal & crinkle. Mineral, silicone & enzyme wash.*
Minimums:	*Low*
Factory Locals:	*Los Angeles - Eli 323-750-9900*

WGCI

2130 Laura Avenue
Huntington Park, CA 90255
Michael or Jeff
(1) (323) 583 9832   Fax: (1) (323) 584 0023

E-Mail:	*wgci@wgciusa.com*
Web Site:	*www.wgciusa.com*
Description:	*Stone wash, enzyme wash, mineral wash, ozone process hand sand, sand blast, grinding, whiskers, resin, potassium wash/brush/spray.*
Specialties:	*Specialize in providing wet & dry processes to premium denim jeans. Vintage washes to glitter coating.*
Markets:	*Apparel manufacturers and designers*

AAA PATTERNS & MARKING SERVICES

233 Cypress Lane
Ozark, AL 36360
Michael Smith
(1) (334) 445 4870   Fax: (1) (334) 445 3910

E-Mail:	*patterns@aaapatternsmarking.com*
Web Site:	*www.aaapatternsmarking.com*
Description:	*Accurate & cost-effective pattern making service.*
Year Est:	*2001*
Categories:	*Pattern Making, Grading/Marking*
Markets:	*All markets, all sizes & all styles.*

AVB DESIGNS

1628 Palm Avenue
San Mateo, CA 94402
Alexandria von Bromssen
(1) (650) 346 1533

E-Mail:	*vonbromssen@mac.com*
Web Site:	*www.avbdesigns.com*
Description:	*Fashion design, fashion illustration, patternmaking, sample making, sourcing, small production runs, grading & consulting.*
Year Est:	*2004*
Categories:	*Sample Rooms/Small Production*
Specialties:	*Pattern engineering, pattern corrections and grading production patterns.*
Markets:	*Womenswear, Mens, Childrens and Home Furnishings.*
Packages:	*Complete packages available.*
Agent:	*Production Sourcing: USA, China, Brazil*
Minimums:	*None*
Production Capacity:	*Depends on the project.*

AXIS MOON DESIGN AND PRODUCTION

809 S. Brighton
Dallas, TX 75208
Ellen Kreager
(1) (214) 395 1277

E-Mail:	*ellenkreager@gmail.com*
Web Site:	*www.axismoon.com*
Description:	*Sewing contractor of all types of apparel. Small and large production runs. Also, design, consulting and sourcing.*
Year Est:	*1986*
Specialties:	*Patternmaking, production, sourcing, cutting & graphic art work. Own Cutting Room on premises.*
Markets:	*Menswear, Womenswear, Children, Accessories, Home.*
Machinery:	*4 single needle, 1buttonhole, 3 serger, 1 button, 2 merrow, 1 leather/walking foot, 1 blindstitch.*
Packages:	*Complete & CMT packages.*
Minimums:	*50*
Production Capacity:	*3000 pcs/monthly*

BRIARCLIFF APPAREL TECHNOLOGIES LTD.

246 West 38th Street
New York, NY 10018
Edward Kostyra, President
(1) (212) 840 7666   Fax: (1) (212) 840 7168

E-Mail:	*fashionprofessor@hotmail.com*
Description:	*Over 30 years experience in patternmaking, apparel development & production.*
Year Est:	*1994*
Categories:	*Active/Athleticwear, Knit Sportswear, Woven Sportswear, Outerwear, Tee Shirts, Dresses/Suits, Robes/Sleepwear.*
Specialties:	*An adjunct professor in the patternmaking department at F.I.T.*
Markets:	*Menswear, Womenswear, Childrens & Infantwear.*
Packages:	*Full, CMT, Samples, Patterns & all production services.*
Minimums:	*Flexible*
Factory Locals:	*New York, NY & throughout tri-state area.*
Production Capacity:	*No limit*

CALIFORNIA APPAREL SERVICE

2109 S. Standard Avenue
Santa Ana, CA 92707
Tom Lo/Helen Lo
(1) (714) 222 1970   Fax: (1) (714) 442 2788

E-Mail:	*tom@californiaapparelservice.com*
Web Site:	*www.californiaapparelservice.com*
Description:	*We provide complete apparel manufacturing from pattern through finishing. We specialize in smaller run productions.*
Year Est:	*2003*
Categories:	*T-Shirts, Shirts/Tops, Pants/Shorts/Skirts, Childrenswear, Dresses/Blouses, Sportswear*
Specialties:	*Full service apparel manufacturing from design, patterns and grading to cutting, sewing and finishing.*
Markets:	*All markets.*
Packages:	*Full package services & private label programs.*
Minimums:	*50 pieces/style*
Factory Locals:	*Work done in-house.*
	http://www.youtube.com/caapparel
Production Capacity:	*2500 - 3000/month - various styles*

CHERIE BIXLER   See our ad on page 71

135 Fort Lee Road
Leonia, NJ 07605
Cherie Bixler
(1) (201) 944 2886

E-Mail:	*cheriebixler@verizon.net*
Web Site:	*www.cheriebixler.com*
Description:	*Patternmaking and consulting service. We take you from your initial idea through production process. Production done in USA.*
Categories:	*Sample Room/Small Production*
Specialties:	*Product Development, patterns of all types with flat sketch & fittings. Work with people new to the industry.*

Markets: Menswear, Womenswear, Childrenswear.

CREATE-A-MARKER, INC.

254 West 35th Street
New York, NY 10001
Sadat Mamirova
(1) (212) 730 5615   Fax: (1) (212) 730 5616

E-Mail:	cad@createamarkernyc.com
Web Site:	www.createamarkernyc.com
Description:	Digitizing, grading, marker making, emailing patterns, plotting paterns, cutting patterns on oak tag, scanning patterns & copying markers.
Year Est:	1993
Exporting Since:	1999
Categories:	Grading & Marking Services
Specialties:	Cutting edge digital cutting system for samples & patterns. Optimum fabric utilization & cost effectiveness.
Markets:	Womens, Mens, Kids, Bride/Evening, Swimwear, Intimate, Leather/Fur
Machinery:	State-of-the-art equipment. 7 plotters, 2 digertizers, 2 scanners, 5 graders, 8 marker makers, 1 computer cutter, 1 photo copier machines (amonia type).
Export to:	China, Italy, Vietnam, Canada, Japan, Turkey, Taiwan, India, Pakistan, Sri Lanka, Guatemala, SDomingo
Minimums:	None
Production Capacity:	160 patterns/month

CREATIVE PATTERN AND SAMPLE

112 West 9th Street
Los Angeles, CA 90015
Isabel Martinez
(1) (213) 233 0253   Fax: (1) (213) 233 4857

E-Mail:	contact@creativepatternandsample.com
Web Site:	www.creativepatternandsample.com
Description:	Grades & marker, showroom samples, mock ups, sewing, sample making, design consultation, prototypes, fittings.
Categories:	Swimwear, jeans, dresses, suits, lingerie
Specialties:	Quality crafted patterns, 1st patterns, production patterns, spec sheets, pattern corrections. By appointment only.
Markets:	Womenswear

CYCLE FASHION PATTERN INC.

306 West 37th Street, 2nd Floor
New York, NY 10018

(1) (212) 216 9668

Web Site:	www.cyclefashionpattern.com
Description:	We are a sample room dedicated to making patterns & samples using draping. We provide small lot production service to meet your needs.
Categories:	Sample Room/Small Production
Specialties:	We specialize in jackets, pants, jeans, dresses, skirts & eveningwear.
Markets:	Womenswear

DESIGN PRINCIPLES LLC, THE

1914 Cordova Road
Ft. Lauderdale, FL 33316
Hollis Dominick
(1) 727 488 8162   Fax: (1) 954 756 7325

E-Mail:	*hollis@thedesignprinciples.com*
Web Site:	*www.thedesignprinciples.com*
Description:	*Design, sketching, patternmaking, samples, marking/grading, sourcing and production services.*
Categories:	*Sample Room/Small Production*
Specialties:	*Specialize in servicing the startup to emerging designer brands for their production needs.*
Markets:	*Menswear, Womenswear, Childrens & Accessories.*
Factory Locals:	*Development Office: 305 879 6863*

FACTORY 212, THE

306 West 38th Street
New York, NY 10018
Angela Kim
(1) (212) 944 6900   Fax: (1) (212) 944 6909

E-Mail:	*angela@thefactory212.com*
Web Site:	*www.thefactory212.com*
Description:	*Patternmaking, samplemaking for runway/showroom, design assistance, duplications, consulting, small production lots.*
Year Est:	*2010*
Specialties:	*We can make anything from tee shirts to jeans to dresses and jackets.*
Markets:	*Menswear & Womenswear*
Machinery:	*Straight stitch, double needle, merrow, coverstitch, bartack.*
Packages:	*Complete Packages*
Minimums:	*None*

FASHIONS UNLIMITED, INC.

1100 Wicomico Street
Baltimore, MD 21230
Mary Murphy
(1) (410) 783 1584

E-Mail:	*fashionsu@verizon.net*
Web Site:	*www.fashionsu.net*
Description:	*Full service patternmaking/development department on premises.*
Year Est:	*1976*
Categories:	*Active/Athleticwear, Lingerie/Intimate Apparel, Sportswear-Knits, Swimwear/Dancewear.*
Specialties:	*We specialize in seamless development. We have seamless knitting capabilities on Santoni Machines. Bras, tops, pants, underwear, swim.*
Markets:	*Womenswear, Childrenswear*
Machinery:	*Overlock, single needle, coverstitch (1 and 2 needle) zig zag, walking foot machines, flat locks.*
Packages:	*Full service, CMT & complete packages.*
Minimums:	*None*
Factory Locals:	*Baltimore MD, Hellam PA, Charlotte NC (Seamless)*
Production Capacity:	*Swim: 1,000 units/week, Activewear: 1,500 units/week,*

Dance: 1,500 units/week, Sportswear: 1,000 units/week

FINE LINE, INC.
12457 Gladstone Avenue
Sylmar, CA 91342
Michael Collier
(1) (818) 361 8103   Fax: (1) (818) 361 1194

E-Mail:	*info@finelineinc.com*
Web Site:	*www.finelineinc.com*
Description:	*Patternmaking & grading service.*
Categories:	*Cutting/Fusing Contractors, Grading/Marking,*
	Patternmaking.
Specialties:	*Domestic production and sourcing solutions...all made in the USA.*
Markets:	*All*
Machinery:	*Fully automated cutting machines.*

FRENCH CURVE DESIGNS
906 West McDermott Drive
Allen, TX 75013
Heather Madrid
(1) 972 571 1196   Fax: (1) 972 534 1218

E-Mail:	*hmadrid@frenchcurvedesigns.com*
Web Site:	*www.frenchcurvedesigns.com*
Description:	*First patterns, production patterns and samples.*
Categories:	*Grading/Marking*
Specialties:	*Tech design, spec writing, patternmaking, grading/marking.*
Markets:	*Menswear, Womenswear & Childrenswear.*

G & M SERVICES
2807 Satsuma Drive
Dallas, TX 75229

(1) (214) 358 0041   Fax: (1) (214) 358 0042

E-Mail:	*gary@gmser.com*
Web Site:	*www.gmser.com*
Year Est:	*1992*
Specialties:	*Samples & patternmaking with Pattern Maker onsite.*
Markets:	*Menswear, Womenswear & Childrenswear.*
Machinery:	*Infinity I Plotter, Infinity II Plotter, Gerber Accumark System,*
	Lectra System, Microdynamics System.

HEATHER MENZIES PATTERN DESIGN
Bournedale Road
Manhasset, NY 11030
Heather Menzies
(1) (516) 375 3807

E-Mail:	*heather@nypatternmaker.com*
Web Site:	*www.nypatternmaker.com*
Description:	*First through production patterns for women's & children's market.*
	Specialize in bridge dresses, designer & moderate sportswear & bridal.
Year Est:	*2008*

> **Specialties:** *Fittings via SKYPE, mock-ups, technical sketches and consulting.*

IN STYLE USA, INC.

307 West 36th Street
New York, NY 10018
James Mallon
(1) (212) 631 0278   Fax: (1) (212) 631 0279

E-Mail:	*instyleusa@instyleusa.net*
Description:	*Contractor & private label manufacturer.*
Categories:	*Dresses/Blouses, Sample Room/Small Production, Suits/Tailored Garments*
Specialties:	*Experienced patternmaking for samples & production. On-time delivery.*
Markets:	*Womenswear*
Packages:	*All*
Minimums:	*None*
Factory Locals:	*New York City.*
Production Capacity:	*12,000 to 20,000 pcs/month*

IN.STYLE EXCHANGE™

See our ad on page 75

1844 W. Division Street
Arlington, TX 76012
Sales Manager
(1) (817) 886 9222

E-Mail:	*info@instyleexchange.com*
Web Site:	*www.instyleexchange.com*
Description:	*Expert patternmaking service starting from an idea/sketch or a technical spec to beautiful, commercial patterns.*
Categories:	*Sample Rooms/Small Production, Production Sourcing, Shirts & Tops, Childrens Wear, Dresses & Blouses, Lingerie, Sleepwear & Robes.*
Specialties:	*Full service, 'one-stop-shop', including design, patterns, grading/marking, samples and small run production.*
Packages:	*Private label & full packages.*
Minimums:	*50 pieces per color per style*
Production Capacity:	*50,000 pcs/month*

JJ PATTERN INC.

580 8th Avenue
New York, NY 10018

(1) (212) 391 8089   Fax: (1) (212) 391 2030

E-Mail:	*myjjpatternnyc@gmail.com*
Web Site:	*www.jjpatternnyc.com*
Description:	*One stop service from patternmaking & sample development to production including grading and marking.*

JUN'S PATTERN

254 West 35th Street
New York, NY 10001
Jenny Kwon
(1) (212) 221 6130   Fax: (1) (212) 575 0656

E-Mail:	*jennykwon64@gmail.com*
Description:	*Patterns for samples & duplicates.*
Year Est:	*1994*
Specialties:	*Expertise with knit & woven styles. Small production.*
Markets:	*Menswear, Womenswear, Childrenswear.*
Minimums:	*None*

KATRINA PATTERNS

555 Eighth Avenue
New York, NY 10018
Valentina
(1) (212) 563 7332   Fax: (1) (212) 563 7394

Web Site:	*www.katrinapatterns.com*
Description:	*Patterns, samples & duplicates. Fast delivery & turn-around.*
Categories:	*Patternmaking, Sample Room/Small Production.*
Specialties:	*Specialize in women's woven sportswear.*
Markets:	*Womenswear*
Machinery:	*6 sewing, 3 merrow, 3 irons, hindstitch & cutting machine.*
Minimums:	*None*
Production Capacity:	*20 units/week (jackets, dresses), 30 units/week (pants, blouses)*

LEFT IN STITCHES INC.

55 Ericson Court
Arcata, CA 95521

(1) (707) 822 3041   Fax: (1) (707) 822 3042

E-Mail:	*info@leftinstitches.com*
Web Site:	*www.leftinstitches.com*
Description:	*Over 29 years of patternmaking, grading and sewing. Samples, prototypes. Work with knits and wovens.*
Categories:	*Grading/Marking, Dresses/Blouses, Samples/Small Production*
Specialties:	*Creative design and development from concept to production. Specialize in working with small and startup companies.*
Markets:	*Menswear, Womenswear & Childrenswear.*

LORI ANN DESIGN

1515 Rose Avenue
Ferndale, CA 95536
Lori Ann Knowles
(1) (707) 845 5043

E-Mail:	*lori@lorianndesign.com*
Web Site:	*www.lorianndesign.com*
Description:	*Professional pattern maker, flat sketches, figure sketches, pattern cards, cutters musts, specs, line sheets and size charts.*
Specialties:	*All work done in-house.*

MAGNATEX APPAREL SERVICES

4790 Irvine Boulevard
Irvine, CA 92620
Kirk Linn
(1) (949) 551 9624

E-Mail:	*magnatex@cox.net*
Description:	*Pre-production technical design packages and computer marking and grading.*
Specialties:	*Specialize in pattern making services.*

ME'LANSON PATTERNS

870 N Richmond
Chicago, IL 60622
Maribel Melanson
(1) (702) 742 3082

E-Mail:	*thepatternmaker14@gmail.com*
Web Site:	*www.coroflot.com/marfig*
Description:	*Pattern draft, initial first samples and small production. Will do runs of 6 pieces to 2 dozen for start-up companies.*
Categories:	*Sample Room/Small Production, Product Development*
Specialties:	*Design studio that offers patternmaking, fabric sourcing, technical flat drawings, fittings, grading, marker making, tech packs & branding.*
Markets:	*Menswear, Womenswear, Childrens & Accessories.*
Minimums:	*None*

MEHERA SHAW TEXTILES PVT LTD.

3307 Trice Atwater Road
Chapel Hill, NC 27516
Shari Keller
(1) (919) 969 2572   Fax: (1) (919) 969 6909

E-Mail:	*info@meherashaw.com*
Web Site:	*www.meherashaw.com*
Description:	*We are a full production company offering pattern making and grading, including designer support, fabric sourcing, sampling & CMT services.*
Year Est:	*2007*
Exporting Since:	*2008*
Categories:	*Samples/Small Production*
Specialties:	*Specialize in small-scale designers wishing to produce private label collections using natural fibers, artisan textiles and/or organic fabrics.*
Markets:	*Womenswear & Girlswear.*
Export to:	*USA, Europe, Japan*
Minimums:	*Small minimums & lots of start-up support*
Factory Locals:	*India*

MICHAEL CALDERONE, INC.

265 West 37th Street
New York, NY 10018
Michael
(1) (212) 465 1093   Fax: (1) (212) 868 0628

E-Mail:	*mcpatterns@aol.com*
Description:	*Expert patternmaking service.*

Categories:	Grading/Marking, Sample Room/Small Production
Specialties:	Specialize in plaids, stripes & cemetric type of prints.
Markets:	All.

NY STUDIO LLC
213 West 35th Street
New York, NY 10001
Robert Forehand
(1) (212) 244 1269   Fax: (1) (212) 244 4788

E-Mail:	robert@nystudiollc.com
Web Site:	www.nystudiollc.com
Description:	New York sample room for 1st proto & dups, pattern scanning/plotting, hand-made patterns or digital pattern service.
Year Est:	1998
Specialties:	Tech packs for China can be created in our New York facility.
Packages:	Full service, CMT & complete packages.
Factory Locals:	Shenzhen & Nantong, China
Production Capacity:	3,000 pcs/month

PATTERN DESIGN UNLIMITED, INC.
See our ad on page 73

550 West Rt. 897
Reinholds, PA 17569
Pamela Urban
(1) (717) 336 0500   Fax: (1) (717) 336 0309

E-Mail:	pdu@patterndesign.com
Web Site:	www.patterndesign.com
Description:	20+year product development company; designing, patterns, grading, marking & samples.
Year Est:	1987
Categories:	Grading/Marking, Sample Rooms/Small Production
Specialties:	On contract with GGT, Gerber Garment Technology to insure up-to-date technology. Expertise with mens, womens & kids markets.
Markets:	Menswear, Womenswear & Childrenswear.
Packages:	Complete & CMT packages.
Minimums:	None

PATTERN GRADING & MARKER SERVICES
3650 S.W. 141 Avenue
Miramar, FL 33027
Regina Gottlieb, Owner
(1) (954) 441 4432   Fax: (1) (954) 441 4344

E-Mail:	regina@pattern-maker.com
Web Site:	www.pattern-maker.com
Description:	Technical consulting services and expert patternmaking, and grading & marking.
Year Est:	1999
Categories:	Grading/Marking
Specialties:	Make patterns from an existing garment, a customer defined speck or sketch. Grading & marking specific to your specs and fabric.
Machinery:	10 machines
Export to:	Dominican Republic

Minimums: Low: 1 to 200 units/style

POPULAR PATTERN CO.
340 West 39th Street
New York, NY 10018
Stephen or Ian
(1) (212) 947 2902   Fax: (1) (212) 947 2716

E-Mail:	ssinger1@aol.com
Description:	Patternmaking, costing of yardage, specs & more.
Categories:	Patternmaking, Grading/Marking
Specialties:	Fast service, affordable prices, instant overseas delivery available by modem.
Markets:	Menswear, Womenswear, Children/Infantwear.
Machinery:	25 Accumark
Export to:	China, Vietnam, Domican Republic
Production Capacity:	400 graded patterns/monthly

QUICK FUSING INC.
260 West 36th Street
New York, NY 10018
Igor Goldenberg
(1) (212) 967 0311   Fax: (1) (212) 967 1432

E-Mail:	quickfuse5@aol.com
Web Site:	www.apparelexpert.com
Description:	Cut and sew contractor from start to finish. All done in the USA.
Year Est:	1987
Categories:	Samples/Small Production, Cutting/Fusing
Specialties:	Cutting, fusing, sponging, bonding fabrics & leather, patternmaking, sewing, samples. Full production small and large lots.
Markets:	Womenswear, Childrenswear, Accessories.
Packages:	Complete packages.
Minimums:	Small

RAINBOW STYLE
242 West 38th Street
New York, NY 10018

(1) (212) 290 0209

E-Mail:	info@rainbowpattern.com
Web Site:	www.rainbowpattern.com
Description:	One-stop service from concept to production. We can cover all types of fabric for knit, chiffon, jersey, netting, denim, wool, leather etc.
Categories:	Samples/Small Production, Sportswear/Knits
Markets:	Menswear, Womenswear, Childrenswear

ROBKO LLC
214 Oak Street
Nazareth, PA 18064
Arthur Rader
(1) (610) 746 4933   Fax: (1) (610) 746 5563

E-Mail:	art@customapparelzone.com

Web Site:	*www.customapparelzone.com*
Description:	*Full service private label manufacturing. From pattern making, grading, markers, sample making, cut and sew.*
Categories:	*Sample Room/Small Production, Grading/Marking*
Specialties:	*Specialize in t-shirts, sport shirts, oxfords, onesies, sweatshirts, camp shirts, rib t-shirts, sports specialty wear.*
Markets:	*Menswear, Womenswear, Childrenswear*

S. KANOUNI DESIGN & PATTERN STUDIO

824 Los Angeles Street
Los Angeles, CA 90014
Soad
(1) (213) 627 2281

E-Mail:	*skfashion@att.net*
Description:	*First & production patternmaking.*
Categories:	*Patternmaking, Sample Rooms/Small Production.*
Specialties:	*In-house cut & sew. One stop service.*
Markets:	*Menswear, Womenswear & Childrenswear.*
Packages:	*CMT packages available.*
Factory Locals:	*Second address: 7171 Grandoaks Dr., Stanton, CA 90680 Cell: 213-880-0515*

SEWN PRODUCT SERVICES

111 S. Lander Street
Seattle, WA 98134
Kristine Carlton/Jenny Mae Miller
(1) (206) 467 5459   Fax: (1) (206) 467 5459

E-Mail:	*contact@sewnproductservices.com*
Web Site:	*www.sewnproductservices.com*
Description:	*Design consultation, patternmaking, sample sewing, raw goods sourcing, grading & marking, fit assesments, tech pack development.*
Categories:	*Athletic/Activewear, Lingerie/Intimate Apparel, Sleepwear, Leather Apparel, Swimwear, Costuming, Dancewear, Soft Goods Accessories*
Specialties:	*We offer a full menu of services supporting sewn product development including production management & small run production.*
Markets:	*Menswear, Womenswear & Childrenswear.*

SHEHU

333 S. 20th Street
Philadelphia, PA 19148
Bela Shehu
(1) (267) 496 5208

E-Mail:	*bela@shehu.net*
Web Site:	*www.shehu.net*
Description:	*Full service design & development company. We specialize in pattern & sample making. Contractor of small production lots.*
Year Est:	*2007*
Categories:	*Small Production/Samples*
Specialties:	*All types of women & girls apparel. Dresses, bottoms, tops, sleepwear, uniforms, sportswear, scarves/shawls.*
Markets:	*Womenswear & Girlswear.*

Machinery:	5 Straight Stitch, 4 Marrow, 1 Cover Stitch, 1 Pearl Stitch, 2 Zigzag.
Packages:	CMT & Samples
Production Capacity:	500 pcs/month

SOMIYA INC.

307 West 38th Street
New York, NY 10018
Leo and Liz
(1) (212) 302 3089   Fax: (1) (212) 302 3089

E-Mail:	somiyainc@yahoo.com
Description:	Patternmaking, samples, small production is done in New York City, bulk production capabilities at sister factory overseas.
Categories:	Sample Rooms/Small Production
Specialties:	Specialize in pattern and samples.
Markets:	All markets.
Minimums:	None

STUDIO NTK LLC

2946 Welcome Way
Greenwood, IN 46143
Nataliya Kitic
(1) (317) 886 7327

E-Mail:	studiontk@gmail.com
Web Site:	www.studiontk.com
Description:	Apparel design and manufacturing. Our services are for start up & small companies to leading brands.
Year Est:	2011
Categories:	Samples/Small Production
Specialties:	Consulting, concept ideas to detailed sketches, specks, production samples, patternmaking, cut and sew, quality control.
Markets:	Womenswear, Accessories
Packages:	CMT & Samples
Minimums:	None
Production Capacity:	1,000 pcs

STUDIO ONE LEATHER DESIGN INC.

270 West 39th Street
New York, NY 10018
Arthur Cohen
(1) (212) 760 1701   Fax: (1) (212) 760 1702

E-Mail:	arthur@studio1leather.com
Description:	A full service sample room working in the development of men's and women's sportswear and outerwear.
Categories:	Sample Room/Small Production, Production Sourcing, Leather/Suede
Specialties:	Specialize in leather and suede.
Markets:	Menswear, Womenswear
Machinery:	5 sewing machines, buttonhole, fur sewing machine and merrow.
Minimums:	25 pcs/style (leather garments, woven)
Factory Locals:	All work in done in the USA.

Production Capacity:	*800-1,000 units/month*

STYLE SOURCE INC.
913 Orange Street
Wilmington, NC 28401
Geoffrey Krasnov
(1) (910) 399 2288   Fax: (1) (910) 399 2289

E-Mail:	*geoff@style-source.com*
Web Site:	*www.style-source.com*
Description:	*Full range of pattern making services to the trade. Manufacturing & sourcing, fabric sales, pre-patterned apparel & private label apparel.*
Year Est:	*2002*
Categories:	*Sample Rooms/Small Production*
Specialties:	*Devise first patterns from conceptual drawings & produce first samples & specs, sourcing & manufacturing both domestic & overseas.*
Markets:	*Womenswear, Childrenswear, Accessories.*
Factory Locals:	*All work is done in North Carolina*
Production Capacity:	*5,000 dozen/monthly*

SUNCOAST TRENDS CORP.
2860 21st Avenue North
St. Petersburg, FL 33713
Rosanna Carl
(1) (727) 321 4948   Fax: (1) (727) 321 4320

Description:	*Patternmaking for samples and production.*
Categories:	*Sportswear/Knits, Sportswear/Wovens*
Markets:	*Menswear, Womenswear, Childrens, Accessories.*

SUPERIOR PATTERN SERVICES
1095 East 15th Street
Hialeah, FLorida 33010
Jeff Trieb, President
(1) (305) 805 1540

E-Mail:	*superior_patterns@yahoo.com*
Web Site:	*www.superiorpatterns.com*
Description:	*Provide the highest quality patterns developed by our master patternmaker. We send either zip files or cut files to our customers.*
Year Est:	*1997*
Categories:	*Grading/Marking, Production Sourcing, Sample Room/Small Production*
Specialties:	*All pattern services for woven & knit apparel. Specialize in assisting new designers create their collection.*
Markets:	*Menswear, Womenswear, Childrenswear*
Machinery:	*Gerber Accumark System*
Packages:	*Full packages.*
Minimums:	*Vary*
Factory Locals:	*Factories in Dominican Republic & Guatemala.*

TAG STUDIO PATTERN DESIGN SERVICE

519 Lincoln Way #2
San Francisco, CA 94122
Monica Houlihan, Owner
(1) (415) 664 2408

E-Mail:	*tagpatrn@gmail.com*
Web Site:	*www.tagstudio.biz*
Description:	*Expert pattern design service. Computer patterns, product development consulting services, grading & marking.*
Year Est:	*1993*
Categories:	*Patternmaking Services, Grading/Marking, Sample Making*
Specialties:	*Experience in a wide range of garment & sewn product categories.*
Markets:	*All markets.*
Machinery:	*Computer-aided design PAD software. Gerber converter software.*

TECHS BY TERRY

83 Beach 216th Street
Breezy Point, NY 11697
Terry Maloney
(1) (718) 440 7185

E-Mail:	*terrmaloney@aol.com*
Description:	*Product development, technical design and patternmaking services.*

TRUE MEASURE INC.

1042 S. Gerhart Avenue
City of Commerce, CA 90022

(1) (323) 213 3184

E-Mail:	*melida@truemeasureinc.com*
Web Site:	*www.truemeasureinc.com*
Description:	*Fashion design, pattern making services, samples, full scale manufacturing in the USA and overseas.*
Categories:	*Sample Rooms/Small Production*
Specialties:	*Specialize in menswear, womens formal & casual wear, swimwear, & intimate apparel. We cater to start-ups as well as established brands.*
Markets:	*Menswear & Womenswear.*

WERKSTATT

347 West 36th Street
New York, NY 10018
Tina Schenk
(1) (646) 414 4545   Fax: (1) (646) 559 2824

E-Mail:	*tina@werkstattny.com*
Web Site:	*www.werkstattny.com*
Description:	*Pattern service located in the heart of NYC's garment district. Specialize in intelligent pattern & garment development.*
Year Est:	*2008*
Specialties:	*Fit specialist. First through production patterns.*

Markets:	*Menswear & Womenswear.*
Production Capacity:	*Varies depending on the difficulty of patterns. 35-60 patterns.*

WILLIAM THE PATTERNMAKER

340 West 39th Street
New York, NY 10018
William Smithline
(1) 646 824 2280   Fax: (1) 212 947 2716

E-Mail:	*williamsmithline@yahoo.com*
Web Site:	*www.williamthepatternmaker.com*
Description:	*Master Patternmaker. Initial idea thru production. Samplemaking. Work with large & small companies as well as emerging designers.*
Specialties:	*Specialize in proper costing of your designs, help with finding label makers, trim resources, proper cutting rooms, factories & shippers.*
Packages:	*Full service company.*

Z.W. DESIGNS, INC.

443 Flint Hill Court
Lawrenceville, GA 30044
Z. Arthur
(1) (770) 513 0906

E-Mail:	*zwd@zwdesigns.com*
Web Site:	*www.zwdesigns.com*
Description:	*Expert apparel & product development, specifications, digital patterns, grading, markers; plotting, samples, small lot manufacturing.*
Year Est:	*1983*
Categories:	*Grading & Marking Services, Sample Rooms/Small Production, CAD/CAM Software Marketing*
Specialties:	*CAD/CAM patternmaking, technical design, design sketching/flats; choir robes, uniforms, government contractor certified (WOSP,SDB).*
Markets:	*Womenswear, Menswear, Childrenswear.*
Production Capacity:	*Small lots, but varies*

3D INDUSTRIES

20988 Bake Parkway
Lake Forest, CA 92630
Ian Tennant
(1) (949) 588 5884   Fax: (1) (949) 855 4747

E-Mail:	*sales@3d-ind.com*
Web Site:	*www.3d-ind.com*
Description:	*Manufacturer of custom technical apparel, sportswear & accessories for branded customers worldwide by our network of overseas factories.*
Year Est:	*1996*
Specialties:	*Design, develop and deliver. We are not set up to handle small runs.*
Markets:	*Menswear, Womenswear & Childrenswear.*
Minimums:	*1,000 pcs/style - $2500.00*

AIM GARMENTS

8444 Braddock Way
Columbia, MD 21046
Chinh Tran
(1) 443 745 1502   Fax: (1) 410 381 5109

E-Mail:	*info@aimgarments.com*
Web Site:	*www.aimgarments.com*
Description:	*Full-service clothing & apparel manufacturing contractor. Specialty in woven athletic apparel and team sportswear.*
Year Est:	*1995*
Categories:	*Active/Athletic Wear, Dresses, Pants/Shorts/Skirts, Blouses/Tops, Outerwear, Jeans/Denimwear, Childrenswear, Lingerie, Tee-Shirts.*
Specialties:	*Full range of services: design, fabric procurement, patternmaking, product development, cut & sew, tag & bag, shipping & custom clearing.*
Markets:	*Menswear, Womenswear, Boyswear, Girlswear.*
Packages:	*CMT, Patternmaking & Samplemaking.*
Export to:	*U.S.A.*
Minimums:	*2000/style*
Factory Locals:	*Ho Chi Minh City, Vietnam*
Production Capacity:	*300,000 pcs/month*

APPAREL AGENCY, THE

2023 W Carroll Avenue
Chicago, IL 60612
Nichole Rairigh
(1) (312) 265 0900   Fax: (1) (312) 273 1796

E-Mail:	*info@theapparelagency.com*
Web Site:	*www.theapparelagency.com*
Description:	*Full service agency. Product design, sourcing, graphic design, tech packs, pattern making, sample making, costing, small production.*
Year Est:	*2010*
Specialties:	*Production-ready patterns and samples with low minimum production commitments for new & small businesses.*
Markets:	*Menswear, Womenswear & Childrenswear.*
Packages:	*CMT, Full Package*
Minimums:	*1-500 pcs/style/color*

CAROL PETERS INC. (CPI)

75 Livingston Street
Brooklyn, NY 11201
Carol Louie
(1) (347) 256 7804

E-Mail:	*carolcpi512@aol.com*
Description:	*Production Sourcing company for women's & children's active wear, outerwear, sleepwear and intimate apparel.*
Markets:	*Womenswear, Childrenswear*
Factory Locals:	*Production in China and Bangladesh.*

CHERIE BIXLER

See our ad on page 71

135 Fort Lee Road
Leonia, NJ 07605
Cherie Bixler
(1) (201) 944 2886

E-Mail:	*cheriebixler@verizon.net*
Web Site:	*www.cheriebixler.com*
Description:	*Patternmaking and consulting service. We take you from your initial idea through production process. Production done in USA.*
Categories:	*Patternmaking, Sample Rooms/Small Production.*
Specialties:	*Product Development, patterns of all types with flat sketch & fittings. Work with people new to the industry.*
Markets:	*Menswear, Womenswear, Childrenswear.*

CHESTER LINE CORP.

9820 Bell Ranch Drive
Santa Fe Springs, CA 90670
Soung Kim, Owner
(1) (562) 944 2777   Fax: (1) (562) 944 2233

E-Mail:	*soungkim@chesterline.com*
Web Site:	*www.chesterline.com*
Description:	*Factory group specializing in high quality intimate apparel, lingerie, sleepwear & women's foundation apparel.*
Year Est:	*1999*
Categories:	*Lingerie/Intimate Apparel*
Specialties:	*Textile design, new product design, molding & more.*
Markets:	*Womenswear & Girlswear.*
Packages:	*Full packages, patterns, samples, embroidery, beading & more.*
Minimums:	*3,000 units/style, but negotiable*
Factory Locals:	*Shantou & Shenzhen China & Seoul, South Korea*
Production Capacity:	*200,000 pcs/month*

CHINAMINE USA

214 West 39th Street
New York, NY 10018
Aimee Van Brunt
(1) (212) 575 1525   Fax: (1) (212) 575 0003

E-Mail:	*info@chinamineusa.com*
Web Site:	*www.chinamineusa.com*
Description:	*Chinese vertical manufacturer with product development expertise.*

A key supplier to the contemporary & better specialty retailers.

Year Est:	*1989*
Categories:	*Production Sourcing/Factory Agents, Patternmaking Services*
Specialties:	*Design library, embellishment hangers & garments for inspiration.*
	We work with design, sourcing & product development teams.
Markets:	*Womenswear, Menswear, Juniors*
Export to:	*Europe 20%, USA 70%, 10% remains in China*
Factory Locals:	*Five sewing factories and a print, dye & wash facility.*
Production Capacity:	*400,000 - 600,000 pieces/monthly depending on garment type.*

CREATIVE BUSINESS HOUSE

45 West 46th Street
New York, NY 10036
Amandine Berg
(1) (646) 543 1831

E-Mail:	*info@creativebusinesshouse.com*
Web Site:	*www.creativebusinesshouse.com*
Description:	*One stop shop for fashion designers.*
	Let us develop and launch your own private label. CBH does it all!
Specialties:	*Outsource fabrics & trim, create patterns, samples, tech packs, EIN,*
	branding, trademark, patents, packaging, labels, website, logo.
Markets:	*Menswear, Womenswear, Children, Accessories, Home.*

EATONTEX RESOURCES LTD.

11 Penn Plaza
New York, NY 10001
Steven Hershkowitz
(1) 212 221 1473   Fax: (1) 646 688 5299

E-Mail:	*sales@eatontexresources.com*
Web Site:	*www.eatontexresources.com*
Description:	*Location plus our strategic alliance with mills & factories worldwide*
	make us your one-stop resource for your fabric, garment & trim needs.
Year Est:	*2006*
Categories:	*Production Sourcing/Factory Agent*
Specialties:	*Work with well-known small manufacturers. Consulting on import*
	procedures, customs regulations, and letter of credit matters.
Markets:	*Menswear, Womenswear, Infant/Childrenswear.*
Minimums:	*Low*
Factory Locals:	*China, Metro New York Area*
Production Capacity:	*2500 pcs/monthly*

FASHION SOURCES, INC.

1006 East Montgomery Avenue
North Wales, PA 19454
Allen Edelson
(1) (215) 699 6801   Fax: (1) (215) 699 3413

E-Mail:	*fashsource@aol.com*
Description:	*Immediate production of all apparel types & for all markets.*
	Marketing agent for twelve factories worldwide.
Year Est:	*1985*
Exporting Since:	*1985*

Categories:	Active/Athleticwear, Coats/Jackets, Dresses/Blouses, Woven Shirts, Jeans/Denim, Sleepwear/Robes, Sportswear, Mens Slacks
Markets:	Menswear, Womenswear, Childrenswear.
Minimums:	2,000 units/style.
Factory Locals:	USA & import from Mexico, Costa Rica, El Salvador & China.
Production Capacity:	Jeans: 75,000/wk, Slacks: 22,000-100,000/wk, Blazers: 3,000/wk, Sportwear: 5,000/wk

GARMENT INDUSTRY DEVELOPMENT CORP/GIDC

262 West 38th Street
New York, NY 10018

(1) (212) 842 9343   Fax: (1) (212) 842 9344

E-Mail:	award@gidc.org
Web Site:	www.gidc.org
Description:	Your first stop in finding domestic New York contractors.
Year Est:	1984
Categories:	Non-profit Association/Production Sourcing Consultants
Specialties:	Dedicated to strengthening New Yorks garment industry, finding fashion jobs, research, business development services & training.
Markets:	All

GLOBE-TEX

56 Harrison Street
New Rochelle, NY 10801
Robert Hurvitz
(1) (914) 560 8422   Fax: (1) (914) 355 4141

E-Mail:	robert@globe-tex.com
Web Site:	www.globe-tex.com
Description:	Source, design & arrange full programs for the U.S., Japan, Australia & Canadian companies.
Year Est:	1996
Exporting Since:	1996
Categories:	All sports categories
Specialties:	Specialize in technical performance, team sports and fan wear. Also, finance, shipping & quality control services.
Markets:	Womenswear, Menswear, Childrenswear.
Packages:	Full packages.
Export to:	China, Vietnam, Cambodia, Dominican Republic, Peru, Pakistan, India, Taiwan & Indonesia.
Minimums:	1,000 dozen/style
Factory Locals:	Sourcing offices in Shanghai/China, Taipei/Taiwan, Jakarta/Indonesia, Lima/Peru, Dominican Republic.
Production Capacity:	1 million units/month

GOLDEN EGG CORPORATION
10501 Valley Boulevard #1856
El Monte, CA 91731
Calvin Lin
(1) (626) 279 2779   Fax: (1) (626) 288 1512

E-Mail:	*calvinlin123@gmail.com*
Description:	*All types of seamless apparel.*
Categories:	*Production Sourcing/Factory Agents*
Factory Locals:	*Factory located in China.*
Production Capacity:	*1000 - 5000 pcs/month*

HARPER INDUSTRIES, INC.
29 Hillcrest Road
Berkeley, CA 94705
Tom Friedland
(1) (510) 655 5143   Fax: (1) (510) 923 9542

E-Mail:	*tsf@harcrest.com*
Web Site:	*www.harcrest.com*
Description:	*Contractor & manufacturer of tee shirts, sport team uniforms, medical scrubs, smocks.*
Categories:	*Tee Shirts/Sweat Shirts, Uniforms*
Markets:	*Menswear, Womenswear, Unisex.*
Packages:	*CMT, Sewing & Full Packages.*
Factory Locals:	*Yucatan Peninsula Mexico*
Production Capacity:	*1,000,000 pcs/month*

IN.STYLE EXCHANGE™   See our ad on page 75
1844 W. Division Street
Arlington, TX 76012
Sales Manager
(1) (817) 886 9222

E-Mail:	*info@instyleexchange.com*
Web Site:	*www.instyleexchange.com*
Description:	*Full service, 'one-stop-shop' for lingerie & intimate & underwear. Design, patterns, grading/marking, samples & small run production.*
Categories:	*Sample Rooms/Small Production, Patternmaking, Shirts & Tops, Childrens Wear, Dresses & Blouses, Lingerie, Sleepwear & Robes.*
Packages:	*Private label & full packages.*
Minimums:	*50 pieces per color per style*
Production Capacity:	*50,000 pcs/month*

JULIE HUTTON, INC.
140 East 28th Street
New York, NY 10016
Julie Hutton
(1) (212) 532 5126   Fax: (1) (212) 532 0109

E-Mail:	*julie@juliehuttoninc.com*
Web Site:	*www.juliehuttoninc.com*
Description:	*Private label & personal label sourcing & manufacturing. Offers clients a wide range of services. Your garments from concept to delivery.*
Specialties:	*Specialize in cut & sew knits, wovens, sportswear. Design expertise,*

	fabric sourcing, color direction, initial specs, first thru final fits, samples.
Markets:	*Womenswear & Menswear.*
Minimums:	*Low*
Factory Locals:	*China, USA, Turkey*
Production Capacity:	*10,000 pcs.*

LOGOS FASHION SERVICE
3215 RiverView Drive
Triangle, VA 22172
Sylvie Tran
(1) (703) 879 8827   Fax: (1) (703) 995 4336

E-Mail:	*info@logosfashionservice.com*
Web Site:	*www.logosfashionservice.com*
Description:	*One-stop service and sourcing partner for projects small and large for designers, retailers and private label.*
Year Est:	*2009*
Exporting Since:	*2009*
Specialties:	*Design Development, material & trims sourcing, textile printing, tags, patternmaking, fitting, samples, sewing, cutting, grading & marking.*
Markets:	*Menswear, Womenswear, Children*
Machinery:	*200 Single Needle, 30 Double Needle, 5 Flatlock, 2 Buttonhole*
Packages:	*CMT & Complete packages, also screenprinting & embroidery.*
Export to:	*USA 70%, Europe 20%, Asia 5%, Australia 5%*
Minimums:	*No sewing minimums*
Factory Locals:	*181 79 Street, Tan Quy Ward, District 7, Ho Chi Minh City, Vietnam tel:84-8-3775-0529*
Production Capacity:	*100,000 - 500,000 pcs.*

MANUFACTURING IN CHINA
305 West 28th Street
New York, NY 10001
Anya Feinberg
(1) (212) 255 5597   Fax: (1) (212) 255 5597

E-Mail:	*manufacturinginchina@rcn.com*
Web Site:	*www.imexchinaltd.com*
Description:	*Production sourcing for home furnishings, accessories & jewelry.*
Year Est:	*1973*
Specialties:	*Trading partner - we can manufacture your product in China.*
Factory Locals:	*China*

MANZELLA PRODUCTIONS
80 Sonwil Drive
Buffalo, NY 14225

(1) (716) 681 8880   Fax: (1) (716) 681 6888

E-Mail:	*info@manzella.com*
Web Site:	*www.manzella.com*
Description:	*Glove designer, manufacturing, contracting & production sourcing.*
Categories:	*Accessories, Production Sourcing/Factory Agent.*
Packages:	*CMT & complete packages available.*

METRO TEXTILE INC.

9995 Monroe Drive
Dallas, Texas 75220
Zee Maya
(1) 214 352 0219   Fax: (1) 888 672 2091

E-Mail:	*zee@mtcsourcing.com*
Web Site:	*www.mtcsourcing.com*
Description:	*Sourcing, quality management, merchandising, inspection services, logistic assistance & negotiation for its clients.*
Year Est:	*2001*
Specialties:	*Specialize in knitted & woven ready-made garments plus knitted & woven fabrics, hosiery and home textiles.*
Markets:	*Menswear, Womenswear, Childrenswear & Home.*
Export to:	*USA & Europe*
Minimums:	*None*
Factory Locals:	*Work with over 30 different factories in Pakistan, China & Bangladesh. Pakistan Office: 92 300 824 5884.*

MIAMI STYLE INC.

7480 NW 52nd Street
Miami, FL 33166
Amnon Bensimon/Sofia Rincon
(1) (305) 805 1168   Fax: (1) (305) 805 0075

E-Mail:	*sofia@miamistyle.com*
Web Site:	*www.miamistyle.com*
Description:	*Sourcing agent for all types of active wear, bottoms, tops, tee shirts, knit sportswear, beachwear, sports bras, basics and children's wear.*
Year Est:	*1997*
Specialties:	*Production services: Private label, sewing, cutting, patternmaking, printing, embroidery, screenprinting, samplemaking, dyeing, beading & more.*
Markets:	*Menswear, Womenswear, Boyswear, Girlswear.*
Factory Locals:	*Bangladesh and China*
Production Capacity:	*3 million pcs per month*

MOKITA

118 East 60th Street
New York, NY 10022
Stanley Kitman
(1) (917) 664 4864

E-Mail:	*info@mokitaglobal.com*
Web Site:	*www.mokitaglobal.com*
Description:	*Product development, sourcing, negotiating best pricing, production control, quality assurance & delivery date assurance.*
Specialties:	*Eco-friendly sourcing. We connect companies to manufacturing sources in China and India at the best possible prices.*

NEO-CONCEPT (NY) CORPORATION

242 West 38th Street
New York, NY 10018

(1) (212) 242 6808   Fax: (1) (212) 242 4418

E-Mail:	*glenda@neo-concept.com*
Web Site:	*www.neo-concept.com*
Description:	*Sweaters, cut and sew, wovens, and mixed-media.*
Year Est:	*1989*
Specialties:	*Yarn and fabric innovation as we weave our own yarns and weave most of our own cut & sew fabrics.*
Packages:	*Vertical Operation*
Factory Locals:	*Dounguan, Zhongshan, and the Shanghai regions of China. Also Eco-Friendly factory in Zhingshan, China.*

NY STUDIO LLC

213 West 35th Street
New York, NY 10001
Robert Forehand
(1) (212) 244 1269   Fax: (1) (212) 244 4788

E-Mail:	*robert@nystudiollc.com*
Web Site:	*www.nystudiollc.com*
Description:	*Apparel production sourcing in Hong Kong, China, Cambodia & Korea.*
Year Est:	*1998*
Packages:	*Full service, CMT & complete packages.*
Factory Locals:	*Shenzhen & Nantong, China*
Production Capacity:	*3,000 pcs/month*

PERFORMANCE DESIGN STUDIO

330 A Street
San Diego, CA 91911

(1) (619) 623 7692

E-Mail:	*info@performancedesignstudio.com*
Web Site:	*www.performancedesignstudio.com*
Description:	*Services include patternmaking, technical design/tech packs, fabric and trim sourcing. prototypes, consulting & small production lots.*
Year Est:	*2013*
Specialties:	*We specialize in performance activewear apparel for men and women.*
Markets:	*Menswear, Womenswear, Accessories.*
Packages:	*Marking, Cutting and Sewing*
Minimums:	*Low*
Factory Locals:	*We source worldwide*

RAYLON CORPORATION

267 Fifth Avenue
New York, NY 10016
Jay Pollak
(1) (212) 221 3633   Fax: (1) (212) 889 3283

E-Mail:	*jpollak@rayloncorp.com*

Description:	Full package contractor/factory agent & textile converter.
Year Est:	1948
Specialties:	Specialize in board shorts & warm-up jackets plus bedding, shower curtains and window treatments.
Markets:	Menswear, Womenswear, Boyswear, Girlswear.
Minimums:	500-1,000 pcs/style
Factory Locals:	Asia

RAYTEX INDUSTRIES

130 Crossways Park Drive
Woodbury, NY 11797
Jay Hellegers
(1) (516) 584 1111   Fax: (1) (516) 584 1034

E-Mail:	jhellegers@raytexindustries.com
Web Site:	www.raytexindustries.com
Description:	Full package apparel supplier. World wide sourcing. Offices in Central America & Shanghai. From design & samples thru final shipment.
Specialties:	Specialize in loungewear, boxer shorts, performance underwear, tee shirts & activewear.
Minimums:	3,000 dozen

ROOCHI TRADERS INC.

6393 East Washington Blvd
City of Commerce, CA 90040
Mickey Sachdeva
(1) (323) 722 5592   Fax: (1) (323) 724 0045

E-Mail:	mickey@roochi.com
Web Site:	www.cottonheritage.com
Description:	Over 25+ years of sportswear and activewear sourcing for men, women and children, also junior knits.
Categories:	Tee Shirts/Sweat Shirts, Jeans/Denimwear, Outerwear, Polo Shirts
Specialties:	We stock blank inventory in our DC's NJ, FL and CA for at once delivery.
Markets:	Menswear, Womenswear & Childrenswear.
Export to:	Europe, Mexico, Central America, Canada
Production Capacity:	100,000 doz/month + per category

SCOTTEX GLOBAL SOURCING LLC

1672 Jarrettown Road
Dresher, PA 19025
Bradley Flickstein
(1) (215) 540 1244   Fax: (1) (215) 793 0994

E-Mail:	bradley@scottexglobal.com
Web Site:	www.scottexglobal.com
Description:	Direct import private label sweater developer. Offices in Hong Kong and India.
Specialties:	Classified as an agent with design value added.
Factory Locals:	New York Showroom: By Appointment Only. Toll Free: 866-333-7630

SEWN PRODUCT SERVICES

111 S. Lander Street
Seattle, WA 98134
Kristine Carlton/Jenny Mae Miller
(1) (206) 467 5459   Fax: (1) (206) 467 5459

E-Mail:	*contact@sewnproductservices.com*
Web Site:	*www.sewnproductservices.com*
Description:	*We build & print markers & provide raw goods requirement summaries for your production.*
Categories:	*Athletic/Activewear, Lingerie/Intimate Apparel, Sleepwear, Leather Apparel, Swimwear, Costuming, Dancewear, Soft Goods Accessories*
Specialties:	*We specialize in helping you take these materials to the factory of your choosing or we can facilitate & manage the production for you.*
Markets:	*Menswear, Womenswear & Childrenswear.*
Packages:	*Full Packages. From marker to quality control & delivery.*

SOURCE-I

P.O. Box 741
Indian Rocks Beach, FL 33785
Wayne Wilson, President
(1) (727) 725 2981

E-Mail:	*wwilson@source-i.com*
Web Site:	*www.source-i.com*
Year Est:	*1994*
Categories:	*Sportswear-Knits, Sportswear-Wovens, Denimwear, Sleepwear, Pants/Shorts/Skirts, Shirts/Tops, Sweaters, Jackets & Uniforms.*
Specialties:	*Full package apparel sourcing solutions. Vertical knit and woven operation.*
Markets:	*Menswear, Womenswear, Childrenswear, Infantwear.*
Machinery:	*All updated & modern sewing facilities.*
Packages:	*Door-to-door full package & CMT programs.*

STUDIO ONE LEATHER DESIGN INC.

270 West 39th Street
New York, NY 10018
Arthur Cohen
(1) (212) 760 1701   Fax: (1) (212) 760 1702

E-Mail:	*arthur@studio1leather.com*
Description:	*A full service sample room working in the development of men's and women's sportswear and outerwear.*
Categories:	*Patternmaking, Sample Room/Small Production, Leather/Suede*
Specialties:	*Specialize in leather and suede.*
Markets:	*Menswear, Womenswear*
Machinery:	*5 sewing machines, buttonhole, fur sewing machine and merrow.*
Minimums:	*25 pcs/style (leather garments, woven)*
Factory Locals:	*All work in done in the USA.*
Production Capacity:	*800-1,000 units/month*

SWEENIE MANUFACTURING CORPORATION

34 Sedgwick Avenue
Yonkers, NY 10705
Diane Walker
(1) (646) 825 5027   Fax: (1) (646) 825 5027

E-Mail:	*diane@sweeniemanufacturing.com*
Web Site:	*www.sweeniemanufacturing.com*
Description:	*Branded manufacturer. Specialize in design/merchandising, sourcing and production of activewear, swimwear and cut/sew knits.*
Specialties:	*Specialize in swimwear, activewear, tee-shirts, knit & woven sportswear, sportsbags, gym bags, cosmetic bags. Printed & logo trims.*
Markets:	*Menswear, Womenswear, Childrenswear.*
Machinery:	*Flat bed, button holer, spaghetti strap*
Packages:	*Full package or CMT only*
Factory Locals:	*Domestic & Overseas Production Capabilities.*

TANNERY DIRECT

40 West 37th Street
New York, NY 10018
Anne Sampson
(1) (212) 465 1503   Fax: (1) (212) 465 1512

E-Mail:	*asampson@tannerydirect.com*
Description:	*Full leather garment production packages in sportswear & outerwear.*
Categories:	*Leather/Suede*
Specialties:	*Our New York sample studio takes our customers from patternmaking, fit sessions to final production.*
Factory Locals:	*Shearling coats/jackets are made in Turkey, leather coats & sportswear & dresses are done in China or India.*

TEXTILE ARTS MARKETING INC,.

405 Tarrytown Road
White Plains, NY 10607
Ken Noonan
(1) (914) 837 3588   Fax: (1) (914) 428 6557

E-Mail:	*ken@textileartsmarketing.com*
Web Site:	*www.textileartsmarketing.com*
Description:	*We offer full package garment production in the US and abroad.*
Specialties:	*Finished garments and accessories through certified garment factories.*

UPLIFTING SALES, INC.

PO Box 556
North Bellmore, NY 11710
John Paul Brogan
(1) (917) 913 2284

E-Mail:	*jp@jpbrogan.com*
Description:	*Manufacturers of intimate apparel, daywear and swimwear.*
Specialties:	*Production and contracted manufacturing in China and Thailand.*
Packages:	*Full Packages*

VESTIGE DESIGN
209 West 38th Street
New York, NY 10018

(1) (212) 944 4389   Fax: (1) (212) 944 4381

E-Mail:	*info@vestigedesign.com*
Web Site:	*www.vestigedesign.com*
Description:	*An apparel sourcing & product development company and partner with several garment factories in China and Indonesia.*
Specialties:	*Men's, junior sportswear, missy, contemporary, intimate apparel, sleepwear, sweaters, hand embroidery & beading.*
Markets:	*Menswear & Womenswear.*
Packages:	*Complete packages, private label.*

VISHAL ENTERPRISES
226 West 37th Street
New York, NY 10018
Vishal Moorjani
(1) (212) 629 0880   Fax: (1) (212) 629 0882

E-Mail:	*vishal@vishalent.com*
Web Site:	*www.vishalent.com*
Description:	*We are a vertically integrated organization specializing in the manufacturing of textiles and garments. NY based sample room.*
Specialties:	*Structured jackets, soft dressing, active wear, evening & casual dresses, woven, printed & novelty knit tops, accessories.*
Markets:	*Menswear, Womenswear, Accessories.*
Packages:	*Complete production packages.*
Minimums:	*Low*
Factory Locals:	*India and China*
Production Capacity:	*We can cater to small productions (100 pcs per style per colorway) or do large volume productions (25,000 to 50,000 units per month).*

WORLD SOURCE
224 West 35th Street
New York, NY 10001
Alan Novie/Jack Mann
(1) (212) 594 9129   Fax: (1) (212) 202 5298

E-Mail:	*info@worldsourcenyc.com*
Description:	*All types of apparel production services.*
Year Est:	*1993*
Specialties:	*Specialize in leather and suede outerwear, embellished, embroidered and lace dresses and blouses.*
Markets:	*Menswear & Womenswear.*
Packages:	*Complete*
Factory Locals:	*China and India*
Production Capacity:	*Leather garments: 200 pcs/month per style/color, Sequin Dresses: 150 pcs/month, Blouses: 300 pcs/month.*

ACCURATE SERVICES, INC.

951 Broadway
Fall River, MA 02724
Sue Teixeira
(1) (508) 674 5773   Fax: (1) (508) 674 5649

E-Mail:	*suetex@accurateservice.com*
Web Site:	*www.accurateservice.com*
Description:	*Warehousing & distribution for sewn products manufacturers.*
Year Est:	*1955*
Categories:	*Distribution/Warehouse*
Specialties:	*Full range of finishing services: alter, hem, fix patterns, press and steam. Also, label, re-label & package goods.*
Machinery:	*100,000+ sq. ft. of modern shelves, racks, overhead trolleys and conveyors.*

AVALON COUTURE & TEXTILE, LTD.

35 Magerus Street
South Huntington, NY 11746
Cynthia Clark
(1) 877 832 2227

E-Mail:	*service@avaloncouture.com*
Web Site:	*www.avaloncouture.com*
Description:	*Artistry in fine garment and interior textile care.*
Specialties:	*Fine drycleaning, wetcleaning, resolution of problems/mishaps during design/production/shipping/storage.*

CHANGES/INT'L WAREHOUSING & DISTRIBUTION

5959 NW 37th Avenue
Miami, FL 33142

(1) (305) 828 6811   Fax: (1) (305) 828 6814

E-Mail:	*changes440@aol.com*
Description:	*Expert in all the finishing components. Fast turn-around time.*
Categories:	*Distribution/Warehouse Center*
Specialties:	*Pressing, hand & machine sewing, soil & mildew spot removal, ticketing, heat-seal, re-packaging, warehousing & distribution.*
Machinery:	*20 single needle, 20 zig zag, 3 button, 3 coverstitch*
Production Capacity:	*100,000 dz/month*

CRAFTEX REWORK INC.

500 Woodcrest Drive
Lucama, NC 27851
Bobby O'Neal
(1) (252) 239 0123   Fax: (1) (252) 239 1177

E-Mail:	*boneal@craftexinc.com*
Description:	*Expert with all types of production rework.*
Year Est:	*1971*
Specialties:	*Production rework, inspecting, auditing, relabeling, hangtagging, packaging, shipping & all other services.*
Machinery:	*Plain sewers, lock stitch, safety stitch, cover stitch blind stitch, button, chain stitch, sergers & more.*

Packages: *CMT, Production Rework & Warehousing.*

FLOOR-READY SERVICES, INC.
94 Glenn Bridge Road
Arden, NC 28704
Jessica Lewis
(1) (828) 651 8504   Fax: (1) (828) 651 0225

E-Mail:	*contact@floorready.com*
Web Site:	*www.floorready.com*
Description:	*Dedicated to processing & reprocessing both soft-line & hard-line goods for manufacturers, distributors, wholesalers, jobbers, retailers.*
Year Est:	*2001*
Specialties:	*Inspect, grade, sort, label, bundle, pack, ticket, hang, fold, bag, bulk pack, pre-packing, preparing POP displays, box, shrink wrap & ship.*
Machinery:	*We have 12 commercial sewing machines & experienced seamstress on staff. Minimize operating expenses & remain competitive. FRS saves its clients in fixed costs directly related to both processing services as well as operations/management.*
Minimums:	*No job is too big or too small. 100% dedicated workforce.*
Factory Locals:	*3rd Party Processor. All work is done in-house.*
Production Capacity:	*1.5 million units/ week. We make sure we have the correct labor force on hand to meet each and every customer's needs.*

HAGINS INDUSTRIES, INC.
2128 Marion Stage Road
Fairmont, NC 28340
Johnnie Hagins
(1) (910) 628 6777   Fax: (1) (910) 628 5160

E-Mail:	*haginsinds@bellsouth.net*
Description:	*Contractor specializing in knit shirts, tops, golf shirts, polo shirts and sweatpants.*
Year Est:	*1989*
Categories:	*Activewear, Knit Shirts & Tops*
Specialties:	*All type of rework and re-labeling capabilities.*
Markets:	*Menswear, Womenswear & Childrenswear.*
Machinery:	*Overlock & flatlock machines. Full cutting room.*
Packages:	*CMT & complete packages available.*
Minimums:	*None*
Production Capacity:	*4800 pcs/month*

HELMSMAN QUALITY & TECHNOLOGY SERVICES LTD.
801 West End Avenue
New York, NY 10025
Jeff Singleton
(1) (212) 757 2400

E-Mail:	*jeff.singleton@hqts.com*
Web Site:	*www.hqts.com*
Description:	*Production inspection, factory audits, testing & quality control services for companies doing business in Asia.*
Markets:	*All markets.*

LACORP/LEBANON APPAREL CORP.

70 Thornhill Drive
Lebanon, VA 24266
Jeoff Bodenhorst
(1) (276) 889 3656   Fax: (1) (276) 889 2830

E-Mail:	*jeoff@lacorpusa.com*
Web Site:	*www.lacorpusa.com*
Description:	*Any type of repair work, grading of seconds, repackaging.*
Year Est:	*1968*
Categories:	*Pants/shorts/skirts, Childrenswear, Uniforms, Home Furnishings*
Specialties:	*Pants, shorts, skirts, childrenswear, uniforms & home furnishings.*
Markets:	*Menswear, Womenswear, Childrenswear & Home.*
Machinery:	*Over 500 various sewing machines & electronic cutting, embroidery & besum pocket equipment on site.*
Packages:	*CMT, Sewing, Cutting, Sample Making & Embroidery.*
Minimums:	*Will adjust to fit your needs.*
Factory Locals:	*All work is done in-house.*

M. FRANABAR INC. CORRECTIONS & REWORKS

One 43rd Street
Brooklyn, NY 11232
Harvey
(1) (718) 499 5190   Fax: (1) (718) 499 5830

E-Mail:	*info@mfranabar.com*
Web Site:	*www.mfranabar.com*
Description:	*Correction & rework services on apparel, gifts, accessories & novelties. QC inspection, problem solving. Assembling. Drop ship.*
Specialties:	*Label installation/removal, ticketing, bar coding, re-assorting, re-packing, re-sizing, most corrections, dry cleaning, packaging.*
Markets:	*Apparel, Gifts & Accessories*
Minimums:	*3,000 pcs.*
Production Capacity:	*500,000 pcs/month*

NU YALE

6300 Highway 62
Jeffersonville, IN 47130
Mike Maloney
(1) (812) 285 7400   Fax: (1) (812) 285 7421

E-Mail:	*mike@nuyale.com*
Web Site:	*www.nuyale.com*
Description:	*Inspectors of import garments. Rework, inspections, washing, pressing, dry cleaning & warehousing.*
Year Est:	*1950*
Categories:	*Rework/Inspection Services, Laundry/Washing Contractors, Restoration.*
Specialties:	*Wet processing & washing of blue jeans, stone washing, bleaching, pre-washing and restoration of any garment.*
Markets:	*All apparel & accessory markets.*
Machinery:	*4 600-lb. washers, 2 900-lb. washers, 3 900-lb. dryers, 1 600-lb. dryer.*
Minimums:	*None*

Production Capacity: 10,000 dozen/month

QUALITY CORRECTIONS & INSPECTIONS

611 Gildea Drive
Duncansville, PA 16635

(1) (814) 696 3737   Fax: (1) (814) 696 3734

E-Mail:	stacey_burket@qualitycorrections.com
Web Site:	www.qualitycorrections.com
Description:	Toll free#: 1-800-340-8384. Volume apparel & footwear repair facility. Guaranteed workmanship, fast turn-around.
Year Est:	1986
Categories:	Rework/Inspection, Laundry, Warehousing/Distribution Center.
Specialties:	Specialize in QC inspections, rework of defective merchandise, repackaging, label changes, warehouse & distribution.
Machinery:	Sewing & button machinery. Steam tunnels, presses, spot cleaning equipment & assortment of footwear repair equipment.
Minimums:	No job is too big or too small.
Factory Locals:	Henderson, Nevada. Tel: 702-719-2322

AAA PATTERNS & MARKING SERVICES

233 Cypress Lane
Ozark, Alabama 36360
Michael Smith
(1) (334) 445 4870   Fax: (1) (334) 445 3910

E-Mail:	*patterns@aaapatternsmarking.com*
Web Site:	*www.aaapatternsmarking.com*
Description:	*Accurate & cost-effective pattern making service.*
Year Est:	*2001*
Categories:	*Pattern Making, Grading/Marking*
Markets:	*All markets, all sizes & all styles.*

W.Y. SHUGART

405 Beeson Gap Road
Fort Payne, Alabama 35968
Tim Shugart
(1) (256) 845 1251   Fax: (1) (256) 845 4502

E-Mail:	*tshugart@wyshugart.com*
Web Site:	*www.wyshugart.com*
Description:	*Makers of fine gauge hosiery since 1937.*
Categories:	*Accessories*
Specialties:	*Man-made & natural fibers. Basic, fashion, fancy and novelty socks. Also, custom-design capabilities & dye and finishing facilities.*
Markets:	*Womens & Childrens.*

EXPLOSION SPORTSWEAR/ IMAGE SOURCE

4814 South 35th Street
Phoenix, Arizona 85040

(1) (602) 243 2728   Fax: (1) (602) 276 4315

E-Mail:	*info@explosionsportswear.com*
Web Site:	*www.explosionsportswear.com*
Year Est:	*1998*
Categories:	*Embroidery, Screenprinting*
Specialties:	*One stop shop for all apparel, screenprint, embroidery and promotional needs.*
Markets:	*Menswear, Womenswear, Childrenswear, Infants, Accessories.*
Machinery:	*90+ Tajima & Brother machines in factory; plus subcontract and overseas. Also, embroidery, laundering, washing, printing & screenprinting equipment.*
Packages:	*CMT & sewing, finishing & packing.*
Minimums:	*36 pieces/style*

AMERICAN STITCHCO INC.

4662 Highway 62 West
Mountain Home, Arkansas 72653

(1) 888 903 0049   Fax: (1) 870 425 4900

E-Mail: stitchco@stitchco.com
Web Site: www.stitchco.com
Description: Over 500,000 sq ft of floor space and 80 shipping docks for all your inbound & outbound shipping & warehousing needs.
Specialties: Automated conveyors, climate controlled, organized racking systems.

POL SYSTEMS

236 Highway 79 South
Magnolia, Arkansas 71753
Donna Keith
(1) 870 562 2901   Fax: (1) 877 479 7618

E-Mail: mdkeith@suddenlink.net
Web Site: www.polsystems.net
Description: Computerized conveyor cutting center with design & nesting capabilities. Complex patterns & materials are cut precisely including notches & holes.
Year Est: 2005
Categories: Cutting contractor
Specialties: All work done in-house. We can process a wide variety of materials including fabrics, leather, foam, paper, plastic, films & more.
Markets: All Apparel, Accessories, Home.
Packages: Cutting only

California

3D INDUSTRIES

20988 Bake Parkway
Lake Forest, California 92630
Ian Tennant
(1) (949) 588 5884   Fax: (1) (949) 855 4747

E-Mail: sales@3d-ind.com
Web Site: www.3d-ind.com
Description: Manufacturer of custom technical apparel, sportswear & accessories for branded customers worldwide by our network of overseas factories.
Year Est: 1996
Categories: Production Sourcing/Factory Agent
Specialties: Design, develop and deliver. We are not set up to handle small runs.
Markets: Menswear, Womenswear & Childrenswear.
Minimums: 1,000 pcs/style - $2500.00

ACTIVE APPAREL INC.

11076 Venture Drive
Mira Loma, California 91752

(1) (951) 361 0060   Fax: (1) (951) 361 3120

E-Mail: sales@activeapparel.net
Web Site: www.activeapparel.net

Description:	All types of tees, tops and bottoms.
Categories:	Active/Athletic Wear, Small Production/Samples
Specialties:	Specialize in custom creations and have full capabilities to manufacture your creative efforts.
Markets:	Menswear, Womenswear & Childrenswear.
Minimums:	600 pcs per color

ADVANCE PLEATING & BUTTON CO.

750 Florida Street
San Francisco, California 94110
Greg Cruz, Manager
(1) (415) 648 3111   Fax: (1) (415) 648 7284

Description:	Contractor of textile trimmings. Custom trimming and covered buttons for apparel and accessories.
Categories:	Pleating/Tucking/Stitching, Trim Application.
Specialties:	Fancy stitching: pearl & shell edge, shirring, tucking, smocking, strapping, ruching, bias, piping, looping & more.
Minimums:	$25.00/order

AFAP

12000 Slauson Avenue
Santa Fe Springs, California 90670
Ann Huang
(1) (626) 330 6376

E-Mail:	sales@afapfashion.com
Web Site:	www.afapfashion.com
Year Est:	2001
Categories:	Lingerie/Intimate/Underwear
Specialties:	Specialize in seamless undergarments and shapewear.
Markets:	Womenswear
Minimums:	300 dz/style, 150 dz/color
Production Capacity:	150,000 units/month

ALL AMERICAN WASH CO.

2932 East 11th Street
Los Angeles, California 90023
Alex Kahen
(1) (323) 265 2626   Fax: (1) (323) 265 3307

E-Mail:	alexkahen@allamericanwashco.com
Description:	Cut and sew contractor of jeans, denim skirts, denim jackets and tee shirts.
Categories:	Laundry/Washing Contractor, Dyeing Contractor, Jeans/Denimwear, Small Production/Sample Room
Specialties:	Premimum denim wash and garment dyeing. All work is done in house.
Markets:	Menswear, Womenswear, Childrenswear.
Packages:	Complete & CMT packaging available.
Minimums:	Low

ALMORE DYE HOUSE, INC.

6850 North Tujunga Avenue
North Hollywood, California 91605
Jamie Yonover
(1) (818) 506 5444   Fax: (1) (818) 762 3905

E-Mail:	*adh@almoredyehouse.com*
Web Site:	*www.almoredyehouse.com*
Description:	*Garment dyers.*
Year Est:	*1919*
Categories:	*Dyeing/Finishing Contractors.*
Specialties:	*Fiber reactive, disperse, acid, ballwash, pigment and sulphur dyeing. Specialize in cotton, rayon & tencel fabrics.*
Markets:	*All apparel markets.*
Machinery:	*30 washer/dyers*
Minimums:	*3 lbs.*
Production Capacity:	*100,000 to 200,000 pcs/month*

ALVARADO DYE & KNITTING MILL

30542 Union City Boulevard
Union City, California 94587
Raymond Chan
(1) (510) 324 8892   Fax: (1) (510) 324 8704

E-Mail:	*sales@alvaradomills.com*
Web Site:	*www.alvaradomill.wix.com/oursdesign*
Description:	*Dyeing & finishing of knit sportswear, tee shirts & denim. Also, full pressing service.*
Categories:	*Dyeing/Finishing Contractors.*
Specialties:	*Expertise with tencel processing.*
Machinery:	*23 paddle dye & 4 tumbler dye machines. Capacity from 40-600 lbs.*
Export to:	*Japan 20%*
Minimums:	*40 lbs./color*
Production Capacity:	*100,000 pcs/month*

AMERICA'S BEST CLEANERS

107 Koch Road
Corte Madera, California 94925
Christopher White
(1) (415) 857 2378

E-Mail:	*chriswhite@americasbestcleaners.com*
Web Site:	*www.americasbestcleaners.com*
Description:	*Independent certification organization for the dry cleaning industry. Certify individual business with different equipment and process times.*
Categories:	*Laundry/Washing*
Specialties:	*Certification is focused on delivering the best quality to our partners in manufacturing, retail and the end consumer. Cell: 561-301-0431.*
Markets:	*Menswear & Womenswear*

ANDARI FASHION INC.
9626 Telstar Avenue
El Monte, California 91731

(1) (626) 575 2759   Fax: (1) (626) 575 3629

E-Mail:	*info@andari.com*
Web Site:	*www.andari.com*
Description:	*Full service sweater and knits manufacturer.*
Year Est:	*1991*
Categories:	*Sweaters/Knitwear*
Specialties:	*Fast turnaround on sampling and production.*
Machinery:	*Wide range of Stoll and Shima Seiki computerized flat-bed knitting machines.*
Factory Locals:	*Domestic manufacturing capabilities plus facilities in China to offer customers more options.*

ANTAKY QUILTING COMPANY
1849 East 50th Street
Los Angeles, California 90058
Derek Antaky
(1) (323) 233 2500   Fax: (1) (323) 233 2570

E-Mail:	*sales@antakyquilting.com*
Web Site:	*www.antakyquilting.com*
Description:	*Quilting specialists for all types of apparel, robes, jackets, uniforms, sportswear & more.*
Year Est:	*1917*
Categories:	*Quilting Contractors*
Specialties:	*Quilted nylon packages in stock.*
Packages:	*Can do samples & small & large production lots.*
Minimums:	*None, any size quilting orders workable.*

AVB DESIGNS
1628 Palm Avenue
San Mateo, California 94402
Alexandria von Bromssen
(1) (650) 346 1533

E-Mail:	*vonbromssen@mac.com*
Web Site:	*www.avbdesigns.com*
Description:	*Fashion design, fashion illustration, patternmaking, sample making, sourcing, small production runs, grading & consulting.*
Year Est:	*2004*
Categories:	*Sample Rooms/Small Production, Patternmaking*
Specialties:	*Pattern engineering, pattern corrections and grading production patterns.*
Markets:	*Womenswear, Mens, Childrens and Home Furnishings.*
Packages:	*Complete packages available.*
Agent:	*Production Sourcing: USA, China, Brazil*
Minimums:	*None*
Production Capacity:	*Depends on the project.*

BIG FRONT UNIFORMS

4535 Huntington Drive S.
Los Angeles, California 90032

(1) (323) 227 4222   Fax: (1) (323) 227 4111
E-Mail: info@bigfront.com
Web Site: www.bigfrontuniforms.com
Description: Our designers will help you to create custom uniforms. Personalized
embroidery available. All work done in our on-site factory.
Year Est: 1977
Categories: Uniforms
Markets: Menswear & Womenswear.
Minimums: 2 dozen
Factory Locals: Domestic 1-800-234-8383

BIG PRINTING T-SHIRT COMPANY

2110 Adams Avenue
San Leandro, California 94577
Dawaud Muhammad
(1) (510) 638 2782   Fax: (1) (510) 638 2783
E-Mail: bigprinting@gmail.com
Web Site: www.bigprintingtshirts.com
Description: Experts in t-shirt printing, embroidery, digital printing &
heat transfers.
Year Est: 2002
Categories: Screenprinting, Tee Shirts
Specialties: Full service apparel manufacturer including screenprinting,
embroidery, cut n sew, applique embellishment & custom packaging.

BLUE CREATIONS OF CA INC.

22632 S. Avalon Boulevard
Carson, California 90745
Oscar Quintero
(1) (310) 816 3100   Fax: (1) (310) 816 9388
E-Mail: info@bluecreationsinc.com
Web Site: www.bluecreationsinc.com
Description: Denim specialists. Easy washes, stone wash, enzyme wash plus
destruction, sand blast, whiskers, tint and dyeing.
Year Est: 2005
Categories: Laundry/Washing Contractor, Dyeing Contractor
Specialties: Professional denim process & garment dye laundry
specialist.

CALIFORNIA APPAREL SERVICE

2109 S. Standard Avenue
Santa Ana, California 92707
Tom Lo/Helen Lo
(1) (714) 222 1970   Fax: (1) (714) 442 2788
E-Mail: tom@californiaapparelservice.com
Web Site: www.californiaapparelservice.com
Description: Knit & woven tops. Complete T-shirt program. One-stop shop solution

for your apparel ideas---tops, bottoms, skirts, dresses.

Year Est:	*2003*
Categories:	*T-Shirts, Shirts/Tops, Pants/Shorts/Skirts, Childrenswear, Dresses/Blouses, Sportswear, Small Production*
Specialties:	*Full service apparel manufacturing from design, patterns and grading to cutting, sewing and finishing. From concept through to completion.*
Markets:	*All markets.*
Packages:	*Full package services & private label programs.*
Minimums:	*100 pieces/style*
Factory Locals:	*Work done in-house.*
	http://www.youtube.com/caapparel
Production Capacity:	*2500 - 3000/month - various styles*

CALIFORNIA RAIN

1213 E. 14th Street
Los Angeles, California 90021

(1) (213) 623 6061   Fax: (1) (213) 627 5703

E-Mail:	*info@californiarainla.com*
Web Site:	*www.californiarainla.com*
Description:	*Vertically integrated manufacturing facility. Custom design and manufacture all types of garments to your specs, size, scale & color.*
Year Est:	*1988*
Categories:	*Screenprinting, Tee Shirts/Sweat Shirts*
Specialties:	*Screenprint or embroider on any type of material. Also, application of rhinestones, nailheading and transfers. Hangtag & polybag.*
Markets:	*Menswear, Womenswear & Childrenswear.*
Packages:	*Complete package programs*
Minimums:	*Small*
Factory Locals:	*U.S.A., Latin American, Asia*

CANDILEJAS CLOTHING CO.

742 South Hill Street
Los Angeles, California 90014
Angelina Munoz
(1) (213) 489 2855   Fax: (1) (213) 489 1845

Description:	*Full service contractor.*
Categories:	*Coats/Jackets, Suits/Tailored Apparel.*
Specialties:	*Women's jackets, pants, skirts, skorts in all fabrics.*
Markets:	*Womenswear.*
Packages:	*CMT & complete packages. Sample room on premises.*
Minimums:	*None*

CARMICHAEL INTERNATIONAL SERVICE

533 Glendale Boulevard
Los Angeles, California 90026
Khim Lim
(1) (213) 353 0800   Fax: (1) (213) 975 0057

E-Mail:	*sales@carmnet.com*
Web Site:	*www.carmnet.com*
Description:	*Full-service, independent and privately owned customs broker and*

freight forwarder plus warehousing and distribution.

Year Est:	*1961*
Categories:	*Freight Forwarder/Customs Broker*
Specialties:	*Operate in the ports of LA/Long Beach, New York, Chicago, Seattle, San Francisco, Miami, Boston, Baltimore, Atlanta, Savannah, Memphis.*

CHESTER LINE CORP.

9820 Bell Ranch Drive
Santa Fe Springs, California 90670
Soung Kim, Owner
(1) (562) 944 2777   Fax: (1) (562) 944 2233

E-Mail:	*soungkim@chesterline.com*
Web Site:	*www.chesterline.com*
Description:	*Korean factory specializing in high quality intimate apparel, lingerie, sleepwear & foundation apparel.*
Year Est:	*1999*
Categories:	*Lingerie/Intimate Apparel*
Specialties:	*Textile design, new product design, molding & more.*
Markets:	*Womenswear & Girlswear.*
Packages:	*Full packages, patterns, samples, embroidery, beading & more.*
Minimums:	*3,000 units/style, but negotiable*
Factory Locals:	*Shantou & Shenzhen China & Seoul, South Korea*
Production Capacity:	*200,000 pcs/month*

COLLECTIVE APPAREL

750 East Gage Avenue
Los Angeles, California 90001
Don Valenzuela
(1) 310 770 1093   Fax: (1) 323 750 5010

E-Mail:	*contact@collectiveapparel.us*
Web Site:	*www.collectiveapparel.us*
Description:	*One stop. We design, sketch, prepare patterns, do samples and production.*
Year Est:	*2009*
Categories:	*Jeans/Denimwear, Pants/Shorts/Skirts, Laundry/Washing*
Specialties:	*We specialize in new and innovative wash techniques as well as organic wash and dye processes.*
Markets:	*Menswear, Womenswear, Childrenswear.*
Packages:	*Full packages - premium denim, tops & knits.*
Production Capacity:	*48,000 pcs/month*

CREATIVE PATTERN AND SAMPLE

112 West 9th Street
Los Angeles, California 90015
Isabel Martinez
(1) (213) 233 0253   Fax: (1) (213) 233 4857

E-Mail:	*contact@creativepatternandsample.com*
Web Site:	*www.creativepatternandsample.com*
Description:	*Grades & marker, showroom samples, mock ups, sewing, sample making, design consultation, prototypes, fittings.*
Categories:	*Swimwear, jeans, dresses, suits, lingerie*

Specialties:	*Quality crafted patterns, 1st patterns, production patterns,*
	spec sheets, pattern corrections. By appointment only.
Markets:	*Womenswear*

DELUXE SCREEN PRINTING

1358 E 15th Street
Los Angeles, California 90021
Elsie Acevedo
(1) (213) 765 0838   Fax: (1) (213) 765 8199

E-Mail:	*deluxe@deluxescreenprinting.net*
Web Site:	*www.deluxescreenprinting.net*
Description:	*Provide screenprinted samples & small runs for market week, trade*
	shows, independent clothing lines.
Year Est:	*2007*
Specialties:	*Specialize in waterbase, discharge inks, plastisol, foils, heat transfer*
	lamination & novelty techniques. Work on cut pieces & finished garments.
Markets:	*Contemporary, mens, juniors, kids.*
Minimums:	*None*
Production Capacity:	*5,000 units weekly*

DEPENDABLE DISTRIBUTION CENTERS

2555 East Olympic Boulevard
Los Angeles, California 90023
J.P. Durrer
(1) (323) 526 2200 ext. 2086   Fax: (1) (323) 526 2201

E-Mail:	*jp.durrer@dependableinc.com*
Web Site:	*www.godependable.com*
Description:	*Third-party warehousing throughout California.*
Year Est:	*1956*
Specialties:	*Distribution, automated GOH, racks, pick & pack, order fulfillment,*
	cross docking, flat pack, short or long term storage, EDI.
Markets:	*Menswear, Womenswear & Childrenswear.*
Factory Locals:	*1,350,000 sq. ft. of public warehouse.*

DEPENDABLE GLOBAL EXPRESS

19201 Susana Road
Rancho Dominguez, California 90221
Brad Dechter
(1) (310) 669 8888   Fax: (1) (310) 537 3291

E-Mail:	*brad.dechter@dhx.com*
Web Site:	*www.dgxglobal.com*
Description:	*An International shipping & logistics company. Your single source for*
	reliable, cost-effective shipment of goods worldwide & here at home.
Specialties:	*We ship to virtually all global and domestic points - both ocean*
	and air.
Machinery:	*Both box trucks and tractor/container combinations*

DEPENDABLE LOGISTICS SERVICES

2555 East Olympic Boulevard
Los Angeles, California 90023
J.P. Durrer
(1) (323) 526 2200   Fax: (1) (323) 526 2252

E-Mail:	*jp.durrer@dependableinc.com*
Web Site:	*www.godependable.com*
Description:	*Complete distribution, warehouseing & freight forwarding service center.*
Year Est:	*1956*
Categories:	*Distribution/Warehouse Center, Freight Forwarders/Customs Broker*
Specialties:	*Warehousing, trucking & repackaging under one roof.*
Markets:	*Menswear, Womenswear & Childrenswear.*
Factory Locals:	*1,350,000 sq. ft. of public warehouse.*

DIDI OF CALIFORNIA

5816 Piedmont Avenue
Los Angeles, California 90042
Aldo Garrolini
(1) (323) 256 4514   Fax: (1) (323) 256 4514

Description:	*Contractor of better ladies dresses, skirts & blouses.*
Categories:	*Dresses/Blouses*
Markets:	*Womenswear.*
Machinery:	*Over 50 machines on premises.*
Packages:	*Sewing & CMT.*
Minimums:	*100-200 pieces/style*

DYNASHAPE INTIMA CORPORATION

2121 Orange Street
Alhambra, California 91803

(1) (626) 289 8418   Fax: (1) (626) 289 8309

E-Mail:	*stewart@dynashapeintima.com*
Web Site:	*www.dynashapeintima.com*
Description:	*Manufacturer of bras, nursing bras, panties, seamless intimate/ yoga apparel and sleepwear.*
Year Est:	*1984*
Categories:	*Lingerie/Intimate/Underwear*
Specialties:	*Our design team works closely with our overseas office to produce samples based on the customer's design, concept and budget.*
Markets:	*Womenswear*
Factory Locals:	*Domestic design center, warehouse and showroom. Import from 12 overseas certified factories.*

EAST BAY GARMENT CUTTING & SEWING SERVICE

3315 Farnam Street
Oakland, California 94601
Kelvin Lam
(1) (510) 261 6688   Fax: (1) (510) 261 6688

E-Mail:	*annielam6688@gmail.com*
Description:	*Patterns, cutting, grading, marking, samples & production*

sewing.

Categories:	*Sample Rooms/Small Production Contractors,* *Cutting/Fusing Contractors.*
Specialties:	*Great with shirts, outerwear, dresses, lingerie, sportswear, uniforms & vests.*
Markets:	*Menswear, Womenswear*
Minimums:	*None*

EMBROIDERY ONE CORPORATION

1359 Channing Street
Los Angeles, California 90021

(1) (213) 572 0280   Fax: (1) (213) 572 0283

E-Mail:	*emb1@pacbell.net*
Web Site:	*www.embroidery-one.com*
Description:	*Embroidery and screenprinting contractor.*
Categories:	*Embroidery, Screenprinting*
Specialties:	*Fast turnaround, high quality, reliable and committed to excellence.*

ESTEPHANIAN ORIGINALS INC.

2666 East Huntington Drive
Duarte, California 91010
Mark Estephanian
(1) (626) 358 7265   Fax: (1) (626) 358 4286

E-Mail:	*mark@eodye.com*
Web Site:	*www.eodye.com*
Description:	*Garment dyed and screen printed looks on nylon, silk, cotton, rayon finished garments in a variety of dip dye and tie-dye looks.*
Year Est:	*1976*
Categories:	*Dyeing, Screenprinting*
Specialties:	*Specialize in tie dye, dip dye, airbrush, contracting services, discharge prints, burnouts. All work done in-house.*
Markets:	*Womenswear & Girlswear.*
Machinery:	*Custom machinery*

FANTASY DESIGNS

23136 Arroyo Vista
Rancho Santa Margarita, California 92688
David Gleckman
(1) (949) 635 9591   Fax: (1) (949) 635 9592

E-Mail:	*dgleck@fantasydesigns.net*
Web Site:	*www.fantasydesigns.net*
Description:	*Custom screenprinting, embroidery, graphic design & digitizing on apparel, team uniforms, promo products and catalogs.*
Year Est:	*1994*
Categories:	*Screenprinting*
Specialties:	*Specialize in low minimums.*
Machinery:	*12 color auto, manual press, numbering machine. Embroidery - 14 heads plus two single heads for small work & personalization.*
Production Capacity:	*60,000 units/monthly*

FINE LINE, INC.
12457 Gladstone Avenue
Sylmar, California 91342
Michael Collier
(1) (818) 361 8103   Fax: (1) (818) 361 1194

E-Mail:	*info@finelineinc.com*
Web Site:	*www.finelineinc.com*
Categories:	*Cutting/Fusing Contractors, Grading/Marking, Patternmaking.*
Specialties:	*Domestic production and sourcing solutions...all made in the USA.*
Markets:	*All*
Machinery:	*Fully automated cutting machines.*

FLEXSYSTEMS USA INC.
727 West Main Street
El Cajon, California 92020
Gary Smith
(1) (619) 401 1858   Fax: (1) (619) 401 1848

E-Mail:	*sales@flexsystems.com*
Web Site:	*www.flexsystems.com*
Description:	*Manufacturer of custom PVC, corn plastic labels, zip pulls, promotional products.*
Year Est:	*1994*
Categories:	*Trim Application, Small Production*
Specialties:	*Sourcing, assembly, fulfillment, custom R&D, sewing, warehousing and packaging.*
Markets:	*Menswear, Womenswear, Children, Accessories, Home.*
Export to:	*Canada 8%, Mexico 2%*
Minimums:	*None*

FRSTEAM BY WEST COVINA CLEANERS
537 South Glendora Avenue
West Covina, California 91790

(1) (626) 960 1911   Fax: (1) (626) 960 0132

E-Mail:	*westcovina@frsteam.com*
Web Site:	*www.frsteamwc.com*
Description:	*Restoration dry cleaning institution. Restoration of couture and specialty garments, leathers, furs etc.*
Year Est:	*1969*
Categories:	*Laundry/Washing Contractors*
Specialties:	*Smoke & odor restoration & dry cleaning. Specialists in rescuing garments considered a "total loss" because of smoke, water or odor damage.*
Markets:	*All Markets*
Factory Locals:	*California*
Production Capacity:	*Largest restoration dry cleaner in the western US with 4 plants, 150 employees.*

G.S. FASHION

2765 Randolph Street
Huntington Park, California 90255
George Simonian
(1) (323) 581 0764   Fax: (1) (323) 581 1253

E-Mail:	*ssimonn@aol.com*
Description:	*Sewing contractor of dresses, evening/formal, skirts, blouses & pants. Interested in partnering with a freelance designer.*
Year Est:	*1988*
Categories:	*Dresses/Blouses, Sample Rooms/Small Production*
Specialties:	*Sewing, finishing, bagging, tagging, repair & change labels. Also fulfillment services for offshore containers.*
Markets:	*Womenswear*
Machinery:	*Single Needle, Double Needle, Overlock, Cover Stitch*

GELTMAN INDUSTRIES

1914 Bay Street
Los Angeles, California 90021
Shari Rezai
(1) (213) 622 2015   Fax: (1) (213) 622 4572

E-Mail:	*info@geltman.com*
Web Site:	*www.geltman.com*
Description:	*All types of textile finishing & laundry processes.*
Year Est:	*1931*
Categories:	*Finishing/Coating Contractors, Laundry/Washing Contractors.*
Specialties:	*Heat-sealing, bonding, sponging, resin finishes, laundry, framing, scouring, pre-shrinking & more.*
Markets:	*All apparel, accessory & home markets.*
Minimums:	*None*

GOLDEN EGG CORPORATION

10501 Valley Boulevard #1856
El Monte, California 91731
Calvin Lin
(1) (626) 279 2779   Fax: (1) (626) 288 1512

E-Mail:	*calvinlin123@gmail.com*
Description:	*All types of seamless apparel.*
Categories:	*Production Sourcing/Factory Agents*
Factory Locals:	*Factory located in China.*
Production Capacity:	*1000 - 5000 pcs/month*

H.T.T. HEADWEAR LTD.

41185 Raintree Court
Murrieta, California 92562

(1) (951) 304 0400   Fax: (1) (951) 304 0420

E-Mail:	*contact@httapparel.com*
Web Site:	*www.httapparel.com*
Description:	*Manufacturer & contractor of headwear & polo shirts.*
Categories:	*Accessories, Shirts/Tops. Outerwear*

Specialties:	*Our factories offer the latest technology such as stain resistant and organic materials along with cutting edge embellishments.*
Markets:	*Womenswear & Menswear.*
Packages:	*All packages.*
Export to:	*United Kingdom & Australia*
Factory Locals:	*Have own domestic plants & can import through Taiwan, China & Pakistan.*
Production Capacity:	*Hats: 5,000 dozen/month & Shirts: 120,00 units/month*

HARPER INDUSTRIES, INC.
29 Hillcrest Road
Berkeley, California 94705
Tom Friedland
(1) (510) 655 5143   Fax: (1) (510) 923 9542

E-Mail:	*tsf@harcrest.com*
Web Site:	*www.harcrest.com*
Description:	*Contractor & manufacturer of tee shirts, sport team uniforms, medical scrubs, smocks.*
Categories:	*Production Sourcing/Factory Agents, Tee Shirts/Sweat Shirts, Uniforms*
Markets:	*Menswear, Womenswear, Unisex.*
Packages:	*CMT, Sewing & Full Packages.*
Factory Locals:	*Yucatan Peninsula Mexico*
Production Capacity:	*1,000,000 pcs/month*

INDU FASHIONS
220 West 25th Street
National City, California 91950
Shashi Pal
(1) (619) 336 4638   Fax: (1) (619) 336 4122

E-Mail:	*shashi@indufashions.com*
Web Site:	*www.indufashions.com*
Description:	*Full service contractor specializing in running shorts, yoga wear, cycle & tri-wear plus all types of athletic sportswear.*
Categories:	*Active/Athleticwear*
Specialties:	*Specialize in flatlock seam construction and excel with fabrics such as lycra and modal fabrics.*
Markets:	*Menswear, Womenswear*
Packages:	*CMT & Full. Cutting, marking & grading in house.*
Minimums:	*250-500 pieces/style*
Production Capacity:	*40,000 pieces/month*

J.B.'S PRIVATE LABEL
1031 South Broadway
Los Angeles, California 90015
Jackie Bender
(1) (213) 747 1922   Fax: (1) (213) 747 1963

E-Mail:	*jackiembender@aol.com*
Web Site:	*www.dunadesigns.com*
Year Est:	*1980*
Categories:	*Sweaters/Knitwear*

Specialties:	Hand-loomed knitwear.
Markets:	Womenswear.
Machinery:	Flatbed machinery in house, no industrial machines.
Minimums:	Low

J.P. SPORTSWEAR/AARON CORP.

1820 East 41st Street
Los Angeles, California 90058
Paul/Paco
(1) (323) 235 5959   Fax: (1) (323) 235 2999

E-Mail:	jppaul2@pacbell.net
Web Site:	www.jpsportswear.net
Description:	Contractor of high-end activewear.
Year Est:	1979
Exporting Since:	1995
Categories:	Active/Athleticwear, Sportswear-Knits.
Specialties:	In house pattern makers, sample department, full inspection.
Markets:	Menswear, Womenswear
Machinery:	40 flat seam, 50 overlock, 35 single needle, 25 coverstitch, 7 bartack, 5 button, 4 zigzag, 5 double & 4 multi-needle.
Packages:	CMT & Full packages available.
Minimums:	1,000 pieces - steady volume only.
Factory Locals:	Los Angeles

JUST JEN

23510 Telo Avenue
Torrance, California 90505
Lawrence Smith/Jennifer Smith
(1) 310 539 6000   Fax: (1) 323 903 0308

E-Mail:	jennifer@justjen.com
Web Site:	www.justjen.com
Description:	Rhinestone setter with great service & fast turnaround times on all designs. Great designs on t-shirts made with Swarovski crystal.
Categories:	Trim Application, Embroidery
Specialties:	Wholesale rhinestone t-shirt orders from retailers, organizations and individuals. We also do embroidery decoration.
Markets:	Menswear, Womenswear, Childrens/Infantwear.
Minimums:	None

L.S.W. CUTTING & SEWING SERVICE

670 Ninth Street
Oakland, California 94607
Lana Wong
(1) (510) 891 9246

E-Mail:	lswcuttingandsewing@hotmail.com
Description:	Contractor of cut & sew knit sportswear for all markets.
Categories:	Childrenswear, Dresses, Pants/Shorts/Skirts, Home Furnishings, Sportswear-Knits.
Specialties:	Complete patternmaking services.
Markets:	Menswear, Womenswear, Chldrenswear.
Packages:	Full service, CMT & complete packages.

Minimums:	*300 units/style*
Production Capacity:	*30,000 pcs/month*

LEAHPATRA KNITTING

7543 Trask Avenue
Los Angeles, California 90293
Leah Walton
(1) 310 951 9095

E-Mail:	*leahpatra@leahpatra.com*
Web Site:	*www.leahpatra.com*
Description:	*Domestic knitting contractor. Design, sample making services, small & large production capabilities. By appointment only.*
Categories:	*Sweaters/Knitwear, Sample Room/Small Production*
Specialties:	*Specialty is cashmere & high end novelty knitwear, scarves, handbags, sweaters.*
Minimums:	*None*
Production Capacity:	*1500 units/month*

LEFT IN STITCHES INC.

55 Ericson Court
Arcata, California 95521

(1) (707) 822 3041   Fax: (1) (707) 822 3042

E-Mail:	*info@leftinstitches.com*
Web Site:	*www.leftinstitches.com*
Description:	*Over 29 years of patternmaking, grading and sewing. Samples, prototypes. Work with knits and wovens.*
Categories:	*Grading/Marking, Patternmaking, Dresses/Blouses, Samples/Small Production*
Specialties:	*Creative design and development from concept to production. Specialize in working with small and startup companies.*
Markets:	*Menswear, Womenswear & Childrenswear.*

LORI ANN DESIGN

1515 Rose Avenue
Ferndale, California 95536
Lori Ann Knowles
(1) (707) 845 5043

E-Mail:	*lori@lorianndesign.com*
Web Site:	*www.lorianndesign.com*
Description:	*Professional pattern maker, flat sketches, figure sketches, pattern cards, cutters musts, specs, line sheets and size charts.*
Categories:	*Patternmaking Service*
Specialties:	*All work done in-house.*

MAGNATEX APPAREL SERVICES

4790 Irvine Boulevard
Irvine, California 92620
Kirk Linn
(1) (949) 551 9624

E-Mail:	*magnatex@cox.net*

Description:	*Pre-production technical design packages and computer marking and grading.*
Categories:	*Patternmaking*
Specialties:	*Specialize in pattern making services.*

MARGARET'S CLEANERS

5150 Convoy Street
San Diego, California 92111
Scott Horst
(1) (858) 454 2375   Fax: (1) (858) 454 4303

E-Mail:	*generalmail@margarets.com*
Web Site:	*www.margarets.com*
Description:	*Premier dry & wet professional cleaner.*
Year Est:	*1953*
Categories:	*Laundry/Washing*
Specialties:	*Handbag cleaning & restoration, bridal cleaning, drapery/blind cleaning, leather & suede cleaning, garment & knit repairs, vintage restoration.*
Markets:	*All markets.*
Factory Locals:	*La Jolla, Del Mar, Newport Beach, Los Angeles California*
Production Capacity:	*150+ employees, multiple "green cleaning" technologies, including Green Earth and System K4. Environmentally friendly.*

MARKER EXPRESS INC.

2773 Napa Valley Corporate Drive
Napa, California 94558
Mary Ann Parker
(1) (707) 259 5201   Fax: (1) (707) 259 5205

E-Mail:	*maryann@markerxpress.com*
Web Site:	*www.markerxpress.com*
Description:	*Full grading & marking service. Computerized Gerber AccuMark, PAD, OptiTex, and MicroMark software systems.*
Categories:	*Grading/Marking*
Specialties:	*Offer grading, marker making, plotting & remote data support to CAD users.*
Markets:	*All markets.*

NORTHRIDGE MILLS INC.

1901 First Street
San Fernando, California 91340
Rocio Maldonado
(1) (818) 361 7373   Fax: (1) (818) 365 5369

E-Mail:	*rocio@northridgemills.com*
Description:	*Sewing, cutting, logo heat-transfer & computer sewing, specialty stitching.*
Categories:	*Athletic/Activewear*
Specialties:	*Specialize in activewear, bikewear, swimwear, pants, tops & bottoms in knits, lycra, cotton-lycra, nylon, cotton & nylon flatlock stitching.*
Markets:	*Menswear, Womenswear & Childrenswear.*
Machinery:	*Over 300 various sewing machines and equipment.*
Minimums:	*400 pieces*

PERFORMANCE DESIGN STUDIO

330 A Street
San Diego, California 91911

(1) (619) 623 7692

E-Mail:	*info@performancedesignstudio.com*
Web Site:	*www.performancedesignstudio.com*
Description:	*Services include patternmaking, technical design/tech packs, fabric and trim sourcing. prototypes, consulting & small production lots.*
Year Est:	*2013*
Categories:	*Production Sourcing/Factory Agent*
Specialties:	*We specialize in performance activewear apparel for men and women.*
Markets:	*Menswear, Womenswear, Accessories.*
Packages:	*Marking, Cutting and Sewing*
Minimums:	*Low*
Factory Locals:	*We source worldwide*

PRECISION WAREHOUSING & DISTRIBUTION

16055 Heron Avenue
La Mirada, California 90638
Rob Boissevain
(1) (714) 690 9344   Fax: (1) (714) 690 9345

E-Mail:	*rob@precisioninc.com*
Web Site:	*www.precisioninc.com*
Description:	*Full line of supply chain services including container unloading, cross-docking, storage, shipping and the coordinating of pick ups & deliveries.*
Categories:	*Distribution/Warehouse Center*
Specialties:	*Southern California Warehousing and Distribution Center.*

PRO WASH

9117 South Main Street
Los Angeles, California 90003
Steve Koo
(1) (323) 756 6000   Fax: (1) (323) 756 8370

E-Mail:	*ykoo@aol.com*
Description:	*All types of washing & bleaching of garments & piece goods.*
Categories:	*Laundry/Washing Contractors*
Specialties:	*Stone, acid, chemical power & vintage washing & bleaching. Plus sand blasting, potassium processing & dyeing.*

QUETICO LOGISTICS LLC

5521 Schaefer Avenue
Chino, California 91710
Nick
(1) (909) 628 6200   Fax: (1) (909) 628 8340

E-Mail:	*nick@queticollc.com*
Web Site:	*www.queticollc.com*
Description:	*Custom-tailored warehousing services including the latest in distribution technology & computerization.*

Specialties:	*Pick & pack, product fulfillment, merchandise pallet display, kit assembly, design & manufacturing point of purchase display.*
Factory Locals:	*Partnerships in facilities in Texas, Canada & Mexico.*

QUINTIN CO.

2630 Humboldt Street
Los Angeles, California 90031

(1) (323) 221 9202   Fax: (1) (323) 221 7304

E-Mail:	*info@quintinco.com*
Web Site:	*www.quintinco.com*
Description:	*Embroidery, screenprinting & wide selection of fully customized hat styles.*
Categories:	*Embroidery, Screenprinting, Accessories*
Specialties:	*Specialize in headwear, tops, bottoms and tees.*
Markets:	*Menswear & Womenswear, Childrenswear, Infants*
Machinery:	*Large plant with wide variety of machinery.*
Minimums:	*200 pieces/style*

RENATO'S CUTTING SERVICE

2193 East 14th Street
Los Angeles, California 90021
Renato Molina
(1) (213) 489 0944   Fax: (1) (213) 489 0944

Description:	*Garment cutting service.*
Year Est:	*1984*
Categories:	*Cutting/Fusing Contractors*
Specialties:	*Women's dresses, skirts, shorts & tops.*
Minimums:	*100-200 pieces. All size lots welcome.*

ROOCHI TRADERS INC.

6393 East Washington Blvd
City of Commerce, California 90040
Mickey Sachdeva
(1) (323) 722 5592   Fax: (1) (323) 724 0045

E-Mail:	*mickey@roochi.com*
Web Site:	*www.cottonheritage.com*
Description:	*Over 25+ years of sportswear and activewear sourcing for men, women and children, also junior knits.*
Categories:	*Production Sourcing/Factory Agent, Tee Shirts/Sweat Shirts, Jeans/Denimwear, Outerwear, Polo Shirts*
Specialties:	*We stock blank inventory in our DC's NJ, FL and CA for at once delivery.*
Markets:	*Menswear, Womenswear & Childrenswear.*
Export to:	*Europe, Mexico, Central America, Canada*
Production Capacity:	*100,000 doz/month + per category*

ROYAL BLUE INTERNATIONAL

9025 Wilshire Boulevard #301
Beverly Hills, California 90211
Sami Kahen/Eli Kahen
(1) (310) 888 0156   Fax: (1) (310) 888 0157

E-Mail:	*samikahen@aol.com*
Description:	*Dyeing & washing/laundry contractor of all types of finished garments including denim.*
Year Est:	*1986*
Categories:	*Dyeing Contractor, Laundry/Washing Contractor*
Specialties:	*All types of garment dye, tie-dye & garment washes. Direct, pigment, distress, dip-dye, crystal & crinkle. Mineral, silicone & enzyme wash.*
Minimums:	*Low*
Factory Locals:	*Los Angeles - Eli 323-750-9900*

S. KANOUNI DESIGN & PATTERN STUDIO

824 Los Angeles Street
Los Angeles, California 90014
Soad
(1) (213) 627 2281

E-Mail:	*skfashion@att.net*
Description:	*Patterns, samples, duplicates & small production lots.*
Categories:	*Patternmaking, Sample Rooms/Small Production.*
Specialties:	*In-house cut & sew. One stop service.*
Markets:	*Menswear, Womenswear & Childrenswear.*
Packages:	*CMT packages available.*
Minimums:	*None*
Factory Locals:	*Second address: 7171 Grandoaks Dr., Stanton, CA 90680 Cell: 213-880-0515*

SAN FRANCISCO PLEATING CO.

233 23rd Avenue
San Mateo, California 94403
Rusty O'Keefe
(1) (415) 982 3003

E-Mail:	*rustysfpleating@comcast.net*
Description:	*All types of pleating on all types of fabric.*
Categories:	*Pleating/Tucking*
Markets:	*Womenswear & home furnishing fabrics.*
Minimums:	*None*

SKY BLUE SEWING

960 Mission Street
San Fransicso, California 94103
Steven
(1) (415) 777 9978   Fax: (1) (415) 777 9938

E-Mail:	*skyblueswg@sbcglobal.net*
Description:	*Private label manufacturer. Provides CMT, sample making, hand pressing, tagging, poly bagging and packing.*
Year Est:	*1988*
Categories:	*Jeans/Denimwear, Sample Rooms/Small Production*

Specialties:	Specialize in the cutting and sewing of denim, and other medium and heavy weight woven fabrics.
Markets:	Menswear, Womenswear & Childrenswear.
Machinery:	Electric cutting knife, keyhole, automatic belt loop, hemming, side seam serger, open seam press.
Packages:	CMT & private label.
Production Capacity:	20,000-30,000 units/month (basic five pocket jeans)

TAG STUDIO PATTERN DESIGN SERVICE

519 Lincoln Way #2
San Francisco, California 94122
Monica Houlihan, Owner
(1) (415) 664 2408

E-Mail:	tagpatrn@gmail.com
Web Site:	www.tagstudio.biz
Description:	Expert pattern design service. Computer patterns, product development consulting services, grading & marking.
Year Est:	1993
Categories:	Patternmaking Services, Grading/Marking, Sample Making
Specialties:	Experience in a wide range of garment & sewn product categories.
Markets:	All markets.
Machinery:	Computer-aided design PAD software. Gerber converter software.

TODD RUTKIN

5801 South Alameda Street
Los Angeles, California 90001
Abe Garcia
(1) (323) 584 9225   Fax: (1) (323) 584 9295

E-Mail:	jan@toddrutkin.com
Web Site:	www.toddrutkin.com
Description:	A complete source for cutting, fusing, grading, marking, slitting & embroidery.
Categories:	Cutting & Fusing, Grading & Marking, Embroidery
Machinery:	Gerber Accumark and Tajima machinery.

TOUCHDOWN FREIGHT COMPANY

20250 South Alameda Street
E. Compton, California 90221

(1) (310) 973 7112   Fax: (1) (310) 973 7113

E-Mail:	touch@touchdownco.com
Description:	Air/ocean import & export, air/ocean consolidations, modern packing & crating, customs clearance, domestic/local trucking.
Categories:	Freight Forwarder/Customs Broker, Distribution/Warehouse
Specialties:	Staff members speak Chinese, Tagalog, Korean, Japanese, Portuguese, Spanish and English.

TRINITY SPORTS INC.

2067 East 55th Street
Vernon, California 90058
Kate McHale Jensen
(1) (323) 277 9288   Fax: (1) (323) 277 9883

E-Mail:	*info@trinitysportsinc.com*
Web Site:	*www.trinitysportsinc.com*
Description:	*Jean specialist. Five bottoms jeans, low waist jeans, fray jeans, carpenter plus skirts, shorts.*
Categories:	*Jeans/Denimwear*
Specialties:	*Cut & sew contractor at competitive prices & exceptional quality.*
Markets:	*Menswear, Womenswear & Childrenswear.*
Machinery:	*Automatic back pocket setter, belt loop machine, design machine, label machine, welt pocket, double needele, single needle overlock*
Packages:	*CMT & Full packages available.*

TRUE MEASURE INC.

1042 S. Gerhart Avenue
City of Commerce, California 90022

(1) (323) 213 3184

E-Mail:	*melida@truemeasureinc.com*
Web Site:	*www.truemeasureinc.com*
Description:	*Fashion design, pattern making services, samples, full scale manufacturing in the USA and overseas.*
Categories:	*Patternmaking Services, Sample Rooms/Small Production*
Specialties:	*Specialize in menswear, womens formal & casual wear, swimwear, & intimate apparel. We cater to start-ups as well as established brands.*
Markets:	*Menswear & Womenswear.*

WGCI

2130 Laura Avenue
Huntington Park, California 90255
Michael or Jeff
(1) (323) 583 9832   Fax: (1) (323) 584 0023

E-Mail:	*wgci@wgciusa.com*
Web Site:	*www.wgciusa.com*
Description:	*Stone wash, enzyme wash, mineral wash, ozone process hand sand, sand blast, grinding, whiskers, resin, potassium wash/brush/spray.*
Categories:	*Laundry/Washing*
Specialties:	*Specialize in providing wet & dry processes to premium denim jeans. Vintage washes to glitter coating.*
Markets:	*Apparel manufacturers and designers*

YOONIMEX INC. DBA/U.S. EMBROIDERY

13953 Valley View Avenue
La Mirada, California 90638
Edward Yoon, President
(1) (562) 906 2100   Fax: (1) (562) 906 2330

E-Mail:	*info@us-embroidery.com*
Web Site:	*www.us-embroidery.com*

Description:	Embroidery and applique on finished garment or cut pieces.
	Best creative & experienced in-house digitizers in the industry.
Categories:	Embroidery
Specialties:	Quick turnaround. Custom patches, embroidered patches &
	heat seal patches available.
Machinery:	1,000 heads
Factory Locals:	25,000 sq. ft. plant in Santa Fe Springs, CA.
Production Capacity:	400,000 pcs/month

Colorado

COLORADO CONTRACT CUT & SEW

2300 West 2nd Avenue, Unit 3
Denver, Colorado 80223

(1) (303) 733 5376   Fax: (1) (303) 777 6117

E-Mail:	jane@coloradocut.com
Web Site:	www.coloradocut.com
Description:	Cut and sew contractor of all types of yoga pants.
Year Est:	1989
Categories:	Pants/Shorts/Skirts, Samples/Small Production
Specialties:	Prototyping & sample run production available.
Markets:	Menswear, Womenswear
Minimums:	250+
Factory Locals:	USA

FIBERLOK, INC.

811 Stockton Avenue
Fort Collins, Colorado 80522
Brown Abrams
(1) (970) 221 1200   Fax: (1) (970) 221 0200

E-Mail:	info@fiberlok.com
Web Site:	www.fiberlok.com
Description:	Exclusive sew-on or heat applied Lextra® and TackleKnit™ and
	ChromaFlex® Graphics.
Categories:	Embroidery
Specialties:	Distribution limited to select-up market brands and partners,
	ChromaFlex brand metallized and die-formed graphics.
Markets:	All apparel & uniform markets.
Machinery:	5 - Lextra, 6 TackleKnit, 8 ChromaFlex
Export to:	Europe, Asia, Latin America
Production Capacity:	7 million units/month

Connecticut

GIMASPORT

241 Ledyard Street
Hartford, Connecticut 06114
Roberto S. Giansiracusa
(1) (860) 296 4441   Fax: (1) (860) 296 8423

E-Mail:	sales@gimasport.com
Web Site:	www.gimasport.com

Description:	*Embroidery & screen printing contractor on all types of apparel.*
	Fulfillment services.
Year Est:	*1992*
Categories:	*Embroidery, Screenprinting*
Specialties:	*Quality, delivery and attention to detail are our specialties.*
Machinery:	*55 Barudan Embroidery Multi-head.*
Packages:	*All work done in house.*
Factory Locals:	*25,000 sq. ft. building in Hartford, CT.*
Production Capacity:	*75,000 pcs/month*

Florida

AMERICAN TEXTILE & APPAREL INC.
10408 W State Road 84
Davie, Florida 33324
Luis Mejia
(1) (954) 734 9988   Fax: (1) (954) 734 9966

E-Mail:	*luis.mejia@ata-usa.com*
Web Site:	*www.ata-usa.com*
Description:	*Contractor of knits & woven athletic sportswear, tee shirts,*
	polo shirts and ladies underwear.
Year Est:	*2002*
Specialties:	*Specialize in private label manufacturing in both knits*
	and woven apparel.
Markets:	*Menswear, Womenswear, Childrenswear.*
Packages:	*CMT & Full Packages*
Factory Locals:	*Davie Florida plus a network of the best apparel and*
	textile manufacturers from both hemispheres.
Production Capacity:	*T-Shirts 50,000 doz/month, Polo Shirts 35,000 doz/month,*
	Sportwear 10,000 doz/month, Underwear 100,000 doz/month

ANTILLEAN MARINE SHIPPING CORP.
3038 Teofilo Babun Drive
Miami, Florida 33142

(1) (305) 633 6361   Fax: (1) (305) 638 0579

E-Mail:	*antillean@antillean.com*
Web Site:	*www.antillean.com*
Description:	*Marine transport, logistics, trucking and*
	intermodal services, warehousing & cargo consolidation.
Year Est:	*1963*
Categories:	*Freight Forwarder/Customs Broker*

CHANGES/INT'L WAREHOUSING & DISTRIBUTION
5959 NW 37th Avenue
Miami, Florida 33142

(1) (305) 828 6811   Fax: (1) (305) 828 6814

E-Mail:	*changes440@aol.com*
Description:	*Expert in all the finishing components plus customized methods to*
	receive, maintain & distribute inventory.

Categories:	*Rework & Inspection, Warehouse & Distribution*
Specialties:	*Pressing, hand & machine sewing, soil & mildew spot removal, ticketing, heat-seal, re-packaging, warehousing & distribution.*
Machinery:	*20 single needle, 20 zig zag, 3 button, 3 coverstitch*
Production Capacity:	*100,000 dz/month*

COTTON & ELSE INC.

2921 N.W. 28th Street
Lauderdale Lakes, Florida 33311

(1) (954) 677 8010   Fax: (1) (954) 677 0270

E-Mail:	*cottonet@bellsouth.net*
Web Site:	*www.cottonandelse.net*
Year Est:	*1992*
Categories:	*Dyeing, Sleepwear/Robes, Active/Athletic Wear*
Specialties:	*Specialize in knitting, dyeing and sewing of cotton knitted garments. We offer a wide range of Tee-Shirts.*
Markets:	*Menswear, Womenswear & Childrenswear.*
Export to:	*Canada, Europe, Middle East, South America*
Factory Locals:	*Florida*
Production Capacity:	*10,000 doz/week (garments)*

DESIGN PRINCIPLES LLC, THE

1914 Cordova Road
Ft. Lauderdale, Florida 33316
Hollis Dominick
(1) 727 488 8162   Fax: (1) 954 756 7325

E-Mail:	*hollis@thedesignprinciples.com*
Web Site:	*www.thedesignprinciples.com*
Description:	*Design, sketching, patternmaking, samples, marking/grading, sourcing and production services.*
Categories:	*Sample Rooms/Small Production, Patternmaking*
Specialties:	*Specialize in servicing the startup to emerging designer brands for their production needs.*
Markets:	*Menswear, Womenswear, Childrens & Accessories.*
Factory Locals:	*Development Office: 305 879 6863*

HARDRIVE PRODUCTIONS, INC.

4605 L.B. McLeod Road
Orlando, Florida 32811
Michael
(1) (407) 872 3030   Fax: (1) (407) 872 1474

E-Mail:	*hdrivemike@aol.com*
Web Site:	*www.hardriveinc.com*
Description:	*Sewing contract work.*
Categories:	*Swimwear/Dancewear*
	Production
Specialties:	*Expertise with theatrical costumes, dancewear, show choirs & various other apparel types.*
Markets:	*Womenswear, Childrenswear.*
Packages:	*Patternmaking, samples & small production sewing.*

INTERNATIONAL FULFILLMENT, INC.

7395 West 18th Lane
Hialeah, Florida 33014
Tristan Cuadrado/Stuart Friedman
(1) (305) 825 1040   Fax: (1) (305) 825 1912

E-Mail:	*tristan@jessicainternational.com*
Web Site:	*www.jessicainternational.com*
Description:	*A complete solution enterprise dedicated to warehousing/distribution, fulfillment services and sales & marketing.*
Categories:	*Distribution/Warehouse Center*
Specialties:	*Assembly, packing, inspection, E-Commerce, returns center, government contracts, kitting, pick & pack, inventory control.*

KEMESTRY

1221 Stirling Road
Dania Beach, Florida 33004
Fred Kinigsberg
(1) (954) 922 2802   Fax: (1) (954) 922 2012

E-Mail:	*elj1978@aol.com*
Web Site:	*www.kemestryonline.com*
Description:	*Custom contracting house specializing in belts, nailhead & stud application & covered buckles & hair accessories.*
Categories:	*Accessories, Trim Applcation.*
Specialties:	*Nailhead, rhinestone, eyeletting, rivetting, laminating & stud work.*
Markets:	*Middle to high-end.*
Minimums:	*None*

LEONORA FASHIONS, INC.

1095 East 15th Street
Hialeah, Florida 33010
Michael Fiorilli
(1) (305) 885 8148   Fax: (1) (305) 885 8148

E-Mail:	*mike@leonorafashions.com*
Web Site:	*www.leonorafashions.com*
Description:	*Contractor specialized in outerwear, coats, jackets, suits & uniforms of all types.*
Categories:	*Coats/Jackets, Active Outerwear, Uniforms, Suits/Formal*
Specialties:	*Designing, pattern making and grading.*
Markets:	*Menswear, Womenswear.*
Machinery:	*State-of-the-art machinery.*
Packages:	*Full package.*
Factory Locals:	*20,000 sq. ft. factory with warehouse in Hialeah, FL.*
Production Capacity:	*5,000 pieces/week*

MIAMI STYLE INC.

7480 NW 52nd Street
Miami, Florida 33166
Amnon Bensimon/Sofia Rincon
(1) (305) 805 1168   Fax: (1) (305) 805 0075

E-Mail:	*sofia@miamistyle.com*

Web Site:	*www.miamistyle.com*
Description:	*Sourcing agent for all types of active wear, bottoms, tops, tee shirts, knit sportswear, beachwear, sports bras, basics and children's wear.*
Year Est:	*1997*
Categories:	*Production Sourcing/Factory Agent, Active Wear/Athletic Wear, Pants/Shorts/Skirts, Shirts/Tops, Tee Shirts/ Sweat Shirts*
Specialties:	*Production services: Private label, sewing, cutting, patternmaking, printing, embroidery, screenprinting, samplemaking, dyeing, beading & more.*
Markets:	*Menswear, Womenswear, Boyswear, Girlswear.*
Factory Locals:	*Bangladesh and China*
Production Capacity:	*3 million pcs per month*

OCEAN AIR LOGISTICS
1800 NW 133rd Avenue
Miami, Florida 33182

(1) (305) 599 0966   Fax: (1) (305) 599 0766

E-Mail:	*sales@oceanairlogistics.com*
Web Site:	*www.oceanairlogistics.com*
Description:	*International & domestic freight forwarder & freight consolidator serving Latin America. Air freight, air cargo, ocean cargo.*
Categories:	*Freight Forwarder/Customs Broker*
Specialties:	*Customs clearance & transport services, packing & crating, warehouse & distribution. Consulting on all imports.*

PATTERN GRADING & MARKER SERVICES
3650 S.W. 141 Avenue
Miramar, Florida 33027
Regina Gottlieb, Owner
(1) (954) 441 4432   Fax: (1) (954) 441 4344

E-Mail:	*regina@pattern-maker.com*
Web Site:	*www.pattern-maker.com*
Description:	*Technical consulting services and expert patternmaking, and grading & marking.*
Year Est:	*1999*
Categories:	*Patternmaking, Grading/Marking*
Specialties:	*Make patterns from an existing garment, a customer defined speck or sketch. Grading & marking specific to your specs and fabric.*
Machinery:	*10 machines*
Export to:	*Dominican Republic*
Minimums:	*Low: 1 to 200 units/style*
Production Capacity:	*200 pieces/week*

PRIORITY MANUFACTURING
571 N.W. 29th Street
Miami, Florida 33127
Richard Levy
(1) (305) 576 3000   Fax: (1) (305) 576 2672

E-Mail:	*richard@customuniforms.com*
Web Site:	*www.customuniforms.com*
Description:	*Manufacturer & contractor of uniforms for restaurants, theme*

	parks, cruise lines, resorts, industrial, chef apparel & more.
Year Est:	1972
Categories:	Uniforms
Specialties:	Custom embroidery & screen printing to any specifications. Toll free-1-800-835-5528
Markets:	Menswear & Womenswear
Packages:	Cutting & sewing, complete & CMT packages available.
Minimums:	36 pieces
Production Capacity:	2000 pcs/month

SOURCE-I

P.O. Box 741
Indian Rocks Beach, Florida 33785
Wayne Wilson, President
(1) (727) 725 2981

E-Mail:	wwilson@source-i.com
Web Site:	www.source-i.com
Year Est:	1994
Categories:	Sportswear-Knits, Sportswear-Wovens, Denimwear, Sleepwear, Pants/Shorts/Skirts, Shirts/Tops, Sweaters, Jackets & Uniforms.
Specialties:	Full package apparel sourcing solutions. Vertical knit and woven operation.
Markets:	Menswear, Womenswear, Childrenswear, Infantwear.
Machinery:	All updated & modern sewing facilities.
Packages:	Door-to-door full package & CMT programs.

SUNCOAST TRENDS CORP.

2860 21st Avenue North
St. Petersburg, Florida 33713
Rosanna Carl
(1) (727) 321 4948   Fax: (1) (727) 321 4320

Description:	Cut & sew contractor of all types of casual knit & woven sportswear plus cosmetic bags & accessories.
Categories:	Sportswear/Knits, Sportswear/Wovens, Patternmaking Services
Markets:	Menswear, Womenswear, Childrens, Accessories.
Minimums:	12 dozen

SUPERIOR PATTERN SERVICES

1095 East 15th Street
Hialeah, FLorida 33010
Jeff Trieb, President
(1) (305) 805 1540

E-Mail:	superior_patterns@yahoo.com
Web Site:	www.superiorpatterns.com
Description:	Grading/Marking and Patternmaking services for all types of woven and knit apparel. Also, assist with sourcing.
Year Est:	1997
Categories:	Grading/Marking, Patternmaking, Sample Room/Small Production
Specialties:	Specialize in assisting new designers create their collection.
Markets:	Menswear, Womenswear, Childrenswear
Machinery:	Gerber Accumark System

Packages:	*Full packages.*
Minimums:	*Vary*
Factory Locals:	*Factories in Dominican Republic & Guatemala.*

TRANN TECHNOLOGIES INC.

12526 U.S. Highway 90
Mossy Head, Florida 32434
Samuel A. Goldstein
(1) (888) 668 6700   Fax: (1) (888) 308 7266

E-Mail:	*sales@tranntech.com*
Web Site:	*www.tranntech.com*
Description:	*Over 50 years of fabric coating and raw material processing.*
Categories:	*Finishing/Coating*
Specialties:	*Specialize in applications to nylon, Lycra/Spandex, cotton and other knit fabrics and nonwovens.*
Machinery:	*Unwinding systems, padding, laminating and vertical coating, paralell tenter entry with overfeeding capability, on-frame knife coater, levitator tenter dryer system and more.*
Packages:	*Full service.*

Georgia

A&S CLOTHING

1130 Ada Street, Suite C
Blue Ridge, Georgia 30513
Salma Adam
(1) (706) 632 2133   Fax: (1) (706) 632 8638

E-Mail:	*asclothing@tds.net*
Description:	*Sewing contractor of mens and womens jeans & chinos.*
Year Est:	*1989*
Categories:	*Jeans/Denimwear, Pants/Shorts/Skirts*
Markets:	*Menswear & Womenswear.*
Machinery:	*12 straight needle, 8 double needle, 7 serger, 2 bander, 1 auto belt loop, 2 waistband end u-tack, 2 bar tacker, 1 zig-zag, 1 auto label sewer, 1 monogram, 2 belt loop maker, 1 heat sealer, 2 needle chain stitch, 2 felling, 2 bulldog hem, 1 rivet, 4 walking foot*
Packages:	*CMT packaages.*
Factory Locals:	*Our 20,000 sq ft facility is equipped with a warehouse and loading dock.*
Production Capacity:	*20,000 units/monthly*

ATLANTA SEWING & PATTERN-MAKING SERVICE

1930 Airport Industrial Park Drive
Marietta, Georgia 30060
Myriam Belasse
(1) (770) 952 9211

E-Mail:	*info@asapsewingservice.com*
Web Site:	*www.asapsewingservice.com*
Description:	*Designing, patternmaking, sample making, fabric sourcing and production sewing. Your idea from concept to final product.*
Categories:	*Sample Rooms/Small Production*

Specialties: We also do label changes in small and large quantities. Qualified to do garment inspection and repairs. By appointment only.
Markets: All markets
Minimums: None
Factory Locals: Cell Number: 404-849-0473

DARWOOD MANUFACTURING CO.

620 West Railroad Street
Pelham, Georgia 31779
Allen Burford, President
(1) (229) 294 4932   Fax: (1) (229) 294 9323
E-Mail: darwood@bellsouth.net
Web Site: www.darwoodmfg.com
Description: Cut & sew shirt & garment contractor. Grading/marking, patternmaking, sample making, washing & more.
Year Est: 1960
Categories: Grading/Marking, Patternmaking, Sample Rooms, Washing, Embroidery, Shirts/Tops
Specialties: Expertise with all kinds of shirts, tops, pants, shorts, skirts, uniforms & outerwear.
Markets: Menswear, Womenswear, Boyswear & Accessories.
Packages: CMT & complete packages available.
Minimums: 5 dozen/style
Factory Locals: Pelham, GA

E.T. MANUFACTURING CO.

192 E. Athens Street
Winder, Georgia 30680

(1) (770) 867 8152   Fax: (1) (770) 867 0025
E-Mail: info@etmanufacturing.com
Web Site: www.etmanufacturing.com
Description: We work with start-ups and apparel/uniform manufacturers by designing & developing your product from concept to production.
Year Est: 1990
Categories: Uniforms
Specialties: Specialize in industrial uniforms. Aprons, vests, smocks, lab coats, bias binding and tote bags.
Machinery: Our cutting room is equipped with a manual spreader & cutter & can manage fabrics as wide as 60 inches. Our sewing room is equipped with multiple range of singe needle, serger, bar-tack, button-hole & more.
Packages: CMT

JORO, INC.

296 Fayette Drive
Winder, Georgia 30680
John Robinson
(1) (770) 867 7364   Fax: (1) (770) 867 5834
E-Mail: joro@joroinc.comcastbiz.net
Description: Press, trim & inspect goods, apply hangtags/pocket flashers. Curing oven resin, waterproofing, wrinklefree, desize, enzyme & stone washes.

Year Est:	*1987*
Categories:	*Finishing, Washing/Laundry*
Specialties:	*Handsand/destruct denim & other fabrics. Dyeing & specialty finishes. All work done in-house.*
Markets:	*Menswear & Womenswear.*
Minimums:	*None*
Factory Locals:	*58 West May Street, Winder, Ga 30680*
Production Capacity:	*70,000 pcs per month*

Z.W. DESIGNS, INC.
443 Flint Hill Court
Lawrenceville, Georgia 30044
Z. Arthur
(1) (770) 513 0906

E-Mail:	*zwd@zwdesigns.com*
Web Site:	*www.zwdesigns.com*
Description:	*Expert apparel & product development, specifications, digital patterns, grading, markers; plotting, samples, small lot manufacturing.*
Year Est:	*1983*
Categories:	*Patternmaking, Sample Rooms/Small Production, Grading & Marking, CAD/CAM Software Marketing*
Specialties:	*CAD/CAM patternmaking, technical design, design sketching/flats; choir robes, uniforms, government contractor certified (WOSP,SDB).*
Markets:	*Womenswear, Menswear, Childrenswear.*
Production Capacity:	*Small lots, but varies*

Idaho

EMBROIDERED CORPORATE IMAGE
10318 North U.S. Highway 95
Hayden Lake, Idaho 83835
Robert Allen, Owner
(1) (208) 772 4044   Fax: (1) (208) 772 4723

E-Mail:	*rla@eci-embroidery.com*
Web Site:	*www.eci-embroidery.com*
Description:	*High quality, high speed contract embroidery for all apparel & accessory markets.*
Year Est:	*1989*
Categories:	*Embroidery*
Specialties:	*Embroidery on accessories, jackets, caps, polos, sweats & athletic wear.*
Markets:	*All*
Machinery:	*Operate Tajima, Barudan & Melco equipment 24 hours a day & 7 days a week.*
Minimums:	*Vary*
Factory Locals:	*1-800-858-4044*

Illinois

AMERICAN SEWING DYNAMICS, INC.

2441 Vermont Avenue #154
Blue Island, Illinois 60406
Bob Choi
(1) (773) 394 9544   Fax: (1) (773) 394 9610

E-Mail:	*sales@americansewingdynamics.com*
Web Site:	*www.americansewingdynamics.com*
Description:	*Sewing, cutting & assembly services for military & commercial uniforms, casual wear, shoe uppers, leather goods, home & specialty.*
Categories:	*Leather Accessories, Coats/Jackets, Casual Wear, Uniforms*
Specialties:	*Specialize in coveralls, pants, combat uniforms, casual shirts, sportswear, leather & military shoe & boot uppers, leather goods.*
Markets:	*Menswear, Womenswear, Accessories.*
Machinery:	*Multiple - Single needle, double needle, walking, cylinder, felling, pattern tacker, riveting, grommeting, eyeletting, snap, splitting, skiving, button hole, button sewing, bartacker, die cutting, table cutting, puritan, autobarr, zigzag, web cutting, folding, trimming.*
Minimums:	*Vary*
Factory Locals:	*Chicago, IL*
Production Capacity:	*500 - 25,000 units/month depending on material & design.*

APPAREL AGENCY, THE

2023 W Carroll Avenue
Chicago, Illinois 60612
Nichole Rairigh
(1) (312) 265 0900   Fax: (1) (312) 273 1796

E-Mail:	*info@theapparelagency.com*
Web Site:	*www.theapparelagency.com*
Description:	*Full service agency. Product design, sourcing, graphic design, tech packs, pattern making, sample making, costing, small production.*
Year Est:	*2010*
Categories:	*Production Sourcing/Factory Agents*
Specialties:	*Production-ready patterns and samples with low minimum production commitments for new & small businesses.*
Markets:	*Menswear, Womenswear & Childrenswear.*
Packages:	*CMT, Full Package*
Minimums:	*1-500 pcs/style/color*

DREAMBAGS INC

2441 Vermont Avenue #154
Blue Island, Illinois 60406
Bob Choi
(1) (773) 394 3136   Fax: (1) (773) 394 9610

E-Mail:	*sales@dreambags.com*
Web Site:	*www.dreambags.com*
Description:	*Manufacturer & contractor of leather goods, handbags, backpacks, totes, travelware, computer cases, pet carriers, specialty cases.*
Categories:	*Leather Accessories, Fashion Accessories, Home Accessories*
Specialties:	*Leather shoe/boot uppers, sample development services.*
Markets:	*Mid-high range women, men, commercial accounts*
Machinery:	*Multiple single needle, double needle, zigzag, walking, cylinder,*

splitting, skiving, rivet, eyelet, grommet, snap, clickers, travel head, table cutting knives, web cutter, pattern tacker

Minimums: *Varies per model and color*
Factory Locals: *Chicago, IL*

ELEGANT EMBROIDERY/MELON INK SCREEN PRINT

100 B Oakwood Road
Lake Zurich, Illinois 60047
Nancy Needham
(1) (847) 540 8003   Fax: (1) (847) 540 8477

E-Mail: *nancy@elegantembroidery.com*
Web Site: *www.elegantembroidery.com*
Description: *Custom embroidery & screen printing.*
Year Est: *1995*
Categories: *Embroidery*
Specialties: *Specialize in embroidery & screen printing on towels, linens, table linens & outerwear.*
Markets: *Accessories, Home Furnishings.*
Machinery: *SWF four-head, 2 SWF single-head embroidery machines. (2) 6 Color & 6 Station Screen Print, one automatic, one manual heat transfer presses, rhinestone.*
Minimums: *None*

GIL SEWING CORPORATION

3500 N. Kostner Avenue
Chicago, Illinois 60641

(1) (773) 545 0990   Fax: (1) (773) 545 0778

E-Mail: *gilsewing@sbcglobal.net*
Web Site: *www.gilsewing.com*
Description: *Garment manufacturer. Pattern creation, cut, sew, quality control & shipped according to client's specs.*
Year Est: *1993*
Categories: *Uniforms*
Specialties: *Specialize in uniforms, tailored and work clothing.*
Markets: *Womenswear & Menswear.*
Machinery: *Gerber GTXL Computer Cutter*

HENDERSON ADVERTIZING

2508 East Cook Street
Springfield, Illinois 62703
Leon Henderson
(1) (217) 544 9419   Fax: (1) (217) 522 8155

E-Mail: *hendersonart@ameritech.net*
Web Site: *www.henderson-advertising.com*
Description: *We provide a variety of custom embroidery, embossing, or silk-screening to help you create your product.*
Categories: *Embroidery, Screenprinting*
Specialties: *A large selection of promotional products. Custom shirts, hats, jackets, sportswear, aprons.*
Markets: *Menswear, Womenswear, Childrens & Accessories.*

SEW PRECISE COMPANY

3212 N. Kilpatrick Avenue
Chicago, Illinois 60641

(1) (773) 481 1400   Fax: (1) (773) 481 1335

E-Mail:	*info@sewprecise.com*
Web Site:	*www.sewprecise.com*
Description:	*Full service cutting and sewing contractor of all types of apparel.*
Categories:	*Grading/Marking, Childrenswear, Small Production*
Specialties:	*Grading/marker, pressing/finishing, embroidery.*
Markets:	*Menswear, Womenswear, Childrenswear.*
Machinery:	*80 machines of all types including fusing machines, pressing equipment, and 2 40ft. cutting tables.*

SHURCO MANUFACTURING INC.

4638 North Ravenwood Avenue
Chicago, Illinois 60640
Seymour Ferdman
(1) (773) 907 8400   Fax: (1) (773) 907 8476

E-Mail:	*sy924@sbcglobal.net*
Description:	*Contractor of accessories, handbags, bags & apparel items in leather, suede, plastic, vinyl & cloth.*
Year Est:	*1950*
Categories:	*Accessories, Leather/Suede*
Specialties:	*We provide embossing, embroidery & silk screening. Quick delivery & quick turn-around.*
Markets:	*Accessories*
Machinery:	*Kick-press, 5 die-cutting & 25 sewing machines.*
Packages:	*Cutting & Sewing & CMT.*
Minimums:	*None*
Production Capacity:	*8,000 pcs/month*

Illinos

ME'LANSON PATTERNS

870 N Richmond
Chicago, Illinos 60622
Maribel Melanson
(1) (702) 742 3082

E-Mail:	*thepatternmaker14@gmail.com*
Web Site:	*www.coroflot.com/marfig*
Description:	*Pattern draft, initial first samples and small production. Will do runs of 6 pieces to 2 dozen for start-up companies.*
Categories:	*Patternmaking, Sample Room/Small Production, Product Development*
Specialties:	*Design studio that offers patternmaking, fabric sourcing, technical flat drawings, fittings, grading, marker making, tech packs & branding.*
Markets:	*Menswear, Womenswear, Childrens & Accessories.*
Minimums:	*None*

Indiana

NU YALE

6300 Highway 62
Jeffersonville, Indiana 47130
Mike Maloney
(1) (812) 285 7400   Fax: (1) (812) 285 7421

E-Mail:	*mike@nuyale.com*
Web Site:	*www.nuyale.com*
Description:	*Inspectors of import garments. Rework, inspections, washing, pressing, dry cleaning & warehousing.*
Year Est:	*1950*
Categories:	*Rework/Inspection Services, Laundry/Washing Contractors, Restoration.*
Specialties:	*Wet processing & washing of blue jeans, stone washing, bleaching, pre-washing and restoration of any garment.*
Markets:	*All apparel & accessory markets.*
Machinery:	*4 600-lb. washers, 2 900-lb. washers, 3 900-lb. dryers, 1 600-lb. dryer.*
Minimums:	*None*
Production Capacity:	*10,000 dozen/month*

STUDIO NTK LLC

2946 Welcome Way
Greenwood, Indiana 46143
Nataliya Kitic
(1) (317) 886 7327

E-Mail:	*studiontk@gmail.com*
Web Site:	*www.studiontk.com*
Description:	*Apparel design and manufacturing. Our services are for start up & small companies to leading brands.*
Year Est:	*2011*
Categories:	*Samples/Small Production, Patternmaking*
Specialties:	*Consulting, concept ideas to detailed sketches, specks, production samples, patternmaking, cut and sew, quality control.*
Markets:	*Womenswear, Accessories*
Packages:	*CMT & Samples*
Minimums:	*None*
Production Capacity:	*1,000 pcs*

TOPPS SAFETY APPAREL INC.

2516 East State Road 14
Rochester, Indiana 46975

(1) (574) 223 4311   Fax: (1) (574) 223 8622

E-Mail:	*info@toppssafetyapparel.com*
Web Site:	*www.toppssafetyapparel.com*
Description:	*Contractor & manufacturer of flame resistant industrial uniforms & workclothes, such as: cover-alls & jumpsuits.*
Categories:	*Uniforms*
Specialties:	*Specialize in safety apparel.*
Machinery:	*Automatic cutting & marking in house.*
Packages:	*CMT, Sewing & Complete.*

Minimums:	*25 dozen/style*
Factory Locals:	*3 factories in Kentucky*

Kansas

BRANDED EMBLEM
7920 Foster
Overland Park, Kansas 66024
Danny
(1) (913) 648 7920   Fax: (1) (913) 648 7444

E-Mail:	*dannys@campdavid.com*
Web Site:	*www.campdavid.com*
Description:	*Toll free:#1-800-747-7920. Contract embroidery, embroidered emblems, appliques & imported woven labels.*
Year Est:	*1969*
Exporting Since:	*1997*
Categories:	*Embroidery.*
Specialties:	*Laser cut, heat seal embroidered emblems & appliques for the direct embroidery look.*
Minimums:	*50 pieces/style*

Kentucky

STITCH DESIGNERS
1601 Crums Lane
Louisville, Kentucky 40216
John Home
(1) (502) 637 8619

E-Mail:	*marketing@dbswebsite.com*
Web Site:	*www.stitchdesigners.com*
Description:	*Premier contract embroiderer in the United States.*
Categories:	*Embroidery*
Specialties:	*Full range of embroidery services to promotional products distributors & various other resellers of embroidered goods.*

Maine

LIBERTY GRAPHICS
44 Main Street
Liberty, Maine 04949

(1) (207) 589 4596   Fax: (1) (207) 589 4415

E-Mail:	*sales@lgtees.com*
Web Site:	*www.lgtees.com*
Description:	*Toll free#: 1-800-338-0015. Contract screen printer. Screen print on sportswear, outerwear & tees.*
Year Est:	*Special handling, folding, tagging & bagging.*
Categories:	*Screenprinting Contractors*
Specialties:	*Nature-oriented tee shirt design & production, with 100% water based ink. Cotton or cool-max substrates.*
Markets:	*Menswear, Womenswear.*
Machinery:	*2 automatic screen print presses for textiles, 1 hand*

	screen print press & full pre-press dept & separationists.
Minimums:	*50 units per ink color*

ACE BINDING CO.,INC.
3031 James Street
Baltimore, Maryland 21230
Larry Cohen
(1) (410) 525 0700   Fax: (1) (410) 525 0714

E-Mail:	*larry@acebinding.com*
Web Site:	*www.acebinding.com*
Description:	*Waist-band, binding, cutting & sewing services.*
Year Est:	*1942*
Categories:	*Cutting & Fusing Contractor*
Specialties:	*Die cutting, table cutting, roll cutting (score, razor, hot knife, pinked), perforating and slotting. Fusing: 72"" capacity, roll to roll.*
Packages:	*807 & CBI Programs*
Minimums:	*Low*

AETNA SHIRT/ON CALL MEDICAL COATS
620 Franklin Avenue
Baltimore, Maryland 21221
Dan Kohn
(1) (410) 574 2657   Fax: (1) (410) 574 6307

E-Mail:	*customerservice@medicalcoats.com*
Web Site:	*www.medicalcoats.com*
Description:	*CMT contractors of high quality formalwear accessories, shirts & blouses plus scrub tops & bottoms.*
Year Est:	*1916*
Categories:	*Dress & Sport Shirts, Formalwear, Accessories, Uniforms*
Specialties:	*Dress shirts, formal shirts, ladies blouses, medical coats, bowties, cummerbunds & more. Can do custom collars, cuffs & tucking.*
Markets:	*Menswear, Womenswear*
Machinery:	*Over 50 sewing machines: single needle, felling, embroidery, formal shirt pleating & more.*
Packages:	*Sewing, CMT & Complete packages available.*
Export to:	*Japan*
Agent:	*Dan or Wayne. Tel: 877-355-2898.*
Minimums:	*None*
Factory Locals:	*Baltimore, MD*
Production Capacity:	*250 labcoats/week, 1500-2000 woven shirts/week*

AIM GARMENTS
8444 Braddock Way
Columbia, Maryland 21046
Chinh Tran
(1) 443 745 1502   Fax: (1) 410 381 5109

E-Mail:	*info@aimgarments.com*
Web Site:	*www.aimgarments.com*
Description:	*Full-service clothing & apparel manufacturing contractor.*

Specialty in woven athletic apparel and team sportswear.

Year Est:	*1995*
Categories:	*Active/Athletic Wear, Dresses, Pants/Shorts/Skirts, Blouses/Tops, Outerwear, Jeans/Denimwear, Childrenswear, Lingerie, Tee-Shirts.*
Specialties:	*Full range of services: design, fabric procurement, patternmaking, product development, cut & sew, tag & bag, shipping & custom clearing.*
Markets:	*Menswear, Womenswear, Boyswear, Girlswear.*
Packages:	*CMT, Patternmaking & Samplemaking.*
Export to:	*U.S.A.*
Minimums:	*2000/style*
Factory Locals:	*Ho Chi Minh City, Vietnam*
Production Capacity:	*300,000 pcs/month*

FASHIONS UNLIMITED, INC.

1100 Wicomico Street
Baltimore, Maryland 21230
Mary Murphy
(1) (410) 783 1584

E-Mail:	*fashionsu@verizon.net*
Web Site:	*www.fashionsu.net*
Description:	*Contractor of swim, active, bodywear & innerwear. Patternmaker & sample room on premises.*
Year Est:	*1976*
Categories:	*Active/Athleticwear, Lingerie/Intimate Apparel, Sportswear-Knits, Swimwear/Dancewear, Patternmaking*
Specialties:	*We specialize in seamless development. We have seamless knitting capabilities on Santoni Machines. Bras, tops, pants, underwear, swim.*
Markets:	*Womenswear, Childrenswear*
Machinery:	*Overlock, single needle, coverstitch (1 and 2 needle) zig zag, walking foot machines, flat locks.*
Packages:	*Full service, CMT & complete packages.*
Minimums:	*None*
Factory Locals:	*Baltimore MD, Hellam PA, Charlotte NC (Seamless)*
Production Capacity:	*Swim: 1,000 units/week, Activewear: 1,500 units/week, Dance: 1,500 units/week, Sportswear: 1,000 units/week*

Massachusetts

ACCURATE SERVICES, INC.

951 Broadway
Fall River, Massachusetts 02724
Sue Teixeira
(1) (508) 674 5773   Fax: (1) (508) 674 5649

E-Mail:	*suetex@accurateservice.com*
Web Site:	*www.accurateservice.com*
Description:	*Warehousing & distribution for sewn products manufacturers.*
Year Est:	*1955*
Categories:	*Distribution/Warehouse Center, Rework/Inspection Services*
Specialties:	*Full range of finishing services: alter, hem, fix patterns, press and steam. Also, label, re-label & package goods.*
Machinery:	*100,000+ sq. ft. of modern shelves, racks, overhead trolleys and conveyors.*

C.R.C. DESIGN SERVICES

19 Buena Vista Avenue
Asonet, Massachusetts 02702
Carlos Custodio/Lucy
(1) (508) 644 3166   Fax: (1) (508) 644 3166

E-Mail:	*carlos.c@comcast.net*
Description:	*Pattern grading & marking for the apparel industry.* *Affordable, up-to-the-minute computerized capabilities.*
Categories:	*Grading/Marking*
Specialties:	*Experience in maximum fabric utilization. Exceptional marker quality. Easy pattern changes.*
Markets:	*All*
Machinery:	*Gerber system.*

CUSTOM APPAREL PROCESSING

994 Jefferson Street
Fall River, Massachusetts 02721

(1) (508) 675 2962

Description:	*Textile dyeing and finishing.*
Categories:	*Dyeing Contractor*
Specialties:	*Custom dyeing and tie-dyeing of apparel, including neon.*

DURO INDUSTRIES

110 Chace Street
Fall River, Massachusetts 02724
Bryan Boulis
(1) (508) 675 0101   Fax: (1) (508) 677 6791

E-Mail:	*boulis_bryan@durolink.com*
Web Site:	*www.duroindustries.com*
Description:	*Nylon, polyesters, coated fabrics, flame retard fabrics, military fabrics, exclusive commercial distributor of Multicam® camo.*
Year Est:	*1948*
Specialties:	*Full service lab testing.*
Minimums:	*Varies on each fabric*

GRIFFIN MANUFACTURING CO., INC.

502 Bedford Street
Fall River, Massachusetts 02722
Gene Laudon
(1) (508) 677 0048   Fax: (1) (508) 674 1268

E-Mail:	*sales@griffinmanufacturing.com*
Web Site:	*www.griffinmanufacturing.com*
Description:	*Cut & sew contractor plus design, development, patternmaking, sample making & warehousing.*
Year Est:	*1936*
Categories:	*Active/Athleticwear, Samples/Small Production*
Specialties:	*Athleticwear, performance knits, knit & woven sportswear & outerwear.*
Markets:	*Menswear, Womenswear & Childrenswear.*
Machinery:	*Sewing machines, flatlock stitch machines, automatic cutting machines,*

in-house embroidery & heat transfers.

Minimums:	*200 to 2,000 pieces*
Factory Locals:	*Fall River, MA & Costa Rica*

MOONLITE GRAPHICS CO., INC.

951 Broadway
Fall River, Massachusetts 02724
Bill Boudreau
(1) (508) 676 6674   Fax: (1) (508) 679 8128

E-Mail:	*moonlite79@verizon.net*
Description:	*Wholesale/contract screenprinting plus embroidery on all types of apparel.*
Year Est:	*1979*
Categories:	*Screenprinting Contractors, Embroidery*
Specialties:	*In-house graphics. Four-color process, cut part printing, familiar with hi-tech fabrics & large volume.*
Markets:	*All apparel markets & all price points.*
Machinery:	*2 automatics & 6 manuals*
Factory Locals:	*14,000 sq. ft. facility*

STERLINGWEAR OF BOSTON, INC.

175 McClellan Highway
East Boston, Massachusetts 02128
David Fredella
(1) (617) 567 6465   Fax: (1) (617) 567 6472

E-Mail:	*dfredella@sterlingwear.com*
Web Site:	*www.sterlingwear.com*
Description:	*Manufacturers of quality outerwear for men, women & children plus military outerwear clothing.*
Categories:	*Uniforms, Coats & Jackets*
Specialties:	*Will do contract work for private label uniforms.*
Minimums:	*Vary*

SWAN DYEING

372 Stevens Street
Fall River, Massachusetts 02721
Mike Rodriques
(1) (508) 674 4611   Fax: (1) (508) 676 3730

E-Mail:	*swansales@swandyeandprint.com*
Web Site:	*www.swandyeandprint.com*
Description:	*Commission dyeing & printing on all types of fabrics. Domestic.*
Categories:	*Dyeing Contractor/Finishing/Coating Contractor*
Specialties:	*Finishing services include brushing/sanding & napping, sanforization, laundering, calendaring, embossing & more.*
Minimums:	*1,500 yds/color*

UNWRAPPED, INC.

95 Rock Street
Lowell, Massachusetts 01854
Steven Katz
(1) (978) 441 0242   Fax: (1) (978) 441 0929

E-Mail:	*skatz@unwrappedinc.com*
Web Site:	*www.unwrappedinc.com*
Description:	*Sewing factory specializing in contract manufacturing of stitched goods including mesh, nylon & canvas bags & OEM production.*
Specialties:	*Cosmetic bags, toy bags, shoe bags, gear bags, pillows & pillow liners.*
Markets:	*Accessories, Home Furnishings.*

Mississippi

DYEHOUSE, INC., THE

601 Harris Avenue
Quitman, Mississippi 39355
Paul Brown
(1) (601) 776 3777   Fax: (1) (601) 776 5008

E-Mail:	*prb21439@aol.com*
Description:	*All types of garment dyeing & denim garment washing.*
Categories:	*Dyeing Contractors, Laundry/Washing Contractors*
Specialties:	*Dyeing on any type of fabric or apparel.*
Machinery:	*Dye extract & testing machinery on premises.*
Minimums:	*None*

Missouri

FABRI-QUILT INC.

901 East 14th Avenue
North Kansas City, Missouri 64116
John Linam
(1) (816) 421 2000   Fax: (1) (816) 471 2853

E-Mail:	*jhlinam@msn.com*
Web Site:	*www.fabri-quilt.com*
Description:	*Toll-Free#1-800-279-0622. Contractor of custom quilting on your fabric or Fabri-Quilt can supply the fabric on custom packages.*
Year Est:	*1962*
Exporting Since:	*1986*
Categories:	*Quilting Contractors.*
Specialties:	*All types of quilting patterns & printed cottons for fabric stores.*
Export to:	*France, Germany, Australia, Netherlands, Canada, Spain, Korea, England, Denmark, Italy & Finland.*
Agent:	*Distributors throughout Europe, North America & Asia.*
Minimums:	*$250.00/order*

HENSCHEL HAT CO.

1706 Olive Street
St. Louis, Missouri 63103
Tarek Deiab, President
(1) (314) 421 0009   Fax: (1) (314) 421 1317

E-Mail:	*usahat@aol.com*
Web Site:	*www.henschelhats.com*
Description:	*Hat manufacturer open for contract work of all hat styles.*
Year Est:	*1947*
Exporting Since:	*1985*
Categories:	*Accessories*
Specialties:	*Men's high fashion, classic & leather hats.*
Markets:	*Menswear*
Packages:	*All*
Export to:	*Germany, Holland, Austria, France, Spain, Japan, Mexico & Korea.*
Minimums:	*Special orders: 6 doz/style; regular orders: 1 doz/style.*
Factory Locals:	*Factory in Missouri.*
Production Capacity:	*200-400 dozen/week*

PARAMOUNT APPAREL INTERNATIONAL

1 Paramount Drive
Bourbon, Missouri 65441

(1) (573) 732 4411   Fax: (1) (573) 732 5211

E-Mail:	*sales@paramountapparel.com*
Web Site:	*www.paramountapparel.com*
Description:	*Largest domestic & off shore headwear contractor & manufacturer. Custom screenprinted t-shirts.*
Categories:	*Accessories, Tee Shirts*
Specialties:	*Fashion knit headwear & fedoras. Cap & Tee combos. .Cutting edge designs.*
Markets:	*Menswear, Womenswear, Boyswear, Girlswear.*
Packages:	*Full service including embroidery & silk-screening.*
Minimums:	*Vary*

New Hampshire

RED FISH BLUE FISH DYE WORKS INC.

145 Green Street
Somersworth, New Hampshire 03878
Jeff Basseches/David Bailey
(1) (603) 692 3900   Fax: (1) (603) 692 2733

E-Mail:	*jeff@rfbfdyeworks.com*
Web Site:	*www.rfbfdyeworks.com*
Description:	*Full service garment dye house. Service on your garments or ours.*
Year Est:	*1994*
Categories:	*Dyeing*
Specialties:	*Garment direct dyeing, including specialty dye effects. Tie-dyeing and heat transfer printing.*
Markets:	*Menswear, Womenswear & Childrenswear.*

5 KIDS EMBROIDERY GROUP LLC

37 Highway 35
Neptune City, New Jersey 07753
Phil Miller
(1) (732) 774 5331   Fax: (1) (732) 774 3311

E-Mail:	*philm@5kidsembroidery.com*
Web Site:	*www.5kidsembroidery.com*
Description:	*Multi head embroidery. Domestic.*
Categories:	*Embroidery*
Specialties:	*First samples. Digitizing. Overseas sourcing of all promotional products.*
Markets:	*Cater to all production runs of all sizes.*

AA WORLD CLASS EMBROIDERY & EMBELLISHMENT CO.

450 Murray Hill Parkway
East Rutherford, New Jersey 07073
Ben Amoruso
(1) (201) 313 0022   Fax: (1) (201) 313 0044

E-Mail:	*bena@aaworld.com*
Web Site:	*www.aaworld.com*
Description:	*Toll-free:1-800-526-0411. Contractor expert with all types of new embroidery & embellishments.*
Year Est:	*1986*
Exporting Since:	*1990*
Categories:	*Embroidery, Trim Application*
Specialties:	*Loloft embroidery, PVC, hi-resolution transfers, appliques,, novelties & many exciting processes. Any design can be made.*
Markets:	*Menswear, Womenswear, Childrenswear, Accessories.*
Export to:	*Worldwide*
Minimums:	*250-1,000/style per size*
Production Capacity:	*Unlimited*

ACCURATE FLANNEL BAG COMPANY

468 Totowa Avenue
Paterson, New Jersey 07522

(1) (973) 720 1800   Fax: (1) (973) 689 6774

E-Mail:	*service@accuratebags.com*
Web Site:	*www.accuratebags.com*
Description:	*Bags and pouches contractor using all fabrics such as flannel, suede, velvet, canvas, silk, satin, nylon and more.*
Categories:	*Accessories*
Markets:	*Accessories market.*

ARTEX KNITTING MILLS INC.

300 Harvard Avenue
Westville, New Jersey 08093
Jill Ann Bal
(1) (856) 456 2800   Fax: (1) (856) 456 4111

E-Mail:	*sales@artexknit.com*
Web Site:	*www.artexknit.com*
Description:	*Knitting contractor of hats, leg warmers, gloves, men's ties and more.*
Year Est:	*1926*
Categories:	*Sweaters/Knitwear, Embroidery, Accessories*
Specialties:	*Specialize in custom knitted accessories, embroidery and custom color.*
Machinery:	*Knitting, embroidery and sewing machines. Production done in-house.*
Minimums:	*None*
Factory Locals:	*Above*
Production Capacity:	*100,000 doz/month*

AVITEX

461 Frelinghuysen Avenue
Newark, New Jersey 07114
Avi
(1) (973) 242 2410   Fax: (1) (973) 242 7258

E-Mail:	*avi@avitex.com*
Web Site:	*www.celioavitex.com*
Description:	*Knitting contractor catering to outerwear, athletic, sportswear, uniform & military markets.*
Categories:	*Sweaters/Knitwear*
Specialties:	*Full-fashion sweaters in course & fine gauge knit.*
Markets:	*Menswear, Womenswear, Children/Infantwear.*
Packages:	*Full packages available*

BERGEN SCREEN PRINTING

255 West Broadway
Paterson, New Jersey 07522
Uday Patel
(1) (973) 595 1222   Fax: (1) (973) 595 5707

E-Mail:	*uday@bergenscreen.com*
Web Site:	*www.bergenscreen.com*
Description:	*One point source. Cotton, linen, silk, spandex, nylon, polyester roll-to-roll textile printing.*
Categories:	*Digital Textile Printing/Screenprinting*
Specialties:	*Specialize in digital textile printing - short run & commercial production.*
Markets:	*All apparel, accessory & home markets.*
Machinery:	*1 - Kornit Allegro Digital Textile Printer*
	4 - M&R Screen Printers
Production Capacity:	*5,000 yards/monthly*

BONNAZ EMBROIDERY CO.

6000 Adams Street
West New York, New Jersey 07093
Alex Faraj
(1) (201) 552 94 94

E-Mail:	*embroideryusa@msn.com*
Description:	*Embroidery contract work. Also do theatrical custom embroidery.*
Year Est:	*1983*
Categories:	*Embroidery.*
Markets:	*Designer & couture markets.*
Machinery:	*10 Cornely embroidery machines, 2 Tajima multi-head, 10 fancy stitching machines.*
Minimums:	*Sample & small production lot capabilities.*
Production Capacity:	*1,000 pcs/month*

CAROLACE EMBROIDERY CO., INC.

450 Murray Hill Parkway
East Rutherford, New Jersey 07073
Howard Mann
(1) (201) 945 2151   Fax: (1) (201) 943 1990

E-Mail:	*info@carolace.com*
Web Site:	*www.carolace.com*
Description:	*Contract embroiderer.*
Categories:	*Embroidery*
Specialties:	*Custom embroideries, embroidered nets, novelties & Schiffli laces. Cater to all price points.*
Markets:	*Lingerie, blouse & childrens markets.*
Minimums:	*Low*

CHERIE BIXLER   See our ad on page 71

135 Fort Lee Road
Leonia, New Jersey 07605
Cherie Bixler
(1) (201) 944 2886

E-Mail:	*cheriebixler@verizon.net*
Web Site:	*www.cheriebixler.com*
Description:	*Patternmaking and consulting service. We take you from your initial idea through production process. Production done in USA.*
Categories:	*Patternmaking, Samples/Small Production, Production Sourcing*
Specialties:	*Product Development, patterns of all types with flat sketch & fittings. Work with people new to the industry.*
Markets:	*Menswear, Womenswear, Childrenswear.*

CRAVATTA MANUFACTUERS

110 Harmon Drive, Unit 205
Blackwood, New Jersey 08012
Donielle Martorano
(1) (856) 302 1151

E-Mail:	*info@cravattamfg.com*
Web Site:	*www.cravattamfg.com*
Description:	*American based apparel manufacturer offering small to medium*

production runs. Specialize in patternmaking, prototypes/SMS & CMT.
Categories:	*Samples/Small Production. Patternmaking Services*
Specialties:	*Consulting services for fashion designers. Branding, wholesale fabric and trim sourcing worldwide.*
Markets:	*Menswear, Womenswear & Childrenswear.*
Minimums:	*25 pcs per style/size/color*
Factory Locals:	*100% made in the USA.*

CREATIVE EMBROIDERY CORP.

305 Third Avenue
Newark, New Jersey 07107
Steven Diamond
(1) (973) 497 5700   Fax: (1) (973) 497 5520

E-Mail:	*sdiam43091@aol.com*
Description:	*Contract embroidery, appliques & decorative embroidery. Cut pieces or finished garments.*
Categories:	*Embroidery*
Markets:	*All apparel markets & all price points.*
Minimums:	*None*

EAST COAST EMBOSSING

35 Eighth Street
Passaic, New Jersey 07055

(1) (973) 777 9830   Fax: (1) (973) 777 0678

E-Mail:	*info@sunbritedyeco.com*
Description:	*Contractors specializing in ciré finishing & complete embossing.*
Year Est:	*1961*
Specialties:	*Complete urethane coatings, acrylic coatings, ciré & other sophisticated & fashion coating finishes.*
Markets:	*Apparel, home furnishing & industrial markets.*
Machinery:	*New modern equipment to serve the industry.*
Packages:	*All*
Export to:	*Worldwide*
Minimums:	*Vary*
Factory Locals:	*Passaic, Industrial Park*
Production Capacity:	*No limit*

EXACTA

118 John F. Kennedy Drive North
Bloomfield, New Jersey 07003
Jeff Giberstein
(1) (973) 259 0104   Fax: (1) (973) 259 0107

E-Mail:	*contactus@exactagarment.com*
Web Site:	*www.exactagarment.com*
Description:	*Full service apparel & garment cutting contractor. Computerized cutting, grading, marking, fusing, piece goods warehousing and more.*
Year Est:	*1970*
Categories:	*Cutting & Fusing Contractor, Grading & Marking*
Specialties:	*Local production lets you manufacture and ship the latest styles to*

retailers in two weeks or less. Great for in-season re-order business.

Markets: *All apparel markets.*

FAIR TRADE KNITTERS
12 Brooklawn Drive
East Windsor, New Jersey 08520
Meredith Kubicki
(1) (609) 610 4018   Fax: (1) (609) 426 9266

E-Mail:	*sales@fairtradeknitters.com*
Web Site:	*www.fairtradeknitters.com*
Description:	*We can knit anything that's handknitted, from garments to accessories to home decor, costumes, jewelry. Create samples for knitwear designers.*
Categories:	*Knitwear*
Specialties:	*Hand knit; embroidery, intarsia, cables, stitch patterns, lace color changes, fair isle knitting, crochet.*
Markets:	*Menswear, Womenswear, Children, Accessories, Home.*
Export to:	*Canada, Europe, Australia*
Minimums:	*Production knitting on both a small & large scale.*
Production Capacity:	*250/300 adult sweaters/month*

FIDUCCIA CUSTOM SHIRTS
433 Lincoln Street
Carlstadt, New Jersey 07072
Walter Quiroga
(1) (201) 507 0644

E-Mail:	*walter@fiducciacustomshirts.com*
Web Site:	*www.fiducciacustomshirts.com*
Description:	*Custom made dress and sport shirt specialists. Specialize in wovens. Samples available.*
Year Est:	*1968*
Categories:	*Shirts/Tops*
Specialties:	*Small or large lots.*
Markets:	*Menswear & Boyswear.*

HAMILTON EMBROIDERY CO.
907-909 21st Street
Union City, New Jersey 07087
Frank Blaso
(1) (201) 867 4084   Fax: (1) (201) 867 2066

E-Mail:	*fblaso@cs.com*
Description:	*Schiffli embroidery contract work on customer's fabrics or ours.*
Year Est:	*1935*
Categories:	*Embroidery.*
Specialties:	*We can do custom designs & have an extensive library of existing designs.*
Markets:	*All apparel, accessory & home markets.*
Machinery:	*10 Schiffli machines, 10 Saurer, 1 Epoca plus sample machine.*
Export to:	*China 65%, Turkey 5%*
Production Capacity:	*5,000 yds/day*

HOSPI-TEL MANUFACTURING COMPANY

545 North Arlington Avenue
East Orange, New Jersey 07017

(1) (973) 678 7100   Fax: (1) (973) 678 1482

E-Mail:	*info@hospitel.com*
Web Site:	*www.hospitel.com*
Description:	*Manufacturer/contractor of Safe-t-top shower curtains, drapery treatments, bedspreads, window curtains & vertical blinds.*
Categories:	*Home Furnishings.*

LACOA INC

34 Waite Street
Paterson, New Jersey 07524
Hector E Baralt, President
(1) (973) 754 1000   Fax: (1) (973) 754 1015

E-Mail:	*hector@lacoa.com*
Web Site:	*www.lacoa.com*
Description:	*Contract laminating, embossing, coating, waterproofing, & other finishing processes.*
Year Est:	*1948*
Specialties:	*Mylar & holographic laminating & transfer paper laminating.*
Minimums:	*200-300 yards*
Factory Locals:	*30,000 sq. foot factory in Clifton, NJ*

LOGISTICS ON THE WEST

102 Gracey Street
Edison, New Jersey 08817

(1) (732) 418 0800   Fax: (1) (732) 418 0840

E-Mail:	*info@logisticsonthewest.com*
Web Site:	*www.logisticsonthewest.com*
Description:	*Full service logistics solutions provider for your Pacific West Imports.*
Categories:	*Distribution/Warehouse*
Specialties:	*Warehousing, distribution, vendor compliance, drop ship, routing, palletizing, small parcel, interstate trucking, labeling, bar-coding etc.*

M.S.R. CUSTOM MADE SHIRTS

600 Broad Avenue
Ridgefield, New Jersey 07657
Mike/Robert
(1) (201) 941 7970   Fax: (1) (201) 941 7994

E-Mail:	*msrcostumshirt@verizon.net*
Web Site:	*www.msrcustomshirtmakers.com*
Description:	*Samples & patterns for sport, stretch & dress shirts, costumes & shirt-waist dresses. Custom shirts & blouses made to order.*
Year Est:	*1990*
Categories:	*Shirts/Tops, Sample Rooms/Small Productions, Costumes.*
Specialties:	*Expert with cowboy, dress & tuxedo shirt styling. Costume design.*

Custom & copy design capability. Samples from scratch.

Markets:	*Menswear & Womenswear*
Machinery:	*Patternmaking, sewing, cutting & grading all in house.*
	10 Single Needle, 5 Irons, 1 Button Hole, 2 Cutting
Packages:	*Full service contractor, all packages available.*
Minimums:	*Vary*
Factory Locals:	*Manufacturing done in-house.*
Production Capacity:	*1,000 pcs/month*

SCHOTT BROTHERS, INC.

1000 Jefferson Avenue
Elizabeth, New Jersey 07201
Don King
(1) (908) 527 0011   Fax: (1) (908) 527 6185

E-Mail:	*schott@schottnyc.com*
Web Site:	*www.schottnyc.com*
Description:	*Contractor of leather & wool jackets & outerwear.*
Year Est:	*1913*
Exporting Since:	*1970*
Categories:	*Coats/Jackets, Leather/Suede*
Specialties:	*Specialize in flight, bomber & motorcycle jackets.*
Machinery:	*Over 80 single needle, double needle & safety stitch*
	machines. 20 leather cutters in house.
Packages:	*Cutting & Sewing & CMT.*
Export to:	*Europe, Asia & Middle East.*
Minimums:	*200 pieces/style*

SEMEL'S EMBROIDERY, INC.

1078 Route 46 West
Clifton, New Jersey 07013
Dolly Semel
(1) (973) 473 3959   Fax: (1) (973) 473 8895

E-Mail:	*embroideri@aol.com*
Web Site:	*www.semelsembroidery.com*
Year Est:	*1935*
Exporting Since:	*1990*
Categories:	*Embroidery, Screenprinting Contractors.*
Specialties:	*Same day samples & on-demand delivery. Screen*
	applique, chenille embroidery & bonnaz vintage embroidery.
Minimums:	*Low. small & large runs okay. Also, do samples.*

SILK CITY FIBERS

155 Oxford Street
Paterson, New Jersey 07522
Mady Fechner
(1) 800 899 7455   Fax: (1) 888 899 6737

E-Mail:	*scfserv@aol.com*
Web Site:	*www.silkcityfibers.com*
Description:	*Knit projects from design sketch to samples to offshore production,*
	whether for small or large runs.
Categories:	*Contractors Knitwear*

Specialties: Crochet, embroidery, hand knitting also offered.

SNAPCO MANUFACTURING CORPORATION

140 Central Avenue
Hillside, New Jersey 07205
Ray
(1) (973) 282 0300   Fax: (1) (973) 282 7627

E-Mail:	ray.snapco@gmail.com
Web Site:	www.snapco.com
Description:	Applications of stud, snap, eyelet & nailhead contract work.
Year Est:	1946
Categories:	Trim Application
Minimums:	None

STAR EMBROIDERY

305 3rd Avenue West
Newark, New Jersey 07107
Dean Ganet
(1) (973) 481 4300   Fax: (1) (973) 481 1267

E-Mail:	dwiley921@gmail.com
Web Site:	www.star-embroidery.com
Description:	Embroidered promotional apparel, printed custom clothing, custom tee shirts, custom polo shirts, embroidered towels.
Categories:	Embroidery
Specialties:	Embroidered sportswear, outerwear, team wear, bags & accessories.
Markets:	Menswear, Womenswear, Childrenswear & Home.
Minimums:	Low

SUNBRITE DYE COMPANY

35 Eighth Street
Passaic, New Jersey 07055

(1) (973) 777 9830   Fax: (1) (973) 777 0678

E-Mail:	info@sunbritedyeco.com
Description:	Complete dyeing, coating & finishing contractors.
Year Est:	1961
Categories:	Dyeing
Specialties:	Complete urethane coatings, acrylic coatings, ciré & refinishing on widths up to 74"".
Markets:	All apparel, accessory & home markets.
Machinery:	New modern equipment to serve the industry.
Packages:	All
Export to:	Worldwide
Minimums:	Vary
Factory Locals:	Passaic, Industrial Park
Production Capacity:	No limit

TAYLORED SERVICES INC.
231 Mill Road
Edison, New Jersey 08837
Chris Kearns
(1) (732) 248 7900   Fax: (1) (732) 248 7950

E-Mail:	*ckearns@tpservices.com*
Web Site:	*www.tayloredservices.com*
Description:	*Warehousing, distribution & logistics. Reverse logistics pick & pack operation, blister & RF sealing, bar coding, labeling and more.*
Categories:	*Distribution/Warehouse Center*
Specialties:	*Real time visibility of inventory via TSI's custom website, narrow aisle system using wire-guided equipment.*
Factory Locals:	*Facilities in New Jersey, California (909-548-4048).*

TEX PRINT USA, LLC
20-21 Wagaraw Road
Fair Lawn, New Jersey 07410
Ginetta Marino
(1) (201) 773 6531   Fax: (1) (201) 773 6535

E-Mail:	*ginettam@texprintusa.com*
Web Site:	*www.texprintusa.com*
Description:	*Manufacturer of textile products for the apparel & home trade. We are an evironmentally conscious facility. All work is done in the USA.*
Categories:	*Finishing/Coating*
Specialties:	*Heat Transfer, AirDye™, Pigment Printing, Crush, Broomstick, Cire, Foil, Glitter, Deluster, Puff, Bonding, Lamination & more.*

TOUCH OF LACE, INC.
333 Bergen Boulevard
Fairview, New Jersey 07022
Marvin Greenburg/Gabriel Sasson
(1) (201) 943 1082   Fax: (1) (201) 943 7163

E-Mail:	*sales@touchoflace.com*
Web Site:	*www.touchoflace.com*
Description:	*1-800-742-7506. Schiffli embroidery on various fabrics & puckered all-overs.*
Categories:	*Embroiderers*
Specialties:	*Custom designs.*
Markets:	*Children's, intimate apparel, bridal, dress & sportswear.*

UNIQUE SCREEN PRINTING, INC.
10-16 McKinley Street
Linden, New Jersey 07036
Jose Agrajeda
(1) (908) 925 3773   Fax: (1) (908) 925 3087

E-Mail:	*Jose@uniquescreenprinting.com*
Web Site:	*www.uniquescreenprintings.com*
Description:	*Full range fashion screen printer.*
Categories:	*Screenprinting Contractors*
Specialties:	*Printing & dyeing on cut parts as well as whole garments. Specialize in fashion novelties.*

Markets:	*Menswear, Womenswear & Childrenswear.*
Packages:	*Full packages*
Minimums:	*100 dozen*
Factory Locals:	*Linden, N.J. & Puebla, Mexico*

USA BEADING/FARAJ INC.

422 Cliff Street
Fairview, New Jersey 07022
Zackary Faraj, President
(1) (201) 313 4480   Fax: (1) (201) 313 4485

E-Mail:	*farajinc@aol.com*
Web Site:	*www.farajinc.com*
Description:	*Manual & automatic bonnaz embroidery, embellishment, trims & beading (www.usabeading.com).*
Categories:	*Embroiderers*
Specialties:	*Specialize in bonnaz embroidery, laser cutting, caviar beads, glitter, rhinestones, trims & beading.*

WEBER & DOEBRICH

119 61st Street
West New York, New Jersey 07093
Jane Zellweger
(1) (201) 867 1540   Fax: (1) (201) 854 5564

E-Mail:	*wedoembroidery@gmail.com*
Description:	*Schiffli & multi-head embroideries.*
Categories:	*Embroiderers*
Markets:	*Lingerie, Seventh Avenue & home furnishing trades.*
Minimums:	*None*

WINGOLD EMBROIDERY LLC

5 Monarch Lane
Freehold, New Jersey 07728
Thomas Figliolino
(1) (201) 945 2727

E-Mail:	*tfigliolino@aol.com*
Web Site:	*www.wingoldembroidery.com*
Description:	*Schiffli embroidery.*
Categories:	*Embroiderers*
Specialties:	*Domestic & overseas production from China.*
Markets:	*Apparel, lingerie, intimate apparel & home furnishings.*
Minimums:	*Varies*

New York

A PROMOS USA DBA THE IMAGEMAKER & AARROW PROMOTIONS

143 East Merrick Road
Freeport, New York 11520
Mindy Younger
(1) (516) 377 0186   Fax: (1) (516) 377 0198

E-Mail:	*sales@imagemakerus.com*
Web Site:	*www.apromosusa.com*

Description:	Screenprinted custom t-shirts, embroidery and promotional items. All work done in-house.
Year Est:	1990
Categories:	Screenprinting, Embroidery
Specialties:	Embroidery on polo shirts, golf shirts, t-shirts, sweaters, hats/caps. Oversized printing, specialty inks, 3D embroidery.
Markets:	Menswear, Womenswear, Childrenswear.
Machinery:	Automated presses
Production Capacity:	T-shirts: 15,000/day

A+ LAUNDRY

224 Lawrence Avenue
Lawrence, New York 11559
Tommy Gregoretti
(1) (516) 371 2100   Fax: (1) (516) 371 5649

E-Mail:	linens@aol.com
Description:	Commercial garment laundering, bleaching, pressing.
Year Est:	1976
Categories:	Laundering/Washing
Markets:	Menswear, Womenswear, Childrenswear
Machinery:	6 industrial washers capable of producing 3600 garments per hour as well as the necessary finishing equipment.
Factory Locals:	We are just 5 minutes south of Kennedy Airport
Production Capacity:	200,000 sets/month, 20,000 garments per day.

ABSOLUTELY! DESIGN SERVICE

210 West 80th Street
New York, New York 10024
Nora Littman
(1) (212) 769 0548

E-Mail:	nlittman@mindspring.com
Web Site:	www.batlledesign.com
Description:	Full packages with graded specs and samples
Categories:	Sample Rooms/Small Production
Specialties:	Specialize in sewing of all types. We make samples vs production unless small quantities.

ALL U, INC.

9 Interstate Avenue
Albany, New York 12205
Tina Benson
(1) (518) 438 2558   Fax: (1) (518) 438 7282

E-Mail:	sales@allu.com
Web Site:	www.allu.com
Description:	Quality custom screenprinting and embroidery.
Year Est:	1986
Categories:	Screenprinting, Embroidery
Specialties:	Our in-house digitizing allows us to reproduce even the most demanding designs quickly and accurately.
Machinery:	8 color and two 12 color automatic presses, and 6 color and 2 color manual presses for screenprinting.

ALLIED TRANSPORT SYSTEM

One Cross Island Plaza
Rosedale, New York 11422

(1) (718) 977 9448   Fax: (1) (718) 276 7780

E-Mail:	*teresa@atsnyc.com*
Web Site:	*www.atsnyc.com*
Description:	*All service freight forwarder. All types of ocean and air cargo from the Far East to the USA.*
Specialties:	*US Custom Clearance, Warehousing and Delivery.*

AMERICAN ICON SCREEN PRINTING

392 N. Montgomery Street
Newburgh, New York 12550
Katrina Pulichene
(1) (845) 561 1299   Fax: (1) (845) 913 9067

E-Mail:	*katrina@americaniconmerch.com*
Web Site:	*www.americaniconshirts.com*
Description:	*Screenprinting, discharge printing, process printing, over-zipper printing, tag - less printing/neck labels.*
Year Est:	*2005*
Categories:	*Screen Printing*
Specialties:	*Full service apparel screen printing on all types of tees, sweatshirts, pullover hoods, crewneck sweatshirts, totes bags, caps etc.*
Markets:	*Menswear, Womenswear, Childrens, Accessories.*
Minimums:	*Low but vary depending on process*
Production Capacity:	*50,000 prints/monthly*

APPAREL PRINTING DIV OF KENMAR SHIRTS

1578 White Plains Road
Bronx, New York 10462
Karen Greene
(1) (718) 824 3880   Fax: (1) (718) 823 4233

E-Mail:	*kareng@apparelprinting.com*
Web Site:	*www.apparelprinting.com*
Description:	*Screen printing contractor. Multi-color, high density, glitter, 4CP lites/darks, puff, gel, suede, metallic, crystalline & soft hand printing.*
Year Est:	*1950*
Categories:	*Screenprinting Contractors*
Specialties:	*Can also provide label change, tagging, automatic folding and hanging, drop shipping. Phthalate free inks.*
Markets:	*All markets.*
Machinery:	*2 M&R Challenger 14 color, 1 Precision oval 8 color, 2 Challenger, 1 Folding, 1 Sealing, 1 Oval.*
Minimums:	*12 dozen*
Production Capacity:	*150,000 units/month*

APPAREL PRODUCTION INC.

270 West 39th
New York, New York 10018
Teddy Sadaka
(1) (212) 278 8362   Fax: (1) (212) 278 8357

E-Mail:	*teddyapparelprod@aol.com*
Web Site:	*www.apparelproductionny.com*
Description:	*Manufacture any type of top or bottom from pattern to production.*
Year Est:	*1993*
Categories:	*Pants/shorts/skirts, Tops/shirts/blouses*
Markets:	*Menswear, Womenswear, Boyswear, Girlswear.*
Packages:	*Full service, CMT & Complete.*
Factory Locals:	*Hangzhou China, most patterns however are made in our pattern facility in New York City.*

APPAREL SOLUTIONS CORP.

249 West 34th Street
New York, New York 10001
John Harihar
(1) (212) 868 1700   Fax: (1) (212) 868 1701

E-Mail:	*john@usapparelsolutions.com*
Web Site:	*www.usapparelsolutions.com*
Description:	*Pleating, special stitching, cutting & finishing, embroidery, digitizing & trimming contractor.*
Year Est:	*1975*
Categories:	*Pleating/Tucking/Stitching, Cutting & Fusing, Finishing/Coating.*
Specialties:	*Experts in table & machine pleating & cutting.*

ARI SHIPPING CORP.

80 Sheridan Boulevard
Inwood, New York 10096
Ilan Fidler
(1) (516) 371 7770   Fax: (1) (516) 371 7757

E-Mail:	*ilan@arishipping.com*
Web Site:	*www.arishipping.com*
Description:	*Full service logistics company, air & ocean import/export consolidated services, customs clearance & compliance service.*
Year Est:	*1980*
Categories:	*Distribution/Warehouse Center, Freight Forwarder/Customs Broker*
Specialties:	*Bonded CFS, warehouse & distribution, crating & packing, complete supply-chain management.*

AVALON COUTURE & TEXTILE, LTD.

35 Magerus Street
South Huntington, New York 11746
Cynthia Clark
(1) 877 832 2227

E-Mail:	*service@avaloncouture.com*
Web Site:	*www.avaloncouture.com*
Description:	*Artistry in fine garment and interior textile care.*

> *Categories:* Rework/Inspection Services
> *Specialties:* Fine drycleaning, wetcleaning, resolution of problems/mishaps
> during design/production/shipping/storage.

B.M.A.C.
248 West 35th Street
New York, New York 10001
Mark Krieger
(1) (212) 736 5380   Fax: (1) (212) 629 3943

E-Mail:	bmacservice@aol.com
Web Site:	www.bmacnewyork.com
Description:	Computerized grading & marking service.
Categories:	Grading & Marking
Specialties:	Specialize in specs engineering, pattern scanning, pattern grading, marking, paper cutting, printing and pattern conversion.
Markets:	All markets.
Machinery:	Pattern scanners, Gerber plotters, Pattern cutters
Production Capacity:	100 styles per week

BIANCA GROUP LTD
244 West 39th Street
New York, New York 10018
Richard Garcia
(1) (212) 768 3011   Fax: (1) (212) 768 1657

E-Mail:	biancainc@aol.com
Description:	Computerized capabilities. Gerber system, pattern grading & marking for the men's, women's, children's, spec & inf. sheet.
Categories:	Grading/Marking.
Specialties:	24 hour turn-around. Instant overseas delivery available by modem.
Markets:	All markets.

BLANKET BOSS
87 Windermere Avenue
Greenwood Lake, New York 10925
Barney Lopilato
(1) (845) 477 4774

E-Mail:	blanketboss@aol.com
Web Site:	www.theblanketboss.com
Description:	Specialize in making patterns & samples of knit sweaters & cards for production knitting machines. Also embroidery & silk screening.
Categories:	Sample Rooms/Small Production, Sweaters/Knitwear, Embroidery
Specialties:	Personalized photo blankets & pillows and unique scarves. Sublimation - print high quality photos on apparel & shoulder bags.
Markets:	Mens, womens & childrens sweater makers.
Machinery:	Knitting machines: Stoll 7 gg, Stoll 10 gg, Shima 7 gg, Shima 10 gg.
Production Capacity:	1,000 units/month

BRIARCLIFF APPAREL TECHNOLOGIES LTD.

246 West 38th Street
New York, New York 10018
Edward Kostyra, President
(1) (212) 840 7666   Fax: (1) (212) 840 7168

E-Mail:	*fashionprofessor@hotmail.com*
Description:	*Over 30 years experience in apparel development &*
	production. Small & large production lots okay.
Year Est:	*1994*
Categories:	*Active/Athleticwear, Knit Sportswear, Woven Sportswear,*
	Outerwear, Tee Shirts, Dresses/Suits, Robes/Sleepwear.
Specialties:	*Full package sewing contractor of all styles of cut*
	& sew knits & wovens.
Markets:	*Menswear, Womenswear, Childrens & Infantwear.*
Packages:	*Full, CMT, Samples, Patterns & all production services.*
Minimums:	*Flexible*
Factory Locals:	*New York, NY & throughout tri-state area.*
Production Capacity:	*No limit*

CAROL PETERS INC. (CPI)

75 Livingston Street
Brooklyn, New York 11201
Carol Louie
(1) (347) 256 7804

E-Mail:	*carolcpi512@aol.com*
Description:	*Production Sourcing company for women's & children's active wear,*
	outerwear, sleepwear and intimate apparel.
Categories:	*Production Sourcing*
Markets:	*Womenswear, Childrenswear*
Factory Locals:	*Production in China and Bangladesh.*

CHINAMINE USA

214 West 39th Street
New York, New York 10018
Aimee Van Brunt
(1) (212) 575 1525   Fax: (1) (212) 575 0003

E-Mail:	*info@chinamineusa.com*
Web Site:	*www.chinamineusa.com*
Description:	*Chinese vertical manufacturer with product development expertise.*
	A key supplier to the contemporary & better specialty retailers.
Year Est:	*1989*
Categories:	*Production Sourcing/Factory Agents, Patternmaking Services*
Specialties:	*Design library, embellishment hangers & garments for inspiration.*
	We work with design, sourcing & product development teams.
Markets:	*Womenswear, Menswear, Juniors*
Export to:	*Europe 20%, USA 70%, 10% remains in China*
Factory Locals:	*Five sewing factories and a print, dye & wash facility.*
Production Capacity:	*400,000 - 600,000 pieces/monthly depending on garment type.*

CO2 TEXTILES

88 Greenwich Street
New York, New York 07075
Melody Levy
(1) (212) 269 2222   Fax: (1) (212) 269 2203

E-Mail:	*melodylevy@co2textiles.com*
Description:	*Textile lamination and fabric finishing.*
Categories:	*Finishing/Coating Contractors*
Specialties:	*Laminating, coating, waterproofing, sponging & more.*
	All domestically produced. R&D on site.
Markets:	*Menswear, Womenswear.*

COLORWORKS INC.

161 Canal Street
Ellenville, New York 12428
Russ Damsky
(1) (845) 647 0300

E-Mail:	*dyestudio@colorworksalley.com*
Web Site:	*www.colorworksalley.com*
Description:	*Sample dyeing, piece dyeing, garment dyeing - single &*
	multiple fabric garments.
Year Est:	*1987*
Categories:	*Dyeing Contractor*
Minimums:	*None*

CREATE-A-MARKER, INC.

254 West 35th Street
New York, New York 10001
Sadat Mamirova
(1) (212) 730 5615   Fax: (1) (212) 730 5616

E-Mail:	*cad@createamarkernyc.com*
Web Site:	*www.createamarkernyc.com*
Description:	*Digitizing, grading, marker making, emailing patterns, plotting paterns,*
	cutting patterns on oak tag, scanning patterns & copying markers.
Year Est:	*1993*
Exporting Since:	*1999*
Categories:	*Grading/Marking, Patternmaking Services*
Specialties:	*Cutting edge digital cutting system for samples & patterns.*
	Optimum fabric utilization & cost effectiveness.
Markets:	*Womens, Mens, Kids, Bride/Evening, Swimwear, Intimate, Leather/Fur*
Machinery:	*State-of-the-art equipment. 7 plotters, 2 digertizers, 2 scanners,*
	5 graders, 8 marker makers, 1 computer cutter,
	1 photo copier machines (amonia type).
Export to:	*China, Italy, Vietnam, Canada, Japan, Turkey,*
	Taiwan, India, Pakistan, Sri Lanka, Guatemala, SDomingo
Minimums:	*None*
Production Capacity:	*160 patterns/month*

CREATIVE BUSINESS HOUSE
45 West 46th Street
New York, New York 10036
Amandine Berg
(1) (646) 543 1831

E-Mail:	*info@creativebusinesshouse.com*
Web Site:	*www.creativebusinesshouse.com*
Description:	*One stop shop for fashion designers.*
	Let us develop and launch your own private label. CBH does it all!
Categories:	*Production Sourcing/Factory Agent*
Specialties:	*Outsource fabrics & trim, create patterns, samples, tech packs, EIN,*
	branding, trademark, patents, packaging, labels, website, logo.
Markets:	*Menswear, Womenswear, Children, Accessories, Home.*

CROOKED BROOK
901 Broad Street
Utica, New York 13501
Ray
(1) (315) 733 1992   Fax: (1) (315) 292 1901

E-Mail:	*info@crookedbrook.com*
Web Site:	*www.crookedbrook.com*
Description:	*Apparel & design & reproduction studio offering knit & woven pattern*
	making from spec sheets or renderings, samples.
Categories:	*Sample Rooms/Small Production, Embroidery*
Specialties:	*Small lot production for men's, women's & children's sportswear.*
	Custom embroidery, applique and tackle twill.
Machinery:	*Juki Straight Stitch, Juki Serge, Reece Key Hole, Singer Straight*
	Button Hole, Kansai Coverstitch, Juki Feed Off the Arm,
	Melco EMT 10 Em broidery Machine
Minimums:	*None*

CUSTOM-SEWING-SERVICES
117 11th Street
Brooklyn, New York 11215
Edwin
(1) (516) 499 7304

E-Mail:	*customsewingservices@yahoo.com*
Description:	*Single garments and bridal for men, women and children.*
Categories:	*Samples/Small Production*
Specialties:	*Samples, patternmaker and small production.*
Factory Locals:	*Alternate tel number: 718-314-2041*

CYCLE FASHION PATTERN INC.
306 West 37th Street, 2nd Floor
New York, New York 10018

(1) (212) 216 9668

Web Site:	*www.cyclefashionpattern.com*
Description:	*We are a sample room dedicated to making patterns & samples using*
	draping. We provide small lot production service to meet your needs.
Categories:	*Patternmaking Services, Sample Room/Small Production*

Specialties: We specialize in jackets, pants, jeans, dresses, skirts & eveningwear.
Markets: Womenswear

DALMA DRESS MFG CO INC

251 West 39th Street
New York, New York 10018
Michael Dipalma
(1) (212) 391 8296

Description: Cut and sew contractor of women's dresses & evening wear.
Categories: Dresses/Blouses, Bridal/Eveningwear, Sample Room/Small Production
Markets: Womenswear

DAVE PRESSLEY DESIGN

456 Greenwich Street
New York, New York 10013
David T. Pressley
(1) 917 771 9557

E-Mail: jewelman65@gmail.com
Web Site: www.djphandmade.com
Description: Hardware model maker (proto-type), also does custom work & assists
in design development for handbag hardware, belt buckles & jewelry.
Categories: Accessories
Specialties: Specialize in mechanical handbag locks. Production consultant.
Markets: Menswear, Womenswear, Children, Accessories, Home.
Packages: CMT
Minimums: Small runs for sales samples.

DYE FX

544 Park Avenue
Brooklyn, New York 11205
Carol Perri
(1) 718 596 4611   Fax: (1) 718 596 5646

E-Mail: carolperri@verizon.net
Description: Silk screen printing contractor on cut pieces or finished garments.
Year Est: 2005
Categories: Screenprinting
Specialties: Silk screen printing, flocking, foil, beads, sequins, tie dye, dip dye,
heat transfer application, nail head & rhinestone application.
Markets: Menswear, Womenswear, Children, Accessories, Home.
Machinery: Printing, heat transfer, folding and more.
Minimums: None
Production Capacity: Machine & tie dye: 222,500 doz/month

DYENAMIX INC.

151 Grand Street
New York, New York 10013
Raylene Marasco, President
(1) (212) 941 6642   Fax: (1) (212) 941 7407

E-Mail: info@dyenamix.com
Web Site: www.dyenamix.com
Description: Custom print development, original design collection, silkscreen &

digital printing of sample & production yardage.

Year Est:	*1991*
Categories:	*Dyeing Contractors*
Specialties:	*Solid & specialty dyeing.*
Markets:	*Womenswear, Menswear, Accessories, Home.*
Minimums:	*None*
Production Capacity:	*Up to 350 yards/dye lots & 500 yds for printing.*

EAGLE DYERS

357 Flushing Avenue
Brooklyn, New York 11205
Lucretia/Shelley
(1) 212 947 2712   Fax: (1) 718 338 0848

E-Mail:	*vjsavta@aol.com*
Description:	*All types of dyeing for lace, trims & fabrics.*
Categories:	*Dyeing Contractors.*
Markets:	*All markets & all price points.*
Packages:	*Can do samples & large quantity runs.*
Minimums:	*$75.00 for dye charge.*

EATONTEX RESOURCES LTD.

11 Penn Plaza
New York, New York 10001
Steven Hershkowitz
(1) 212 221 1473   Fax: (1) 646 688 5299

E-Mail:	*sales@eatontexresources.com*
Web Site:	*www.eatontexresources.com*
Description:	*Location plus our strategic alliance with mills & factories worldwide make us your one-stop resource for your fabric, garment & trim needs.*
Year Est:	*2006*
Categories:	*Production Sourcing/Factory Agent*
Specialties:	*Work with well-known small manufacturers. Consulting on import procedures, customs regulations, and letter of credit matters.*
Markets:	*Menswear, Womenswear, Infant/Childrenswear.*
Minimums:	*Low*
Factory Locals:	*China, Metro New York Area*
Production Capacity:	*2500 pcs/monthly*

FABRICLEAN

1139 50th Avenue
Long Island City, New York 11101
Walter Pepper
(1) (888) 692 2532

E-Mail:	*info@nycclean.com*
Web Site:	*www.nycclean.com*
Year Est:	*1988*
Categories:	*Laundry/Washing/Dry Cleaning Contractors*
Specialties:	*Highly specialized dry cleaning, laundry, commercial washing & pressing service.*
Markets:	*All apparel & textile markets.*
Machinery:	*Large variety & assorted sizes of dry cleaning & laundering*

Production Capacity:	*equipment.*
	1,500 pounds/hour

FACTORY 212, THE

306 West 38th Street
New York, New York 10018
Angela Kim
(1) (212) 944 6900   Fax: (1) (212) 944 6909

E-Mail:	angela@thefactory212.com
Web Site:	www.thefactory212.com
Description:	We make samples for runway & showroom, duplicates, small production lots with no minimums. All work done in-house.
Year Est:	2010
Categories:	Sample Rooms/Small Production, Patternmaking Services
Specialties:	We can make anything from tee shirts to jeans to dresses & jackets. Patternmaking, design assistance & consulting.
Markets:	Menswear & Womenswear.
Machinery:	Straight stitch, double needle, merrow, coverstitch, bartack.
Packages:	Complete Packages
Minimums:	None

FINE PRODUCTS/FP SERVICES INC.

90 North Main Street
Florida, New York 10921
Jay Feinberg
(1) (845) 651 4020   Fax: (1) (845) 651 4182

E-Mail:	jay@fineproducts.net
Web Site:	www.fpservicesapparel.com
Description:	From tees to jackets to uniforms and more, we are the source for everything custom. Private Label programs available.
Categories:	Screenprinting, Tee-shirts, Uniforms
Specialties:	Made in USA apparel; poly/spandex blanks/all over sublimation poly/blend apparel.
Markets:	Menswear, Womenswear, Childrenswear.
Packages:	Cut & Sew, design, Ecommerce, production packages.
Production Capacity:	60,000-80,000 units/month

FORMART CORPORATION

312 Fifth Avenue
New York, New York 10001
Sheung Mei Liu
(1) (212) 819 1819   Fax: (1) (212) 921 1992

E-Mail:	bellini_formart@hotmail.com
Web Site:	www.formartcorp.com
Description:	Beading, stone setting contractor for jewelry, accessories and garments.
Year Est:	1988
Categories:	Trim Application
Specialties:	Hot-Fix crystal stones onto all kinds of fabric, leather, garments and accessories.
Minimums:	None

Production Capacity: 5,000 sets/month

GARMENT INDUSTRY DEVELOPMENT CORP/GIDC

262 West 38th Street
New York, New York 10018

(1) (212) 842 9343   Fax: (1) (212) 842 9344

E-Mail:	*award@gidc.org*
Web Site:	*www.gidc.org*
Description:	*Your first stop in finding domestic New York contractors.*
Year Est:	*1984*
Categories:	*Non-profit Association/Production Sourcing Consultants*
Specialties:	*Dedicated to strengthening New Yorks garment industry, finding fashion jobs, research, business development services & training.*
Markets:	*All*

GLOBE-TEX

56 Harrison Street
New Rochelle, New York 10801
Robert Hurvitz
(1) (914) 560 8422   Fax: (1) (914) 355 4141

E-Mail:	*robert@globe-tex.com*
Web Site:	*www.globe-tex.com*
Description:	*Source, design & arrange full programs for the U.S., Japan, Australia & Canadian companies.*
Year Est:	*1996*
Exporting Since:	*1996*
Categories:	*All sports categories*
Specialties:	*Specialize in technical performance, team sports and fan wear. Also, finance, shipping & quality control services.*
Markets:	*Womenswear, Menswear, Childrenswear.*
Packages:	*Full packages.*
Export to:	*China, Vietnam, Cambodia, Dominican Republic, Peru, Pakistan, India, Taiwan & Indonesia.*
Minimums:	*1,000 dozen/style*
Factory Locals:	*Sourcing offices in Shanghai/China, Taipei/Taiwan, Jakarta/Indonesia, Lima/Peru, Dominican Republic.*
Production Capacity:	*1 million units/month*

HEATHER MENZIES PATTERN DESIGN

Bournedale Road
Manhasset, New York 11030
Heather Menzies
(1) (516) 375 3807

E-Mail:	*heather@nypatternmaker.com*
Web Site:	*www.nypatternmaker.com*
Description:	*First through production patterns for women's & children's market. Specialize in bridge dresses, designer & moderate sportswear & bridal.*
Year Est:	*2008*
Categories:	*Patternmaking Services*

Specialties: *Fittings via SKYPE, mock-ups, technical sketches and consulting.*

HELMSMAN QUALITY & TECHNOLOGY SERVICES LTD.
801 West End Avenue
New York, New York 10025
Jeff Singleton
(1) (212) 757 2400

E-Mail:	*jeff.singleton@hqts.com*
Web Site:	*www.hqts.com*
Description:	*Production inspection, factory audits, testing & quality control services for companies doing business in Asia.*
Categories:	*Rework and Inspection Services*
Markets:	*All markets.*

IN STYLE USA, INC.
307 West 36th Street
New York, New York 10018
James Mallon
(1) (212) 631 0278   Fax: (1) (212) 631 0279

E-Mail:	*instyleusa@instyleusa.net*
Description:	*Contractor & private label manufacturer.*
Categories:	*Dresses/Blouses, Patternmaking, Suits/Tailored Gaments, Sample Room/Small Production*
Specialties:	*Patternmaking, sample rooms, small production. Expert with women's dresses, shirts, suits & sportswear. On-time delivery.*
Markets:	*Womenswear*
Machinery:	*Over 100 new machines.*
Packages:	*All*
Minimums:	*None*
Factory Locals:	*New York City.*
Production Capacity:	*12,000 to 20,000 pcs/month*

J.L.S.C./SYDNEY BUSH
728 East 136th Street
Bronx, New York 10454
Michael
(1) (718) 742 9629   Fax: (1) (718) 742 1379

E-Mail:	*michaelraske@msn.com*
Description:	*Contractor of underpinnings & petticoats for wedding & formal dresses.*
Categories:	*Lingerie/Intimate Apparel*
Specialties:	*Domestic*
Markets:	*Womenswear, Girlswear.*
Packages:	*Complete & CMT.*
Minimums:	*None*

JJ PATTERN INC.

580 8th Avenue
New York, New York 10018

(1) (212) 391 8089   Fax: (1) (212) 391 2030

E-Mail:	*myjjpatternnyc@gmail.com*
Web Site:	*www.jjpatternnyc.com*
Description:	*One stop service from patternmaking & sample development to production including grading and marking.*
Categories:	*Patternmaking Services*

JULIE HUTTON, INC.

140 East 28th Street
New York, New York 10016
Julie Hutton
(1) (212) 532 5126   Fax: (1) (212) 532 0109

E-Mail:	*julie@juliehuttoninc.com*
Web Site:	*www.juliehuttoninc.com*
Description:	*Private label & personal label sourcing & manufacturing. Offers clients a wide range of services. Your garments from concept to delivery.*
Categories:	*Production sourcing/factory agent*
Specialties:	*Specialize in cut & sew knits, wovens, sportswear. Design expertise, fabric sourcing, color direction, initial specs, first thru final fits, samples.*
Markets:	*Womenswear & Menswear.*
Minimums:	*Low*
Factory Locals:	*China, USA, Turkey*
Production Capacity:	*10,000 pcs.*

JUN'S PATTERN

254 West 35th Street
New York, New York 10001
Jenny Kwon
(1) (212) 221 6130   Fax: (1) (212) 575 0656

E-Mail:	*jennykwon64@gmail.com*
Description:	*Patterns for samples & duplicates.*
Year Est:	*1994*
Categories:	*Patternmaking.*
Specialties:	*Expertise with knit & woven styles. Small production.*
Markets:	*Menswear, Womenswear, Childrenswear.*
Minimums:	*None*

KATRINA PATTERNS

555 Eighth Avenue
New York, New York 10018
Valentina
(1) (212) 563 7332   Fax: (1) (212) 563 7394

Web Site:	*www.katrinapatterns.com*
Description:	*Patterns, samples & duplicates. Fast delivery & turn-around.*
Categories:	*Patternmaking, Sample Room/Small Production.*
Specialties:	*Specialize in women's woven sportswear.*

Markets:	*Womenswear*
Machinery:	*6 sewing, 3 merrow, 3 irons, hindstitch & cutting machine.*
Minimums:	*None*
Production Capacity:	*20 units/week (jackets, dresses), 30 units/week (pants, blouses)*

L.I. CUTTING

2523 Merrick Road
Bellmore, New York 11710
Peter Romeo
(1) (516) 826 6138   Fax: (1) (516) 826 6148

E-Mail:	*info@licutting.com*
Web Site:	*www.licutting.com*
Description:	*Private label contractor of all types of sportswear knits, swimwear, uniforms and more. Pattern through production.*
Categories:	*Sample Rooms/Small Production, Uniforms, Sportswear/Knits, Swimwear*
Specialties:	*All work done in-house. Screenprinting & sublimation on site.*
Markets:	*Womens & childrens markets.*
Packages:	*CMT, Patternmaking, Samplemaking & Grading.*
Minimums:	*None*

LAMCOM, INC.

224 West 35th Street
New York, New York 10001
Kit Wong
(1) (212) 868 6910   Fax: (1) (212) 868 4050

E-Mail:	*lamcom1@aol.com*
Web Site:	*www.lamcominc.com*
Description:	*Contractor & reliable manufacturing supplier of all types of buttons, zippers, drawcords, patches, snaps & more.*
Categories:	*Trim Application*
Specialties:	*All products meet ASTM standards. Customer designs welcome.*
Minimums:	*Sample, small & large size lots workable.*
Factory Locals:	*Factories in China & Taiwan for worldwide distribution.*

LANDZEG INC.

8025 Grenfell Street
Kew Gardens, New York 11415
Jonathan Lee
(1) (212) 575 0746   Fax: (1) (212) 575 0746

E-Mail:	*landzeg@gmail.com*
Description:	*Pattern grading & marking.*
Year Est:	*1941*
Categories:	*Grading/Marking*
Markets:	*Womenswear*

LLU INC.

108-28 46th Avenue
Corona, New York 11368
James
(1) (718) 271 3228   Fax: (1) (718) 271 3228

E-Mail:	*lluinc@hotmail.com*
Description:	*Cut and sew contractor of womens underwear, lingerie and bras.*
Year Est:	*1997*
Categories:	*Lingerie/Intimate Apparel*
Specialties:	*All work is done in-house.*
Markets:	*Womenswear*
Machinery:	*Sewing machines, needle sewing, horizontal sewing*

M. FRANABAR INC. CORRECTIONS & REWORKS

One 43rd Street
Brooklyn, New York 11232
Harvey
(1) (718) 499 5190   Fax: (1) (718) 499 5830

E-Mail:	*info@mfranabar.com*
Web Site:	*www.mfranabar.com*
Description:	*Correction & rework services on apparel, gifts, accessories & novelties. QC inspection, problem solving. Assembling. Drop ship.*
Specialties:	*Label installation/removal, ticketing, bar coding, re-assorting, re-packing, re-sizing, most corrections, dry cleaning, packaging.*
Markets:	*Apparel, Gifts & Accessories*
Minimums:	*3,000 pcs.*
Production Capacity:	*500,000 pcs/month*

MANUFACTURING IN CHINA

305 West 28th Street
New York, New York 10001
Anya Feinberg
(1) (212) 255 5597   Fax: (1) (212) 255 5597

E-Mail:	*manufacturinginchina@rcn.com*
Web Site:	*www.imexchinaltd.com*
Description:	*Production sourcing for home furnishings, accessories & jewelry.*
Year Est:	*1973*
Categories:	*Production Sourcing/Factory Agent*
Specialties:	*Trading partner - we can manufacture your product in China.*
Factory Locals:	*China*

MANZELLA PRODUCTIONS

80 Sonwil Drive
Buffalo, New York 14225

(1) (716) 681 8880   Fax: (1) (716) 681 6888

E-Mail:	*info@manzella.com*
Web Site:	*www.manzella.com*
Description:	*Glove designer, manufacturing, contracting & production sourcing.*
Categories:	*Accessories, Production Sourcing/Factory Agent.*

Packages: CMT & complete packages available.

MARK D.A., INC.
247 West 37th Street
New York, New York 10018

(1) 212 868 3081   Fax: (1) 866 475 0743

E-Mail: pbartual@msn.com
Description: Expert grading & marking service.
Categories: Grading/Marking
Markets: All
Minimums: None
Production Capacity: Minimum capacity: 100 styles per week.

MERIDIAN SHIPPING CO. INC.
147-20 181st Street
Jamaica, New York 11413
Kenneth Blum
(1) (718) 995 3598   Fax: (1) (718) 244 0874

E-Mail: mershico@cs.com
Description: A.B.I. certified customhouse broker, international freight forwarder & import/export.
Year Est: 1975
Exporting Since: 1975
Categories: Freight Forwarders/Customs Broker
Specialties: Offices throughout the world.

METRO DYEING SERVICES, LTD
306 West 38th Street
New York, New York 10018
John
(1) 212 391 1001   Fax: (1) 646 219 7119

E-Mail: cs@nyfashioncenter.com
Web Site: www.metrodyeing.com
Description: Premiere sample dyers for all fabrics, fibers & apparel.
Categories: Dyeing contractor.
Specialties: Specialize in matching components for intimate apparel & sportswear. 24 hour service.
Markets: All markets.
Minimums: None

METRO TRIMMING CORP.
327 West 36th Street
New York, New York 10018

(1) (212) 564 7966   Fax: (1) (212) 564 6262

E-Mail: metrotrimming@gmail.com
Web Site: www.metrotrimmingcorp.com
Description: On prem manufacturer of dress trimmings & bias binding products.
Year Est: 1955
Categories: Contractor Trim Application

Specialties: Spaghetti straps, braiding, bias in all sizes, belt loops, frogs, ruffles,
cordedge, baby hemming, fabric flowers, straight & cross cutting.
Markets: All womens markets.
Factory Locals: New York, NY

MICHAEL CALDERONE, INC.
265 West 37th Street
New York, New York 10018
Michael
(1) (212) 465 1093   Fax: (1) (212) 868 0628
E-Mail: mcpatterns@aol.com
Description: Expert patternmaking, grading & marking service.
Categories: Grading/Marking, Patternmaking, Sample Room/Small Production
Specialties: Specialize in plaids, stripes & cemetric type of prints.
Markets: All.

MOKITA
118 East 60th Street
New York, New York 10022
Stanley Kitman
(1) (917) 664 4864
E-Mail: info@mokitaglobal.com
Web Site: www.mokitaglobal.com
Description: Product development, sourcing, negotiating best pricing, production
control, quality assurance & delivery date assurance.
Categories: Production Sourcing/Factory Agent
Specialties: Eco-friendly sourcing. We connect companies to manufacturing
sources in China and India at the best possible prices.

NEO-CONCEPT (NY) CORPORATION
242 West 38th Street
New York, New York 10018

(1) (212) 242 6808   Fax: (1) (212) 242 4418
E-Mail: glenda@neo-concept.com
Web Site: www.neo-concept.com
Description: Sweaters, cut and sew, wovens, and mixed-media.
Year Est: 1989
Specialties: Yarn and fabric innovation as we weave our own yarns and weave most
of our own cut & sew fabrics.
Packages: Vertical Operation
Factory Locals: Dounguan, Zhongshan, and the Shanghai regions of China.
Also Eco-Friendly factory in Zhingshan, China.

NETWORK BROKERS INTERNATIONAL
100 N. Centre Avenue
Rockville Centre, New York 11570
Judy Kearney
(1) (516) 825 6623   Fax: (1) (516) 825 3942
E-Mail: info@networkbrokers.com
Web Site: www.networkbrokers.com

Description: *Custom house brokers.*
Year Est: *1981*
Specialties: *Export forwarding, domestic distribution and warehousing.*

NEW CONCEPTS OF NEW YORK LLC

313 West 37th Street
New York, New York 10018
Mel Weiss
(1) (212) 695 4999   Fax: (1) (212) 695 4513

E-Mail: *sales@newconceptsllc.com*
Web Site: *www.newconceptsllc.com*
Description: *Nailhead & rhinestone design work on belts, hats &*
any type of apparel. Also, belt & hat band contractor.
Categories: *Accessories, Trim Application*
Minimums: *None*

NEW YORK BINDING COMPANY

43-01 22nd Street
Long Island City, New York 11101

(1) 718 729 2454
Description: *All kinds of pleating, elastic, ruffles, tucking & samples orders.*
Categories: *Pleating/Tucking*
Markets: *Womenswear, Childrenswear, Costumes & Home Furnishings.*
Minimums: *None*

NOVELTY POM POM COMPANY

247 West 37th Street
New York, New York 10018
John Jones
(1) (212) 391 9175   Fax: (1) (212) 575 9688
Description: *Contractor of macrame & corded belts, tassels, pom poms*
fringes, frogs, braiding & accessories. Domestic.
Categories: *Accessories*
Markets: *Womenswear, Childrenswear. All price points.*
Machinery: *Braiding & knitting machinery in house.*
Minimums: *Low*

NY STUDIO LLC

213 West 35th Street
New York, New York 10001
Robert Forehand
(1) (212) 244 1269   Fax: (1) (212) 244 4788
E-Mail: *robert@nystudiollc.com*
Web Site: *www.nystudiollc.com*
Description: *New York sample room for 1st proto & dups, pattern scanning/plotting,*
hand-made patterns or digital pattern service plus tech packs.
Year Est: *1998*
Specialties: *Apparel production sourcing in Hong Kong, China, Cambodia & Korea.*
Packages: *Full service, CMT & complete packages.*
Factory Locals: *Shenzhen & Nantong, China*

Production Capacity: *3,000 pcs/month*

OCASA
12-12 33rd Avenue
Long Island City, New York 11106

(1) (212) 758 0101   Fax: (1) (212) 758 1286

E-Mail: *customer.service@ocasa.com*
Web Site: *www.ocasa.com*
Description: *Freight Forwarders and Logistics.*
Specialties: *Courier, biological, shipping and distribution, warehousing, loading, file storage, check mail and management.*

PARIS ACCESSORIES
1385 Broadway
New York, New York 10018

(1) (212) 868 0500   Fax: (1) (212) 967 4936

E-Mail: *info@parisacc.com*
Description: *Domestic contractor & manufacturer of women's belts, gloves, hats & scarves.*
Categories: *Accessories*
Specialties: *Better priced belts & accessories.*
Minimums: *None*

PENN & FLETCHER, INC.
21-07 41st Avenue
Long Island City, New York 11101
Ernie Smith
(1) (212) 239 6868   Fax: (1) (212) 239 6914

E-Mail: *pennandfletcher@aol.com*
Web Site: *www.pennandfletcher.com*
Description: *Contractor of custom embroideries by hand or by machine.*
Year Est: *1986*
Categories: *Embroidery Contractors*
Markets: *Higher-end manufacturers.*
Minimums: *None. Small & large production lots & samples.*
Production Capacity: *Modest*

POPULAR PATTERN CO.
340 West 39th Street
New York, New York 10018
Stephen or Ian
(1) (212) 947 2902   Fax: (1) (212) 947 2716

E-Mail: *ssinger1@aol.com*
Description: *Computer grading & marking, patternmaking, mini markers, spec sheet grading & plotting.*
Categories: *Patternmaking, Grading/Marking*
Specialties: *Fast service, affordable prices, instant overseas delivery available by modem.*

Markets:	*Menswear, Womenswear, Children/Infantwear.*
Machinery:	*25 Accumark*
Export to:	*China, Vietnam, Domican Republic*
Production Capacity:	*400 graded patterns/monthly*

PORTCHESTER, USA

42-24 Orchard Street
Long Island City, New York 11101
Kulwant Chouhan
(1) (718) 937 4200   Fax: (1) (718) 937 4223

E-Mail:	*portchester_usa@verizon.net*
Web Site:	*www.portchesterusa.com*
Description:	*Handbag sample maker and manufacturer - we find solutions to your problems when it comes to making a line of handbags.*
Year Est:	*1985*
Categories:	*Accessories*
Specialties:	*From pattern making to samples to production of handbags & belts. Sourcing all kinds of leather, lining & hardware. Made in the USA.*
Packages:	*Complete & CMT packages.*

PRIMO COAT COMPANY

43-15 Queens Street
Long Island City, New York 11101

(1) (718) 349 2070   Fax: (1) (718) 349 7150

E-Mail:	*alan@alandavidnyc.com*
Description:	*Contractor of men's jackets, topcoats, overcoats & all formal wear.*
Categories:	*Coats/Jackets, Sample Rooms/Small Production*
Specialties:	*Small production lots & special orders. Top quality.*
Markets:	*Menswear & Womenswear*
Machinery:	*Sergers, bartack & buttonhole machinery.*
Packages:	*Cutting & CMT packages avail. Design service avail.*
Minimums:	*None. Will do singles.*

PROSTER FASHION

265 West 37th Street
New York, New York 10018
Cecilia
(1) (212) 730 8503   Fax: (1) (212) 730 8348

E-Mail:	*prosterlock23@gmail.com*
Description:	*Cut and Sew contractor.*
Year Est:	*2002*
Categories:	*Sample room/Small Production*
Specialties:	*Make all first prototypes and samples. Sewing on premises.*
Markets:	*Womenswear, Menswear, Ready to Wear.*
Packages:	*Full service*
Minimums:	*Low*

QUICK FUSING INC.

260 West 36th Street
New York, New York 10018
Igor Goldenberg
(1) (212) 967 0311   Fax: (1) (212) 967 1432

E-Mail:	*quickfuse5@aol.com*
Web Site:	*www.apparelexpert.com*
Description:	*Complete garment manufacturing, start to finish production. All done in the USA.*
Year Est:	*1987*
Categories:	*Patternmaking, Samples/Small Production, Cutting/Fusing*
Specialties:	*Cutting, fusing, sponging, bonding fabrics & leather, patternmaking, sewing, samples. Full production small and large lots.*
Markets:	*Womenswear, Childrenswear, Accessories.*
Packages:	*Complete packages.*
Minimums:	*Small*

R & N HEADWEAR

544 Park Avenue
Brooklyn, New York 11211
Fay Green
(1) (718) 522 6990   Fax: (1) (718) 522 3924

Description:	*Contractors & importers of children's hats & accessories.*
Categories:	*Accessories, Childrenswear*
Markets:	*Boyswear, Girlswear, Infantwear.*
Machinery:	*Plant equipped with over 150 sewing machines.*
Packages:	*Sewing.*
Minimums:	*Vary*

RAINBOW STYLE

242 West 38th Street
New York, New York 10018

(1) (212) 290 0209

E-Mail:	*info@rainbowpattern.com*
Web Site:	*www.rainbowpattern.com*
Description:	*One-stop service from concept to production. We can cover all types of fabric for knit, chiffon, jersey, netting, denim, wool, leather etc.*
Categories:	*Patternmaking, Samples/Small Production, Sportswear/Knits*
Markets:	*Menswear, Womenswear, Childrenswear*

RAYLON CORPORATION

267 Fifth Avenue
New York, New York 10016
Jay Pollak
(1) (212) 221 3633   Fax: (1) (212) 889 3283

E-Mail:	*jpollak@rayloncorp.com*
Description:	*Full package contractor/factory agent & textile converter.*
Year Est:	*1948*
Categories:	*Production Sourcing/Factory Agent, Pants/Shorts, Rainwear/Outerwear, home furnishings.*

Specialties:	*Specialize in board shorts & warm-up jackets.*
Markets:	*Menswear, Womenswear, Boyswear, Girlswear.*
Minimums:	*500-1,000 pcs/style*
Factory Locals:	*Asia*

RAYTEX INDUSTRIES

130 Crossways Park Drive
Woodbury, New York 11797
Jay Hellegers
(1) (516) 584 1111   Fax: (1) (516) 584 1034

E-Mail:	*jhellegers@raytexindustries.com*
Web Site:	*www.raytexindustries.com*
Description:	*Full package apparel supplier. World wide sourcing. Offices in Central America & Shanghai. From design & samples thru final shipment.*
Categories:	*Production Sourcing/Factory Agent*
Specialties:	*Specialize in loungewear, boxer shorts, performance underwear, tee shirts & activewear.*
Minimums:	*3,000 dozen*

REGAL ORIGINALS, INC.

43-01 22nd Street
Long Island City, New York 11101
Rodger Cohen
(1) (201) 569 2144   Fax: (1) (201) 569 2246

E-Mail:	*rodger@regaloriginals.com*
Web Site:	*www.regaloriginals.com*
Description:	*Pleating, stitching, novelty trim factory for all types of apparel and accessories.*
Year Est:	*1952*
Specialties:	*Over 60 years experience. All products made on site.*
Markets:	*Menswear, Womenswear, Childrens, Accessories.*
Production Capacity:	*10,000 pcs/month*

ROYAL APPAREL INC.
                                      See our ad on page 9, 113, 129

65 Commerce Street
Hauppauge, New York 11788
Morey Mayeri
(1) (631) 213 8299   Fax: (1) (631) 922 8438

E-Mail:	*sales@royalapparel.net*
Web Site:	*www.royalapparel.net*
Description:	*Manufacturer & private label contractor/converter of premium knit apparel. Made to order custom programs.*
Year Est:	*1993*
Exporting Since:	*1993*
Categories:	*Tee Shirts, Sportswear-Knits, Activewear/Athleticwear, Embroidery, Cutting/Fusing, Sample Room*
Specialties:	*Active sportswear styles in knit jersey, ribs, cotton blends. Graphic designs, cut & sew, screenprinting, flock & embroider, heat transfer.*
Markets:	*Menswear, Womenswear & Childrenswear.*
Packages:	*Full service, complete packages.*
Export to:	*Canada & Europe*

Minimums: 100 dozen per size/per color

SILK CITY SALES INTERNATIONAL
108 West 39th Street
New York, New York 10018
Maureen Kwiat
(1) (212) 382 2235   Fax: (1) (212) 382 0923

E-Mail:	maureen@silkcitysales.com
Description:	Fine quality novelty yarns from Italy, Uruguay & classic cashmere from China. Custom handknit garment programs from South America.
Categories:	Sportswear/Knits
Specialties:	Cashmere machine knits, natural fiber digital printed knits & woven scarves from China. Sourcing & development for volume knitting in China.
Markets:	Menswear & Womenswear.

SOMIYA INC.
307 West 38th Street
New York, New York 10018
Leo and Liz
(1) (212) 302 3089   Fax: (1) (212) 302 3089

E-Mail:	somiyainc@yahoo.com
Description:	Patternmaking, samples, small production is done in New York City, bulk production capabilities at sister factory overseas.
Categories:	Patternmaking, Sample Rooms/Small Production
Specialties:	Specialize in pattern and samples.
Markets:	All markets.
Minimums:	None

SPOILED ROTTEN U.S.A.
605 East 132nd Street
Bronx, New York 10454
Eric Beroff
(1) (718) 993 7006   Fax: (1) (718) 993 6314

E-Mail:	eberoff@yahoo.com
Description:	Cut and sew contractor of knit & wovens for womenswear. All types of tops and bottoms.
Categories:	Sample Room/Small Production
Specialties:	We can also source your fabric.
Minimums:	Very low

STILE ASSOCIATES LTD
181 South Franklin Avenue
Valley Stream, New York 11581
Isaac
(1) (516) 394 2166   Fax: (1) (516) 394 2195

E-Mail:	isaacg@stileintl.com
Web Site:	www.stileintl.com
Description:	Full service logistics company. Air/ocean, import/export, consolidated services, customs clearance and compliance service.
Year Est:	1972
Categories:	Freight Forwarder/Customs Broker

Specialties: *Large roster of licensed customs brokers at our Atlantic & Pacific port offices. Ability to obtain advance clearance & remote location filing.*

STUCKI EMBROIDERY
Box 185, Route 28
Boiceville, New York 12412
Murray Fenwick
(1) (845) 657 2308   Fax: (1) (845) 657 2860

E-Mail: *mail@stuckiembroidery.com*
Web Site: *www.stuckiembroidery.com*
Description: *Custom embroidery and screenprinting.*
Categories: *Embroidery*
Specialties: *Expert with embroidered trims, edges, all-overs, emblems & specialty motifs, ie: animals.*
Machinery: *10 Swiss embroidery looms in house.*
Minimums: *20 yds.*
Factory Locals: *Plants in Boiceville, NY & Fairview, NJ.*

STUDIO ONE LEATHER DESIGN INC.
270 West 39th Street
New York, New York 10018
Arthur Cohen
(1) (212) 760 1701   Fax: (1) (212) 760 1702

E-Mail: *arthur@studio1leather.com*
Description: *A full service sample room working in the development of men's and women's sportswear and outerwear.*
Categories: *Patternmaking, Sample Room/Small Production, Production Sourcing, Leather/Suede*
Specialties: *Specialize in leather and suede.*
Markets: *Menswear, Womenswear*
Machinery: *5 sewing machines, buttonhole, fur sewing machine and merrow.*
Minimums: *25 pcs/style (leather garments, woven)*
Factory Locals: *All work in done in the USA.*
Production Capacity: *800-1,000 units/month*

STYLE COUNCIL, THE
242 West 36th Street
New York, New York 10018
Marissa Porskievies
(1) (212) 564 9380   Fax: (1) (212) 594 2315

E-Mail: *marissa@stylecouncil.com*
Web Site: *www.stylecouncil.com*
Description: *Digital fabric printing for a last minute print for a photo shoot, sales presentation, runway show or short run production domestically in NYC.*
Categories: *Screenprinting*
Specialties: *Colorfast, non-colorfast, dye sublimation and screenprinting.*

SWEATER BRAND INC.

401 Park Avenue
Brooklyn, New York 11205
Moshie Rosenberg
(1) (718) 797 0505   Fax: (1) (718) 875 8028

E-Mail:	*info@sweaterbrand.com*
Description:	*Sweater contracting & private label manufacturing.*
Year Est:	*1983*
Exporting Since:	*1983*
Categories:	*Sweaters/Knitwear*
Markets:	*All*
Machinery:	*75 computer & 150 finishing machines.*
Packages:	*All types of programs & private label import packages.*
Export to:	*Canada 10%*
Minimums:	*50 dozen/style*
Production Capacity:	*15,000 dozen/month*

SWEENIE MANUFACTURING CORPORATION

34 Sedgwick Avenue
Yonkers, New York 10705
Diane Walker
(1) (646) 825 5027   Fax: (1) (646) 825 5027

E-Mail:	*diane@sweeniemanufacturing.com*
Web Site:	*www.sweeniemanufacturing.com*
Description:	*Branded manufacturer. Specialize in design/merchandising, sourcing and production of activewear, swimwear and cut/sew knits.*
Categories:	*Production Sourcing, Swimwear/Dancewear, Active/Athletic Wear, Tee Shirts, Sportswear Knits, Sportswear Wovens.*
Specialties:	*Specialize in swimwear, activewear, tee-shirts, knit & woven sportswear, sportsbags, gym bags, cosmetic bags. Printed & logo trims.*
Markets:	*Menswear, Womenswear, Childrenswear.*
Machinery:	*Flat bed, button holer, spaghetti strap*
Packages:	*Full package or CMT only*
Factory Locals:	*Domestic & Overseas Production Capabilities.*

TANNERY DIRECT

40 West 37th Street
New York, New York 10018
Anne Sampson
(1) (212) 465 1503   Fax: (1) (212) 465 1512

E-Mail:	*asampson@tannerydirect.com*
Description:	*Full leather garment production packages in sportswear & outerwear.*
Categories:	*Production Sourcing/Factory Agent, Leather/Suede*
Specialties:	*Our New York sample studio takes our customers from patternmaking, fit sessions to final production.*
Factory Locals:	*Shearling coats/jackets are made in Turkey, leather coats & sportswear & dresses are done in China or India.*

TECHS BY TERRY

83 Beach 216th Street
Breezy Point, New York 11697
Terry Maloney
(1) (718) 440 7185

E-Mail: *terrmaloney@aol.com*
Description: *Product development, technical design and patternmaking services.*

TEXTILE ARTS MARKETING INC,.

405 Tarrytown Road
White Plains, New York 10607
Ken Noonan
(1) (914) 837 3588   Fax: (1) (914) 428 6557

E-Mail: *ken@textileartsmarketing.com*
Web Site: *www.textileartsmarketing.com*
Description: *We offer full package garment production in the US and abroad.*
Categories: *Production Sourcing/Factory Agent*
Specialties: *Finished garments and accessories through certified garment factories.*

UPLIFTING SALES, INC.

PO Box 556
North Bellmore, New York 11710
John Paul Brogan
(1) (917) 913 2284

E-Mail: *jp@jpbrogan.com*
Description: *Manufacturers of intimate apparel, daywear and swimwear.*
Categories: *Production Sourcing/Factory Agents*
Specialties: *Production and contracted manufacturing in China and Thailand.*
Packages: *Full Packages*

VESTIGE DESIGN

209 West 38th Street
New York, New York 10018

(1) (212) 944 4389   Fax: (1) (212) 944 4381

E-Mail: *info@vestigedesign.com*
Web Site: *www.vestigedesign.com*
Description: *An apparel sourcing & product development company and partner with several garment factories in China and Indonesia.*
Categories: *Production Sourcing/Factory Agent*
Specialties: *Men's, junior sportswear, missy, contemporary, intimate apparel, sleepwear, sweaters, hand embroidery & beading.*
Markets: *Menswear & Womenswear.*
Packages: *Complete packages, private label.*

VISHAL ENTERPRISES

226 West 37th Street
New York, New York 10018
Vishal Moorjani
(1) (212) 629 0880   Fax: (1) (212) 629 0882

E-Mail:	*vishal@vishalent.com*
Web Site:	*www.vishalent.com*
Description:	*We are a vertically integrated organization specializing in the manufacturing of textiles and garments. NY based sample room.*
Categories:	*Production Sourcing/Factory Agent*
Specialties:	*Structured jackets, soft dressing, active wear, evening & casual dresses, woven, printed & novelty knit tops, accessories.*
Markets:	*Menswear, Womenswear, Accessories.*
Packages:	*Complete production packages.*
Minimums:	*Low*
Factory Locals:	*India and China*
Production Capacity:	*We can cater to small productions (100 pcs per style per colorway) or do large volume productions (25,000 to 50,000 units per month).*

VISIONAIRE PLEATING LLC.

1155 Manhattan Avenue
Brooklyn, New York 11222
John Dziewit
(1) 917 520 4100   Fax: (1) 718 349 3309

E-Mail:	*john@visionairepleating.com*
Web Site:	*www.visionairepleating.com*
Year Est:	*2004*
Categories:	*Pleating/Tucking/Stitching*
Specialties:	*All types of pleating.*
Machinery:	*21 different types of pleating machines*
Production Capacity:	*100,000 pcs/month*

VOGUE TOO PLEATING STITCHING AND EMBROIDERY

265 West 37th Street
New York, New York 10018
Larry Geffner
(1) (212) 354 8976   Fax: (1) (212) 354 8975

E-Mail:	*larry@voguetoo.com*
Web Site:	*www.voguetoo.com*
Description:	*Pleating, tucking, decorative & novelty stitching for the apparel trade.*
Year Est:	*2001*
Specialties:	*We can manufacture all types of trimmings. Specialize in tucking, pleated ruffles, picot trim stitching, flower & novelty trims.*

WAITEX INTERNATIONAL

135 West 36th Street
New York, New York 10018
Candice
(1) (212) 967 8100   Fax: (1) (212) 967 8266

E-Mail:	*candice@waitex.com*

Web Site:	*www.waitex.com*
Description:	*Merchandise distribution, warehousing, garment refurbishing, label sewing & more.*
Year Est:	*1981*
Categories:	*Distribution, Warehouse Center*
Machinery:	*Pressing & sewing machinery. 1,200,00 square feet warehousing facility.*
Factory Locals:	*13 plants: North Bergen, Carlstadt, East Rutherford, Clifton & Secaucus, NJ. Rancho Cucamonga, CA., China*

WERKSTATT

347 West 36th Street
New York, New York 10018
Tina Schenk
(1) (646) 414 4545   Fax: (1) (646) 559 2824

E-Mail:	*tina@werkstattny.com*
Web Site:	*www.werkstattny.com*
Description:	*Pattern service located in the heart of NYC's garment district. Specialize in intelligent pattern & garment development.*
Year Est:	*2008*
Categories:	*Patternmaking Services*
Specialties:	*Fit specialist. First through production patterns.*
Markets:	*Menswear & Womenswear.*
Production Capacity:	*Varies depending on the difficulty of patterns. 35-60 patterns.*

WILLIAM THE PATTERNMAKER

340 West 39th Street
New York, New York 10018
William Smithline
(1) 646 824 2280   Fax: (1) 212 947 2716

E-Mail:	*williamsmithline@yahoo.com*
Web Site:	*www.williamthepatternmaker.com*
Description:	*Master Patternmaker. Initial idea thru production. Samplemaking. Work with large & small companies as well as emerging designers.*
Categories:	*Patternmaking*
Specialties:	*Specialize in proper costing of your designs, help with finding label makers, trim resources, proper cutting rooms, factories & shippers.*
Packages:	*Full service company.*

WORLD CLASS SHIPPING

210 Sunrise Highway
Valley Stream, New York 11581
Billy Shaw
(1) (516) 568 8861   Fax: (1) (516) 872 5017

E-Mail:	*billjr@worldclassshipping.com*
Web Site:	*www.worldclassshipping.com*
Description:	*International freight forwarder and customs broker*
Year Est:	*1987*
Categories:	*Freight Forwarder/Custom Broker*
Specialties:	*Knowledge, expertise & resources for your in-house logistic solutions. Network of over 450 agents worldwide.*

WORLD SOURCE

224 West 35th Street
New York, New York 10001
Alan Novie/Jack Mann
(1) (212) 594 9129   Fax: (1) (212) 202 5298

E-Mail:	*info@worldsourcenyc.com*
Description:	*All types of apparel production services.*
Year Est:	*1993*
Categories:	*Production Sourcing/Factory Agent, Leather/Suede, Dresses/Blouses, Coats/Jackets*
Specialties:	*Specialize in leather and suede outerwear, embellished, embroidered and lace dresses and blouses.*
Markets:	*Menswear & Womenswear.*
Packages:	*Complete*
Factory Locals:	*China and India*
Production Capacity:	*Leather garments: 200 pcs/month per style/color, Sequin Dresses: 150 pcs/month, Blouses: 300 pcs/month.*

North Carolina

ARTWEAR EMBROIDERY, INC.

621 A Indeneer Drive
Kernersville, North Carolina 27284
Cindy Cox Wilson
(1) (336) 992 2166   Fax: (1) (336) 992 2167

E-Mail:	*artwear@artwearinc.com*
Web Site:	*www.artwearinc.com*
Description:	*High quality embroidery contractor. On time, every time.*
Year Est:	*1992*
Exporting Since:	*1994*
Categories:	*Embroidery*
Specialties:	*Embroidery, applique, names personalization & multi-media applications on any type of apparel, piece goods or cut pieces.*
Machinery:	*51 Tajima embroidery heads, Pulse signature digitizing equipment.*
Export to:	*England*
Minimums:	*48 pieces/style*
Factory Locals:	*Kernersville, NC*
Production Capacity:	*100,000 pieces/month*

BJ CON-SEW

321 Industrial Park Avenue
Asheboro, North Carolina 27205
Barbara/Jerry Trotter
(1) (336) 629 4550   Fax: (1) (336) 629 2078

E-Mail:	*bjconsew@triadbiz.rr.com*
Web Site:	*www.bjconsew.com*
Description:	*Services include cutting and sewing, slitting, product development, and pattern design.*
Year Est:	*1992*
Specialties:	*Specialize in bedding and pillows. ISO 9001 certified.*

Markets: Home Furnishings.

CATAWBA CREATIONS
PO Box 1159
Hildebran, North Carolina 28637
Doris Houston
(1) (828) 397 7088   Fax: (1) (828) 397 2357

E-Mail:	catawbacreations@msn.com
Description:	Cut and sew family-owned business specializing in knit tops and bottoms for men, women and children.
Categories:	Pants/Shorts/Skirts, Shirts/Tops
Minimums:	Will do small quantities

COVILLE INC.
8065-0 North Point Boulevard
Winston-Salem, North Carolina 27106
Kevin Williams
(1) (336) 759 0115   Fax: (1) (336) 759 2229

E-Mail:	kwilliams@covilleinc.com
Web Site:	www.covilleinc.com
Description:	Full package cut and sew facility producing thermal underwear, performance underwear, Henleys and nightshirts.
Categories:	Underwear Contractor
Specialties:	Contract services, CMT and knitting of cloth.

CRAFTEX REWORK INC.
500 Woodcrest Drive
Lucama, North Carolina 27851
Bobby O'Neal
(1) (252) 239 0123   Fax: (1) (252) 239 1177

E-Mail:	boneal@craftexinc.com
Description:	Expert with all types of production rework.
Year Est:	1971
Categories:	Rework/Inspection.
Specialties:	Rework, inspections, hangtagging, labeling, packing & shipping.
Machinery:	Plain sewers, lock stitch, safety stitch, cover stitch blind stitch, button, chain stitch, sergers & more.
Packages:	CMT, Production Rework & Warehousing.

CREATIVE OUTLET, INC.
1600 Bridges Street
Moorhead City, North Carolina 28557
Jim Garner
(1) (252) 808 3898   Fax: (1) (252) 808 2188

E-Mail:	sscrubs@yahoo.com
Web Site:	www.creativeoutlet.info
Description:	Contractor for healthcare apparel & related textile products.
Categories:	Uniforms.
Specialties:	Specialize in hospital uniforms & hospital pajamas.
Machinery:	Digitized embroidery system on site.

Minimums: None

FLOOR-READY SERVICES, INC.
94 Glenn Bridge Road
Arden, North Carolina 28704
Jessica Lewis
(1) (828) 651 8504   Fax: (1) (828) 651 0225

E-Mail:	*contact@floorready.com*
Web Site:	*www.floorready.com*
Description:	*Dedicated to processing & reprocessing both soft-line & hard-line goods for manufacturers, distributors, wholesalers, jobbers, retailers.*
Year Est:	*2001*
Categories:	*Rework & Inspection Services*
Specialties:	*Inspect, grade, sort, label, bundle, pack, ticket, hang, fold, bag, bulk pack, pre-packing, preparing POP displays, box, shrink wrap & ship.*
Machinery:	*We have 12 commercial sewing machines & experienced seamstress on staff. Minimize operating expenses & remain competitive. FRS saves its clients in fixed costs directly related to both processing services as well as operations/management.*
Minimums:	*No job is too big or too small. 100% dedicated workforce.*
Factory Locals:	*3rd Party Processor. All work is done in-house.*
Production Capacity:	*1.5 million units/ week. We make sure we have the correct labor force on hand to meet each and every customer's needs.*

GRANITE KNITWEAR/DBA CAL CRU
805 S Salisbury Avenue
Granite Quarry, North Carolina 28072
Mike Jones, President
(1) (704) 279 5526   Fax: (1) (704) 279 8205

E-Mail:	*calcru@mindspring.com*
Web Site:	*www.calcru.com*
Description:	*1-800-476-9944. Contractor & manufacturer of knit apparel & tee shirts using Coolmax & Dri-Release performance knit fabrics.*
Year Est:	*1968*
Exporting Since:	*1980*
Categories:	*Sportswear-Knits, Tee Shirts, Active/Athletic Wear*
Specialties:	*Private labeling, custom design & manufacturing, stock inventory & final packaging.*
Markets:	*Menswear, Womenswear, Children/Infantwear.*
Machinery:	*1 flatlock, 30 overedger, 4 coverseam, 4 covertape, 4 single needle, 1 button hole, 1 snap machine, 1 pocket, 1 shirring.*
Packages:	*Full package, screenprinting, embroidery, pattern making.*
Export to:	*Japan*
Minimums:	*60 dozen/color/style*
Production Capacity:	*2,000 doz/month*

GWEN'S CREATIVE SEWING

108 W Bizzell Street
Laurinburg, North Carolina 28352
Gwen Baker
(1) (910) 276 2121

E-Mail:	gebaker@roadrunner.com
Description:	Patternmaking, fabric sourcing, cut and sew, samples, small production.
Specialties:	All types and styles. Menswear, bridal, costums, sportswer, pillows, drapery treatments for the home.
Markets:	Menswear, Womenswear, Home Furnishings.

HAGINS INDUSTRIES, INC.

2128 Marion Stage Road
Fairmont, North Carolina 28340
Johnnie Hagins
(1) (910) 628 6777   Fax: (1) (910) 628 5160

E-Mail:	haginsinds@bellsouth.net
Description:	Contractor specializing in knit shirts, tops, golf shirts, polo shirts and sweatpants.
Year Est:	1989
Categories:	Shirts/Tops, Activewear, Rework/Inspection
Specialties:	All type of rework and re-labeling capabilities.
Markets:	Menswear, Womenswear & Childrenswear.
Machinery:	Overlock & flatlock machines. Full cutting room.
Packages:	CMT & complete packages available.
Minimums:	None
Production Capacity:	4800 pcs/month

HANES DYE & FINISHING COMPANY

600 Northwest Boulevard
Winston-Salem, North Carolina 27101

(1) (336) 725 1391   Fax: (1) (336) 722 0890

E-Mail:	hfcsales@hanesindustries.com
Web Site:	www.hanesfinishing.com
Description:	Latest dyeing technology.
Year Est:	1924
Categories:	Dyeing Contractor
Specialties:	Pad, jigg & beam dyeing. Can dye cottons, polyesters, acrylics & poly blends.
Markets:	Home Furnishings, Apparel & Industrial Fabrics
Machinery:	Pressure beams 800,000 yds, jiggs 500,000 yds, coating range 1,700,000.
Export to:	Europe 10%, Asia 5%, Mexico 5%, Canada 5%
Factory Locals:	Butner, North Carolina and Winston-Salem, North Carolina. 877-453-9476
Production Capacity:	3,000,000 linear yards

HICKORY BRANDS INC.

P.O. Box 429
Hickory, North Carolina 28603
Josh Higgins
(1) (828) 322 2600   Fax: (1) (828) 328 1700

E-Mail:	*josh@hickorybrands.com*
Web Site:	*www.tenseconds.com*
Description:	*Custom fabric trims, drawcords, lanyards, shoe laces, insoles & more.*
Year Est:	*1923*
Categories:	*Trim Application*
Specialties:	*Open line of childrens designs & can do any custom design.*
Markets:	*Casual & activewear markets & all price points.*
Minimums:	*2500 yds.*

MEHERA SHAW TEXTILES PVT LTD.

3307 Trice Atwater Road
Chapel Hill, North Carolina 27516
Shari Keller
(1) (919) 969 2572   Fax: (1) (919) 969 6909

E-Mail:	*info@meherashaw.com*
Web Site:	*www.meherashaw.com*
Description:	*We are a full production company offering pattern making and grading, including designer support, fabric sourcing, sampling & CMT services.*
Year Est:	*2007*
Exporting Since:	*2008*
Categories:	*Samples/Small Production, Patternmaking Services*
Specialties:	*Specialize in small-scale designers wishing to produce private label collections using natural fibers, artisan textiles and/or organic fabrics.*
Markets:	*Womenswear & Girlswear.*
Export to:	*USA, Europe, Japan*
Minimums:	*Small minimums & lots of start-up support*
Factory Locals:	*India*

STYLE SOURCE INC.

913 Orange Street
Wilmington, North Carolina 28401
Geoffrey Krasnov
(1) (910) 399 2288   Fax: (1) (910) 399 2289

E-Mail:	*geoff@style-source.com*
Web Site:	*www.style-source.com*
Description:	*Full range of pattern making services to the trade. Manufacturing & sourcing, fabric sales, pre-patterned apparel & private label apparel.*
Year Est:	*2002*
Categories:	*Patternmaking Services, Sample Rooms/Small Production*
Specialties:	*Devise first patterns from conceptual drawings & produce first samples & specs, sourcing & manufacturing both domestic & overseas.*
Markets:	*Womenswear, Childrenswear, Accessories.*
Factory Locals:	*All work is done in North Carolina*
Production Capacity:	*5,000 dozen/monthly*

SUPERTEX LIBERTY INDUSTRIES INC.

312 West Luther Avenue
Liberty, North Carolina 27298

(1) (336) 622 1000

E-Mail:	*info@supertex-inc.com*
Web Site:	*www.supertex-inc.com*
Description:	*Dyeing, finishing and coating to widths up to 230 inches. We also do slitting and chopping.*
Year Est:	*1982*
Categories:	*Finishing/Coating/Dyeing Contractor*
Specialties:	*Fully integrated and vertical warp knitting mill.*
Packages:	*Full Package*
Factory Locals:	*All work is done in the North Carolina Facility.* *1-800-790-1000*

WELLS HOSIERY MILLS, INC.

1758 South Fayetteville Street
Asheboro, North Carolina 27205

(1) (336) 633 4881   Fax: (1) (336) 633 4862

E-Mail:	*info@wellshosiery.com*
Web Site:	*www.wellshosiery.com*
Description:	*Cut and sew operations specializing in womens high end knit tops.*
Categories:	*Accessories, Shirts/Tops*
Specialties:	*Ladies hosiery. Brand name & private label products. Seamless lines.*
Markets:	*Womenswear.*

North Dakota

SOARING EAGLE OUTERWEAR, INC.

1916 20th Avenue S.E.
Minot, North Dakota 58701
Austin Hall
(1) (701) 838 2110   Fax: (1) (701) 852 4941

E-Mail:	*seagle@srt.com*
Categories:	*Uniforms, Coats/Jackets.*
Machinery:	*Sergers, cover stitch, multi-needle & pressing machinery.*
Packages:	*Sewing & CMT packages.*
Minimums:	*None. Can handle small & large production lots.*

NY

DYNOTEX INC.

236 Greenpoint Avenue
Brooklyn, NY 11222
Annie Kwan
(1) (917) 532 9068

E-Mail:	*dynotexinc@gmail.com*
Web Site:	*www.dynotex.com*

Description:	Manufacture ladies and mens woven & knit bottoms, tops and outerwear. More than just cut & sew services. Quality conscious.
Year Est:	1999
Categories:	Tops/Bottoms/Outerwear
Specialties:	We can provide patternmaking services, cutting room in-house, sample making, grading & marking, 100% inspection,
Markets:	Menswear & Womenswear
Machinery:	18 Single Needle, 8 Merrow, 1 Double Needle, 2 Blind Stitch, 2 Double Needle Cover Stitch, 1 Zig Zag, 2 Purl Stitch, 2 Button, 1 Button Hole Straight, 1 Button Hole Keyhole, 2 Snap Machines, 3 Thread Trimmer, 1 Fabric Steamer, 2 Cutting Tables and more.
Packages:	Comprehensive technical knowledge of fabrics.
Minimums:	None
Factory Locals:	All work is done in-house.
Production Capacity:	Knitwear: 15,000 units/month, Pants: 10,000 units/month, Blouses: 10,000 units/month, Blazers: 5,000 units/month.

Ohio

AIR WAVES, INC.
7787 Graphics Way
Lewis Center, Ohio 43035

(1) (740) 548 1200   Fax: (1) (740) 548 1212

E-Mail:	cs@airwavesinc.com
Web Site:	www.airwavesstore.com
Description:	Toll Free #1-800 468 7335. Contract screenprinting & heat transfers on finished garments or pieces.
Year Est:	1983
Categories:	Screenprinting.
Specialties:	Thousands of stock designs with custom design capabilities. Puff, spot, 4-color process & 4-color process puff printing.
Machinery:	Full line of heat press machines: manual, automatic & specialty.
Export to:	Over 120 countries
Minimums:	Vary
Production Capacity:	100,000-500,000 doz/month

KAM MANUFACTURING INC.
PO Box 407
Van Wert, Ohio 45891

(1) (419) 238 6037   Fax: (1) (419) 238 3489

E-Mail:	ollie@kammfg.com
Web Site:	www.kammfg.com
Description:	Cut, sew, ship contractor specializing in quilted fashion purses.
Categories:	Accessories
Packages:	Full Package

PRIMAL SCREEN

1021 Mason Avenue
Kent, Ohio 44240
Catie Kuchenbecker
(1) (330) 677 1766   Fax: (1) (330) 677 4299

E-Mail:	*catie@primalscreenprinting.com*
Web Site:	*www.primalscreenprinting.com*
Description:	*Design and print t-shirts, sweatshirts, and other printed apparel.*
Year Est:	*1995*
Categories:	*Screenprinting Contractors.*
Specialties:	*Full graphic design and art service, embroidery and other promotions.*
Markets:	*Menswear, Womenswear, Childrens*

Oklahoma

ROUND HOUSE MANUFACTURING

One American Way
Shawnee, Oklahoma 74801
Jim Antosh
(1) (405) 273 0510   Fax: (1) (405) 273 0511

E-Mail:	*info@round-house.com*
Web Site:	*www.round-house.com*
Description:	*Contractor specializing in bib overalls.*
Categories:	*Jeans/Denimwear, Uniforms.*
Specialties:	*All work is produced in the USA.*
Packages:	*CMT & complete packages. Cutting room in house.*
Minimums:	*50 dozen/style*

Oregon

BOULDER PATH DESIGNS

110 E. 2nd Street
The Dalles, Oregon 97058
Luise Langheinrich
(1) (541) 296 4470   Fax: (1) (541) 298 5067

E-Mail:	*info@boulderpathdesigns.com*
Web Site:	*www.boulderpathdesigns.com*
Description:	*Full service contractor. Product development, specifications, patterns, CAD service, grading, marker making, samples, production runs.*
Categories:	*Patternmaking, Samples/Small Production, Activewear, Sportswear/Wovens*
Specialties:	*Problem solving. Experience in work wear, sportswear, hospital gowns, active wear, and more. Can do all styles of tops, bottoms and jackets.*
Markets:	*Menswear, Womenswear & Childrenswear.*
Packages:	*Full service, prototype, development, samplemaking*
Minimums:	*None*
Factory Locals:	*Oregon, USA*

LATITUDES
2425 NE Riverside Way
Portland, Oregon 97211

(1) (503) 248 2060   Fax: (1) (503) 248 2134
E-Mail: *info@latitudespdx.com*
Web Site: *www.latitudespdx.com*
Description: *Custom screen printing, embroidery, design, promotional products.*
We can accommodate all your design needs from concept to production.
Categories: *Embroidery/Screenprinting*
Specialties: *Other services provided - tagging, UPC bar coding, folding, poly-*
bagging, boxing, palletizing, full service shipping worldwide.
Markets: *Menswear, Womenswear, Childrens, Accessories.*
Machinery: *Embroidery: 15 head Tajima, 6 head Tajima, 1 head Melco*
Packages: *Full Package Programs including private label product.*
Factory Locals: *In-house*
Production Capacity: *150,000 prints/weekly*

OREGON SCREEN IMPRESSIONS
3580 NE Broadway
Portland, Oregon 97232

(1) (503) 231 0181   Fax: (1) (503) 231 9756
E-Mail: *tiffanyf@oregonscreen.com*
Web Site: *www.oregonscreen.com*
Description: *Excellence in screenprinting and embroidery. We offer a broad*
range of garments - tees, sweats, polos, dress shirts, jackets & bags.
Categories: *Screenprinting/Embroidery*
Specialties: *We also provide the following services: labeling, hang tags,*
packaging, fulfillment services, shipping.
Markets: *Menswear, Womenswear, Childrens, Accessories.*
Minimums: *Screen Printing 24 pcs, Embroidery 12 pcs.*
Factory Locals: *Our factory is in Oregon but we assist customers*
throughout the US

Pennsylvania

A RIFKIN COMPANY
1400 Sans Souci Parkway
Wilkes-Barre, Pennsylvania 18706
Joe Bachkosky
(1) (570) 825 9551   Fax: (1) (570) 825 5282
E-Mail: *jbachkosky@arifkin.com*
Web Site: *www.rifkinsewing.com*
Description: *Apparel & garment contract sewing. Samples & small runs.*
Finishing, inspection, fold and bag.
Categories: *Sample Rooms/Small Production*
Specialties: *Private label services available using your patterns and fabric.*
All work done in-house.

ABSTRACT GRAPHICS

214 Oak Street
Nazareth, Pennsylvania 18064
Arthur Rader
(1) (610) 746 4933   Fax: (1) (610) 746 5563

E-Mail:	*art@customapparelzone.com*
Web Site:	*www.customapparelzone.com*
Description:	*Provide full service screen printing from creating the logo to imprinting it with a wide variety of specialty inks.*
Categories:	*Screenprinting*
Specialties:	*Complete embroidery services from digitizing the logo to the finished sewn out logo on any apparel or accessory desired.*
Markets:	*Menswear, Womenswear, Childrenswear*

ALL AMERICAN EMBROIDERY

2228 Noblestown Road
Pittsburg, Pennsylvania 15205
Lou Fani
(1) (412) 922 8999   Fax: (1) (412) 922 7712

E-Mail:	*aae2000@aol.com*
Description:	*Contract embroidery work on finished garments or pieces, plus sweatshirts, hats, tees, etc.*
Year Est:	*1980*
Categories:	*Embroidery*
Specialties:	*Applique embroidery*
Markets:	*Menswear, Womenswear, Childrenswear, Accessories.*
Minimums:	*4 dozen/style*
Factory Locals:	*Two plants in the Pittsburg area.*
Production Capacity:	*600 dozen/week*

CALEDONIAN DYE WORKS, INC.

3300 Emerald Street
Philadelphia, Pennsylvania 19134
Richard Fitch
(1) (215) 739 2322   Fax: (1) (215) 739 6121

Description:	*Dyers of cotton, rayon, wool & polyester yarns.*
Year Est:	*1911*
Machinery:	*22 dyeing machines*
Minimums:	*50 lbs.*
Production Capacity:	*130,000 lbs/month*

COLORSTAR CORP.

6464 Ruch Road
Bethlehem, Pennsylvania 18017
Ali Ismail
(1) (610) 837 2400   Fax: (1) (610) 837 8114

E-Mail:	*colorstar@aol.com*
Web Site:	*www.colorstaronline.com*
Description:	*Factory Direct custom heat seal transfers including: plastisol, white-backing/litho, shimmer, glitter, glow in the dark, foil, hot-peel, etc.*
Year Est:	*1950*

Categories: Screenprinting/Heat Transfers
Specialties: Application & finishing provided on site. Provide superior
silkscreen products, iron on letters, jersey numbers, stock designs.
Markets: Womens, Mens & Childrens.

DYE IT UP
1002 E. Pennsylvania Boulevard
Trevose, Pennsylvania 19053
Mark
(1) (267) 288 5545   Fax: (1) (267) 288 5545
E-Mail: sales@dyeitup.com
Web Site: www.dyeitup.com
Description: Tie dye contractor of finished goods.
Markets: Menswear, Womenswear, Children/Infantwear.

EMBROIDERY CONCEPTS
231 South College Street
Washington, Pennsylvania 15301
Kevin Booth
(1) 724 225 3644   Fax: (1) 724 225 3609
E-Mail: kevin@1clickshirts.com
Web Site: www.1clickshirts.com
Description: One stop source for embroidering your corporate apparel, business
logos, and team wear on tee shirts, denim shirts, jackets & hats.
Specialties: Specialize in computerized embroidery.
Markets: Menswear, Womenswear & Childrenswear.
Machinery: 10 Brother Machines
Production Capacity: 4,000/pcs.

F & M HAT CO., INC.
103 Walnut Street
Denver, Pennsylvania 17517
Fred Fichthorn
(1) (717) 336 5505   Fax: (1) (717) 336 0501
E-Mail: customerservice@fmhat.com
Web Site: www.fmhat.com
Description: Contractor of men's & women's wool, felt, straw & western hats.
Categories: Accessories.
Specialties: Wool, straw & cloth hats from start to finish.
Machinery: Cording, pressing, decorating & boxing equipment.
Packages: Complete packages
Minimums: Vary
Factory Locals: 1-800-953-4287

FASHION SOURCES, INC.
1006 East Montgomery Avenue
North Wales, Pennsylvania 19454
Allen Edelson
(1) (215) 699 6801   Fax: (1) (215) 699 3413
E-Mail: fashsource@aol.com
Description: Immediate production of all apparel types & for all markets.

Marketing agent for twelve factories worldwide.

Year Est:	1985
Exporting Since:	1985
Categories:	Production Sourcing/Factory Agent.
Markets:	Menswear, Womenswear, Childrenswear.
Minimums:	2,000 units/style.
Factory Locals:	USA & import from Mexico, Costa Rica, El Salvador & China.
Production Capacity:	Jeans: 75,000/wk, Slacks: 22,000-100,000/wk, Blazers: 3,000/wk, Sportwear: 5,000/wk

GRECO APPAREL

420 North Spring Garden St.
Ambler, Pennsylvania 19002

(1) (215) 628 2557   Fax: (1) (215) 352 0464

E-Mail:	joe@grecoapparel.com
Web Site:	www.grecoapparel.com
Description:	Contract to order - full package or CMT - from product development to delivery duty paid.
Year Est:	1951
Categories:	Suits/Tailored Garments, Shirts/Tops, Uniforms, Outerwear Pants/Shorts/Skirts.
Specialties:	Specialize in pants (dress, work & casual), jeans, tailored clothing, shirts (woven & knit), skirts, dresses, outerwear, flame retardant.
Markets:	Menswear, Womenswear & Childrenswear.
Packages:	Full packages
Factory Locals:	USA (Berry Amendment Compliant for US Government), Dominican Republic, Central America, Far East.
Production Capacity:	125,000 units/week

ID4U JACKETS WITH IDENTITY

344 Hostetter Road
Manheim, Pennsylvania 17545
Daryl Schumacher
(1) 888 968 4348   Fax: (1) 717 644 4397

E-Mail:	daryl@id4u-jackets.com
Web Site:	www.id4u-jackets.com
Description:	1-888-968-4348. Full package contractor & manufacturer of custom jackets. Also offer dye sublimation type decoration on shirts & jackets.
Year Est:	1991
Categories:	Leather/Suede, Coats/Jackets
Specialties:	Specialize in full customization of leather, wool & twill jackets as well as team shirts. Prototypes are offered for a minimal charge.
Markets:	Menswear & Womenswear
Packages:	CMT, samples, embroidery, screenprinting & dyeing.
Minimums:	25 pcs/style
Factory Locals:	Pennsylvania & Madras, India.
Production Capacity:	Variable. Can fill small & large orders.

JADE APPAREL

1017 Race Street
Philadelphia, Pennsylvania 19107
Anh Thai
(1) (215) 922 3953   Fax: (1) (215) 922 7231

E-Mail:	*jadey989@aol.com*
Description:	*Cut and sew moderate size lot contractor.*
Year Est:	*1995*
Categories:	*Blouses/Shirts, Dresses/Suits, Shirts/Tops, Pants Sportswear-Knits*
Specialties:	*Specialize in better knits & woven tops, blouses, dresses and men's button down shirts, pants.*
Markets:	*Menswear, Womenswear & Childrenswear.*
Machinery:	*40 single needle, 4 double needle coverstitch, zig zag, pearl stitch, safety stitch, blind stitch & bar tack machines, welt pocket machine, smocking.*
Packages:	*CMT*
Minimums:	*200 unit per style.*
Factory Locals:	*Philadelphia, PA*
Production Capacity:	*30,000 pieces*

LAUNDRY SPECIALTIES LLC

431 N. Jordan Street
Allentown, Pennsylvania 18102
Richard Koury
(1) (610) 351 3860   Fax: (1) (610) 770 1785

E-Mail:	*richard@laundryspecialties.com*
Web Site:	*www.laundryspecialties.com*
Description:	*Garment washing, bleaching & specialty washing. We can also handle sewing repairs.*
Year Est:	*2000*
Specialties:	*Unpacking & repacking of "finished" garments. Pressing, folding, hanging, pre-ticketing, baging and drop-shipping.*
Production Capacity:	*100,000 units/month*

MONALISA FASHIONS INC.

650 East Green Street
Allentown, Pennsylvania 18109
Mereille Najm
(1) (610) 770 0806   Fax: (1) (610) 770 0823

E-Mail:	*monalisamfg@gmail.com*
Web Site:	*www.monalisamfg.com*
Description:	*Family-owned CMT contractor. The 15,000SF facility includes cutting, sewing, trimming, shipping/storage.*
Year Est:	*1984*
Categories:	*Active & Athletic wear, Childrens Wear, Shirts & Tops, Swimwear, T-Shirts, Sportswear-knits, Sample Rooms/Small Production.*
Specialties:	*Garment dye, organic, contemporary knitwear, infantwear.*
Markets:	*Menswear, Womenswear, Childrens*
Machinery:	*Over-lock, safety, 2-ndl and 3-ndl cover stitch, straight stitch,*

single needle, neck tape, double needle, metal snaps, elastic cover stitch, binding, button hole, button sewer, picot machine, flatlock, heat press, fusing.

Packages:	*CMT, Sewing*
Export to:	*Canada, Europe, Asia*
Minimums:	*200 units/style*
Production Capacity:	*50,000 pcs/month*

PATTERN DESIGN UNLIMITED, INC.

See our ad on page 73

550 West Rt. 897
Reinholds, Pennsylvania 17569
Pamela Urban
(1) (717) 336 0500   Fax: (1) (717) 336 0309

E-Mail:	*pdu@patterndesign.com*
Web Site:	*www.patterndesign.com*
Description:	*20+years in business constructing cut and sew apparel & items with 30 industrial machines. All stitch & folder applications available.*
Year Est:	*1987*
Categories:	*Grading/Marking, Patternmaking, Sample Rooms/Small Production*
Specialties:	*Offering complete ""one-stop"" product development; designing, patterns, grading, marking, samples & small production runs available.*
Markets:	*Menswear, Womenswear & Childrenswear.*
Packages:	*Complete & CMT packages.*
Minimums:	*None*

PATTERN GRADING & MARKING BY ANDREW GLONINGER

5 Roberts Road
Newtown Square, Pennsylvania 19073
Andrew Gloninger
(1) (610) 356 1777   Fax: (1) (610) 356 1193

E-Mail:	*andrew@gradingandmarking.com*
Web Site:	*www.gradingandmarking.com*
Description:	*An experienced professional who provides pattern grading and marking services employing hardware and software from Lectra Systems.*
Categories:	*Grading & Marking Services*
Specialties:	*Over thirty years experience in the apparel industry.*

QUALITY CORRECTIONS & INSPECTIONS

611 Gildea Drive
Duncansville, Pennsylvania 16635

(1) (814) 696 3737   Fax: (1) (814) 696 3734

E-Mail:	*stacey_burket@qualitycorrections.com*
Web Site:	*www.qualitycorrections.com*
Description:	*Toll free#: 1-800-340-8384. Volume apparel & footwear repair facility. Guaranteed workmanship, fast turn-around.*
Year Est:	*1986*
Categories:	*Rework/Inspection, Laundry, Warehousing/Distribution Center.*
Specialties:	*Specialize in QC inspections, rework of defective merchandise, repackaging, label changes, warehouse & distribution.*

Machinery:	Sewing & button machinery. Steam tunnels, presses, spot cleaning equipment & assortment of footwear repair equipment.
Minimums:	No job is too big or too small.
Factory Locals:	Henderson, Nevada. Tel: 702-719-2322

ROBKO LLC

214 Oak Street
Nazareth, Pennsylvania 18064
Arthur Rader
(1) (610) 746 4933   Fax: (1) (610) 746 5563

E-Mail:	art@customapparelzone.com
Web Site:	www.customapparelzone.com
Description:	Full service private label manufacturing. From pattern making, grading, markers, sample making, cut and sew.
Categories:	Patternmaking, Sample Room/Small Production, Grading/Marking
Specialties:	Specialize in t-shirts, sport shirts, oxfords, onesies, sweatshirts, camp shirts, rib t-shirts, sports specialty wear.
Markets:	Menswear, Womenswear, Childrenswear

SARAH LYNN SPORTSWEAR, INC.

431 N. Jordan Street
Allentown, Pennsylvania 18102
Richard Koury
(1) (610) 770 1702   Fax: (1) (610) 770 1785

E-Mail:	rkoury@slsportswear.com
Web Site:	www.slsportswear.com
Description:	Contractor of childrenswear, activewear, knit sportswear & tee shirts.
Year Est:	1985
Categories:	Active/Athletic Wear, Sportswear-Knits, Childrenswear, Tee-Shirts
Specialties:	Experience with stretch fabrics & all types of knits. All work done in-house. Also, patternmaking, sample making & rework/inspection.
Markets:	Menswear, Womenswear & Childrenswear.
Machinery:	20 overlock, 20 safety, 8 coverstitch, 4 button, 4 binding, 9 flat-seam and more.
Packages:	Sewing only, Complete & CMT packages.
Production Capacity:	75,000 pcs/month

SCOTTEX GLOBAL SOURCING LLC

1672 Jarrettown Road
Dresher, Pennsylvania 19025
Bradley Flickstein
(1) (215) 540 1244   Fax: (1) (215) 793 0994

E-Mail:	bradley@scottexglobal.com
Web Site:	www.scottexglobal.com
Description:	Direct import private label sweater developer. Offices in Hong Kong and India.
Categories:	Sweaters/Knitwear.
Specialties:	Classified as an agent with design value added.
Factory Locals:	New York Showroom: By Appointment Only. Toll Free: 866-333-7630

SHEHU

333 S. 20th Street
Philadelphia, Pennsylvania 19148
Bela Shehu
(1) (267) 496 5208

E-Mail:	*bela@shehu.net*
Web Site:	*www.shehu.net*
Description:	*Full service design & development company. We specialize in pattern & sample making. Contractor of small production lots.*
Year Est:	*2007*
Categories:	*Patternmaking, Small Production/Samples*
Specialties:	*All types of women & girls apparel. Dresses, bottoms, tops, sleepwear, uniforms, sportswear, scarves/shawls.*
Markets:	*Womenswear & Girlswear.*
Machinery:	*5 Straight Stitch, 4 Marrow, 1 Cover Stitch, 1 Pearl Stitch, 2 Zigzag.*
Packages:	*CMT & Samples*
Production Capacity:	*500 pcs/month*

TESTFABRICS, INC.

PO Box 3026
West Pittston, Pennsylvania 18643
Tom Klaas
(1) (570) 603 0432   Fax: (1) (570) 603 0433

E-Mail:	*info@testfabrics.com*
Web Site:	*www.testfabrics.com*
Description:	*Custom sourcing/manufacturing including small lot dyeing, we also provide cutting & slitting services & special textile services.*
Categories:	*Samples/Small Production, Sourcing*
Specialties:	*Sewing including overcast merrow stitching, custom assembly of composite test specimens, samples, ""mock"" garments, etc.*
Minimums:	*One Linear Meter*

V.A. PRIVATE LABEL

3237 Amber Street
Philadelphia, Pennsylvania 19134
Sarah
(1) (215) 496 0408   Fax: (1) (215) 496 0925

E-Mail:	*info@vaprivatelabel.com*
Web Site:	*www.vaprivatelabel.com*
Description:	*Full service garment production in wovens & knits. Production samples, grading & marking, cutting, sewing, trim, pressing and packing.*
Categories:	*Sportswear/Knits, Sportswear/Wovens, Samples/Small Production*
Specialties:	*Custom silk screen printing and embroidery.*
Markets:	*Menswear & Womenswear*

Rhode Island

TURFER ATHLETIC

240 Bald Hill Road
Warwick, Rhode Island 02886
Gary Goldberg
(1) (401) 427 1369   Fax: (1) (401) 633 7061

E-Mail:	ggoldberg@turfer.com
Web Site:	www.turfer.com
Description:	We personalize & customize apparel, uniforms & accessory items for schools, teams, colleges and more.
Categories:	Uniforms
Minimums:	None

South Carolina

AIKEN INDUSTRIES, INC.

1910 Richland Avenue
Aiken, South Carolina 29801
Sarah Friedman/Cary Friedman
(1) (803) 648 5467   Fax: (1) (803) 648 5469

E-Mail:	carysarah@aol.com
Web Site:	www.aikenind.com
Description:	Contractor of ladies & mens pants & shorts, plus ladies skirts. Expert with knit & woven fabrications.
Year Est:	1962
Categories:	Pants/Shorts/Skirts, Home Furnishings
Markets:	Menswear & Womenswear.
Packages:	Cutting & Sewing, Complete & CMT packages available.
Minimums:	100 dozen/style
Factory Locals:	Aiken factory also has a controlled environment cleanroom for assembly of sewn & non-sewn health care products.
Production Capacity:	10,000 pcs/month

CAROLINA COTTON WORKS, INC.

14 Commerce Drive
Gaffney, South Carolina 29340
Bryan
(1) (864) 488 2824   Fax: (1) (864) 488 0488

E-Mail:	bryan@carolinacotton.com
Web Site:	www.carolinacotton.com
Description:	Knit fabric dyeing & finishing. Jersey, rib, fleece, french terry, interlock, pique, thermal & herringbone.
Categories:	Dyeing/Finishing Contractors
Machinery:	State-of-the-art equipment yields excellent shrinkage control.
Minimums:	800 lbs.

CRAIG INDUSTRIES
213 Pearl Street
Lamar, South Carolina 29069
Larry Crolley
(1) (843) 326 5561   Fax: (1) (843) 326 1234

E-Mail:	*craig.ind@craigindustries.net*
Categories:	*Shirts/Tops, Tee Shirts.*
Specialties:	*Placket shirts, tee shirts.*
Markets:	*Menswear, Womenswear, Boyswear.*
Machinery:	*Hemmers, pocket setters, placket fusing, serger & embroidery. Also, marking, grading & cutting equipment.*
Packages:	*Complete & CMT.*
Minimums:	*100 dozen/style*
Factory Locals:	*Plants in Lamar & Dalzell, SC.*

HARODITE INDUSTRIES, INC.
2 Henderson Court
Travelers Rest, South Carolina 29690
Tommy Bridges
(1) (864) 834 9066   Fax: (1) (864) 834 9089

E-Mail:	*tbridges@harodite.com*
Web Site:	*www.harodite.com*
Description:	*Custom finishing, coating, laminating, sheeting & die cutting of woven & non-woven textiles.*
Year Est:	*1910*
Categories:	*Finishing/coating*
Specialties:	*Specialize in shirt interlinings.*
Factory Locals:	*Taunton, Massachusetts and Travelers Rest, South Carolina in USA, plus, Aguascalientes, Mexico & Olocuilta, El Salvador.*

HARRIS PILLOW SUPPLY INC.
3026 Trask Parkway
Beaufort, South Carolina 29906
John Harris
(1) 800 845 8240   Fax: (1) 843 846 4196

E-Mail:	*john@harrispillow.com*
Web Site:	*www.harrispillow.com*
Description:	*Contractor & manufacturer specializing in pillows. Quick turn-around.*
Year Est:	*1958*
Exporting Since:	*1980*
Categories:	*Home Furnishings.*
Specialties:	*Feather & down pillows & synthetic down (Comforel) pillows.*
Markets:	*Home Furnishings*
Machinery:	*Sewing, spreading, custom built pillow blower & pillow filling machines in house.*
Packages:	*Full packages available.*
Export to:	*Canada 3%, Europe 2%*
Minimums:	*None*
Production Capacity:	*20,000 pcs/month*

HEMINGWAY APPAREL MFG., INC.

Highway 41 North, P.O. Box 459
Hemingway, South Carolina 29554
Jack Marsh
(1) (843) 558 3482   Fax: (1) (843) 558 9530

E-Mail:	*jmarsh@hemingwayapparel.com*
Web Site:	*www.hemingwayapparel.com*
Description:	*Sewing contractor of ladies tee shirts, sleepwear, panties & lingerie.*
Year Est:	*1978*
Categories:	*Tee Shirts, Lingerie/Intimate Apparel, Sleepwear/Robes.*
Specialties:	*Service for product development.*
Markets:	*Womenswear*
Machinery:	*200 overlock, 20 zig-zag, 80 coverstitch, single needle, double needle, multi-needle, all types of hemmers & more.*
Packages:	*Sewing & CMT. Cutting room on premises.*
Minimums:	*1,000 dozen/style, sleepwear: 500 dozen/style*
Production Capacity:	*32,000 dozen/month*

IDEA LLC.

6331 Fain Street
North Charleston, South Carolina 29406
Tom DeMuth
(1) (843) 744 2727   Fax: (1) (843) 744 9993

E-Mail:	*tomdemuth@ideallc.com*
Web Site:	*www.ideallc.com*
Description:	*3PL, US materials and finished goods distributor, currently working with Wal-Mart, KMart, Target, Marshalls.*
Categories:	*Freight Forwarder/Customs Broker, Distribution/Warehouse*
Specialties:	*LCL/FCL consolidation, door to door US to Honduras, El Salvador, Nicaragua and Guatemala.*
Factory Locals:	*Warehouses in San Pedro Sula Honduras, San Salvador El Salvador and Managua Nicaragua.*

INTEDGE INDUSTRIES INC.

1875 Chumley Road
Woodruff, South Carolina 29388

(1) (864) 969 9601   Fax: (1) (864) 969 9604

E-Mail:	*sales@intedge.com*
Web Site:	*www.intedge.com*
Description:	*Contractor of sewn kitchen products & men's & women's chef wear.*
Year Est:	*1914*
Categories:	*Uniforms, Home Furnishings.*
Markets:	*Mainly restaurant industry, but open to more.*
Machinery:	*3 overlock, 10 single needle, 1 double needle, 1 bartack, 2 buttonhole, & multi-needle quilting machinery.*
Packages:	*Sewing*
Export to:	*Canada 10%, Puerto Rico 2%*

Minimums: None

JOCASSEE DESIGNS INC.
311 Tucapau Road
Duncan, South Carolina 29334
Julie Edwards
(1) (864) 433 1113   Fax: (1) (864) 433 1204

E-Mail:	julie@jocasseedesigns.com
Web Site:	www.jocasseedesigns.com
Description:	Embroidery contractor
Year Est:	1985
Categories:	Embroidery
Specialties:	Custom embroidery on piece or finished goods.
Markets:	All
Machinery:	In-house digitizing, 452 embroidery heads & a complete packing line.

MCBEE MANUFACTURING COMPANY
347 West Cypress Avenue
McBee, South Carolina 29101
John/Tom Campolong
(1) (843) 335 8234   Fax: (1) (843) 335 8236

E-Mail:	vinci@shtc.net
Web Site:	www.vinciclothiers.com
Description:	Contractor of ladies woven sportswear, tops, bottoms, jackets, pants & skirts.
Year Est:	1960
Categories:	Sportswear-Wovens, Coats/Jackets, Pants/Shorts/Skirts.
Markets:	Womenswear
Machinery:	Complete range of machinery.
Packages:	CMT & Full packages available.
Minimums:	Vary
Factory Locals:	McBee & Camden, South Carolina

REST IN BEAUTY, INC.
771 Bridge Street
Bamberg, South Carolina 29003
Teresa Dansby
(1) (803) 245 5126   Fax: (1) (803) 245 5665

E-Mail:	restinbeauty@bellsouth.net
Web Site:	www.restinbeauty.com
Description:	Design & manufacturers of ladies burial garments. Dresses, gowns, accessories, hankies, slippers and gloves.
Categories:	Accessories, Dresses
Specialties:	Design, engineering, cutting room & sourcing available. Quick delivery.
Markets:	Womenswear, Accessories.
Machinery:	Single needle, double needle, sergers, zig-zag & cover stitch machinery.
Packages:	Sewing & CMT.

Minimums:	*250 pieces/style*

VAPOR APPAREL

2120 Noisette Boulevard
North Charleston, South Carolina 29405
Christopher Bernat
(1) (843) 747 4200   Fax: (1) (843) 747 4211

E-Mail:	*sales@sourcesubstrates.com*
Web Site:	*www.vaporapparel.com*
Description:	*High quality performance apparel specifically engineered for digital decorating, screenprinting & embroidery.*
Categories:	*Activewear*
Specialties:	*Offer cut & sew custom garment services as well as full private label programs.*
Markets:	*Menswear, Womenswear, Childrenswear.*
Factory Locals:	*Bogota, Colombia*

Texas

APPAREL MARK SERVICES

7117 Orizaba Avenue
El Paso, Texas 79912
Barbara Bean
(1) (915) 833 2643

E-Mail:	*barbbctx@yahoo.com*
Description:	*Pattern grading and marking services.*
Categories:	*Grading & Marking*
Markets:	*Womenswear, Menswear.*

AXIS MOON DESIGN AND PRODUCTION

809 S. Brighton
Dallas, Texas 75208
Ellen Kreager
(1) (214) 395 1277

E-Mail:	*ellenkreager@gmail.com*
Web Site:	*www.axismoon.com*
Description:	*Sewing contractor of all types of apparel. Small and large production runs. Also, design, consulting and sourcing.*
Year Est:	*1986*
Specialties:	*Patternmaking, production, sourcing, cutting & graphic art work. Own Cutting Room on premises.*
Markets:	*Menswear, Womenswear, Children, Accessories, Home.*
Machinery:	*4 single needle, 1buttonhole, 3 serger, 1 button, 2 merrow, 1 leather/walking foot, 1 blindstitch.*
Packages:	*Complete & CMT packages.*
Minimums:	*50*
Production Capacity:	*3000 pcs/monthly*

CUSTOM CHENILLE EMBROIDERY

11330 Hillguard
Dallas, Texas 75243
Ken Gilmer, President
(1) (214) 343 0888   Fax: (1) (214) 349 8884

E-Mail:	*kgilmer@chenille.com*
Web Site:	*www.chenille.com*
Description:	*1-800-227-2040. Garment decoration, including traditional chenille embroidery appliques & emblems on any type of apparel.*
Categories:	*Embroidery.*
Specialties:	*Sportswear & uniform decoration .*
Markets:	*Menswear, Womenswear, Childrenswear & Home.*
Machinery:	*80 embroidery, 80 chenille embroidery machines.*
Minimums:	*12 dozen/style*
Production Capacity:	*600,000 units/month*

FRENCH CURVE DESIGNS

906 West McDermott Drive
Allen, Texas 75013
Heather Madrid
(1) 972 571 1196   Fax: (1) 972 534 1218

E-Mail:	*hmadrid@frenchcurvedesigns.com*
Web Site:	*www.frenchcurvedesigns.com*
Categories:	*Grading/Marking, Patternmaking*
Specialties:	*Tech design, spec writing, patternmaking, grading/marking*
Markets:	*Menswear, Womenswear & Childrenswear.*

G & M SERVICES

2807 Satsuma Drive
Dallas, Texas 75229

(1) (214) 358 0041   Fax: (1) (214) 358 0042

E-Mail:	*gary@gmser.com*
Web Site:	*www.gmser.com*
Description:	*Grading, marking & copy service, Patternmaking*
Year Est:	*1992*
Specialties:	*Samples & patternmaking with Pattern Maker onsite.*
Markets:	*Menswear, Womenswear & Childrenswear.*
Machinery:	*Infinity I Plotter, Infinity II Plotter, Gerber Accumark System, Lectra System, Microdynamics System.*

GEMBA GROUP, INC.

501 N Bridge Street
Hidalgo, Texas 78557
Jorge Avila Trevino
(1) (956) 607 0890

E-Mail:	*joavila@gembagroup.com*
Description:	*Contract manufacturer of fire retardant garments & Arc Flash Suits up to HRC4.*
Categories:	*Shirts/Tops, Pants, Uniforms*
Specialties:	*Coveralls, hoods, bibs, jackets, pants & lab coats out of FR fabrics like*

Nomex, Westex Indura/Ultrasoft, Milliken Amplitude, Itex & Keviar fabrics.
Factory Locals: *Mexico tel#899 132-6161*

GENESIS IMPORTS
2408 Royal Lytham Drive
Austin, Texas 64500
Art Kimbel
(1) (512) 292 4000   Fax: (1) (512) 292 4515

E-Mail:	*akimbel@aol.com*
Web Site:	*www.genesismexico.com*
Description:	*Cut & sew contractors of work shirts, chef coats, coveralls, promotional articles, aprons, napkins, pillowcases & laundry bags.*
Year Est:	*1993*
Exporting Since:	*1995*
Categories:	*Uniforms, Accessories, Home Furnishings*
Specialties:	*Uniforms*
Machinery:	*160 sewing machines. Single needle, overlocking, double needle, bar tack, flat safety stitch, button, buttonholers & cutting knives, plus 2 20-ton die cut presses & 2 50-foot cutting tables.*
Export to:	*USA & Canada.*
Minimums:	*None*
Factory Locals:	*Promotora Genesis in Monterrey, Mexico. Two locations with over 30,000 sq ft. Registered with the FDA in USA.*

IN.STYLE EXCHANGE™
See our ad on page 75

1844 W. Division Street
Arlington, Texas 76012
Sales Manager
(1) (817) 886 9222

E-Mail:	*info@instyleexchange.com*
Web Site:	*www.instyleexchange.com*
Description:	*Private label sampling and production for men's, women's & kid's apparel & accessories.*
Categories:	*Sample Rooms/Small Production, Production Sourcing, Shirts & Tops, Childrens Wear, Dresses & Blouses, Lingerie, Sleepwear & Robes.*
Specialties:	*Product development, fabric sourcing, sampling, grading/marking, patternmaking, production, embroidery & screenprinting.*
Packages:	*Private label & full packages.*
Minimums:	*50 pieces per color per style*
Production Capacity:	*50,000 pcs/month*

KRISTABEN
233 Yorktown Street
Dallas, Texas 75208
Dinh Yang
(1) (214) 760 9796   Fax: (1) (214) 760 9744

E-Mail:	*dinhyang@hotmail.com*
Web Site:	*www.kristaben.com*
Description:	*Open to small production. Specializing in lingerie, baby and childrenswear.*
Categories:	*Sample Rooms/Small Production*

Specialties:	Start-up companies welcome! Product development and Consulting work provided.
Markets:	Ladies, baby & childrenswear markets.
Packages:	Full Packages.
Minimums:	100 pieces
Factory Locals:	Vietnam

METRO TEXTILE INC.

9995 Monroe Drive
Dallas, Texas 75220
Zee Maya
(1) 214 352 0219   Fax: (1) 888 672 2091

E-Mail:	zee@mtcsourcing.com
Web Site:	www.mtcsourcing.com
Description:	Sourcing, quality management, merchandising, inspection services, logistic assistance & negotiation for its clients.
Year Est:	2001
Categories:	Production Sourcing/Factory Agents
Specialties:	Specialize in knitted & woven ready-made garments plus knitted & woven fabrics, hosiery and home textiles.
Markets:	Menswear, Womenswear, Childrenswear & Home.
Export to:	USA & Europe
Minimums:	None
Factory Locals:	Work with over 30 different factories in Pakistan, China & Bangladesh. Pakistan Office: 92 300 824 5884.

NEW ICM, LP

220 Sam Bishkin Road
El Campo, Texas 77437
R. C. Whitson, Projects Coordinator
(1) (979) 578 0543   Fax: (1) (979) 578 0503

E-Mail:	rcwhitson@newicm.com
Web Site:	www.newicm.com
Description:	Manufacturer, designer & contractor of children's sleepwear, dresses, sportswear & activewear.
Year Est:	1948
Categories:	Childrenswear, Activewear, Sleepwear/Robes, Workwear Uniforms
Specialties:	Flame resistant children's sleepwear, undergarments & slips. Also, industrial workwear coveralls & insulated jackets.
Markets:	Childrenswear
Machinery:	Over 400 serger, safety stitch, double & triple needle, cover stitch, single needle, zig-zag & numerous other special-operations machines.
Export to:	Piece goods & trims for various programs exported to countries in Latin America & Asia.
Minimums:	Domestic - none, overseas - negotiable.
Factory Locals:	El Campo, TX. Also affiliated with factories in Mexico, Dominican Republic, China & Southeast Asia.
Production Capacity:	4,000 units/day for domestic. Virtually unlimited for overseas.

SQUEEGEE PRINTERS

4067 VT Route 102
Canaan, Vermont 05903
Pat Beauregard
(1) (802) 266 3426   Fax: (1) (802) 266 3654

E-Mail:	*squeegee@together.net*
Description:	*Toll-free: 1-800-962-0252. Cater to corporate, special events, advertising specialties & resortwear.*
Year Est:	*1984*
Categories:	*Embroidery, Screenprinting Contractors*
Specialties:	*Full service contract embroiderer & screen printer.*
Machinery:	*M & R Challenger 8-color & M & R Gauntlet II 10-color. 2 Automatic press, 1 14-head embroidery machine.*
Minimums:	*12 dozen*
Production Capacity:	*Screenprinting: 350 units/hour, Embroidery: Varies*

BLOOM FASHION USA

5589-B Guinea Road
Fairfax, Virginia 22032

(1) (703) 323 6793   Fax: (1) (703) 323 6795

E-Mail:	*sales@bloomfashionusa.com*
Web Site:	*www.bloomfashionusa.com*
Description:	*Sewing contractor of all types of casual wear, childrens wear and uniforms.*
Categories:	*Uniforms, Childrens Wear, Pants/Shorts/Skirts*
Specialties:	*We can help you start your new business. 100% of our products are made in the USA.*
Markets:	*Menswear, Womenswear, Childrenswear.*
Minimums:	*Low Minimums*

CHATHAM KNITTING MILLS, INC.

P.O. Box 152
Chatham, Virginia 24531
Matt Harris
(1) (434) 432 4701 x11   Fax: (1) (434) 432 3742

E-Mail:	*mattharris2006@gmail.com*
Description:	*Contract sewing of men's & women's outerwear. Also, correction facility & prison uniforms & work coats.*
Year Est:	*1951*
Categories:	*Coats/Jackets, Uniforms.*
Packages:	*Sewing only & complete packages.*
Minimums:	*None*

HEIDI-HO, INC.
8322 George Washington Hwy
Keysville, Virginia 23947

(1) (434) 736 8763   Fax: (1) (434) 736 0646

E-Mail:	*heidiho@kinex.net*
Description:	*Cut, sew and finish contractor since 1976. Dance costumes, swimwear, kids clothes woven and knit.*
Categories:	*Dancewear/Swimwear*
Markets:	*Womenswear, Girlswear, Infantwear.*

LACORP/LEBANON APPAREL CORP.
70 Thornhill Drive
Lebanon, Virginia 24266
Jeoff Bodenhorst
(1) (276) 889 3656   Fax: (1) (276) 889 2830

E-Mail:	*jeoff@lacorpusa.com*
Web Site:	*www.lacorpusa.com*
Description:	*Contractor of all types of bottoms, childrenswear, uniforms, aprons & home furnishings. Plus rework and inspection services.*
Year Est:	*1968*
Categories:	*Pants/shorts/skirts, Childrenswear, Uniforms, Home Furnishings, Rework & Inspection Services.*
Specialties:	*Specialize in mattress zipper covers, pillows, pillow covers, medical uniforms and re-work.*
Markets:	*Menswear, Womenswear, Childrenswear & Home.*
Machinery:	*Over 500 various sewing machines & electronic cutting, embroidery & besum pocket equipment on site.*
Packages:	*CMT, Sewing, Cutting, Sample Making & Embroidery.*
Minimums:	*Will adjust to fit your needs.*
Factory Locals:	*All work is done in-house.*

LOGOS FASHION SERVICE
3215 RiverView Drive
Triangle, Virginia 22172
Sylvie Tran
(1) (703) 879 8827   Fax: (1) (703) 995 4336

E-Mail:	*info@logosfashionservice.com*
Web Site:	*www.logosfashionservice.com*
Description:	*One-stop service and sourcing partner for projects small and large for designers, retailers and private label.*
Year Est:	*2009*
Exporting Since:	*2009*
Categories:	*Production Sourcing/Factory Agent*
Specialties:	*Design Development, material & trims sourcing, textile printing, tags, patternmaking, fitting, samples, sewing, cutting, grading & marking.*
Markets:	*Menswear, Womenswear, Children*
Machinery:	*200 Single Needle, 30 Double Needle, 5 Flatlock, 2 Buttonhole*
Packages:	*CMT & Complete packages, also screenprinting & embroidery.*
Export to:	*USA 70%, Europe 20%, Asia 5%, Australia 5%*
Minimums:	*No sewing minimums*

Factory Locals:	*181 79 Street, Tan Quy Ward, District 7,*
	Ho Chi Minh City, Vietnam tel:84-8-3775-0529
Production Capacity:	*100,000 - 500,000 pcs.*

SOLID STONE FABRICS
26 Fayette Street
Martinsville, Virginia 24112
David Stone
(1) (276) 634 0115   Fax: (1) (276) 632 8986

E-Mail:	*dstone@solidstonefabrics.com*
Web Site:	*www.solidstonefabrics.com*
Description:	*Cut and sew contractor of dancewear and clothing for athletes such as gymnasts.*
Categories:	*Dancewear, Athleticwear, Small Production*
Specialties:	*Small production lots.*
Markets:	*Menswear & Womenswear.*
Minimums:	*Small*

SUNDOG PRODUCTIONS
3850 Jermantown Road
Fairfax, Virginia 22030
John
(1) (703) 978 0041   Fax: (1) (703) 978 0043

E-Mail:	*j.sague@sunpup.com*
Web Site:	*www.sunpup.com*
Description:	*Custom dye work, design work or screenprinting on tee shirts.*
Categories:	*Screenprinting, Dyeing Contractor*
Specialties:	*Proprietary printing process using seaweed instead of plastisol or traditional water based inks. It has no phalyet PVC's resins or binders.*

Washington

SEWN PRODUCT SERVICES
111 S. Lander Street
Seattle, Washington 98134
Kristine Carlton/Jenny Mae Miller
(1) (206) 467 5459   Fax: (1) (206) 467 5459

E-Mail:	*contact@sewnproductservices.com*
Web Site:	*www.sewnproductservices.com*
Description:	*Design consultation, patternmaking, sample sewing, raw goods sourcing, grading & marking, fit assesments, tech pack development.*
Categories:	*Athletic/Activewear, Lingerie/Intimate Apparel, Sleepwear, Leather Apparel, Swimwear, Costuming, Dancewear, Soft Goods Accessories*
Specialties:	*We offer a full menu of services supporting sewn product development including production management & small run production.*
Markets:	*Menswear, Womenswear & Childrenswear.*

Wisconsin

JONCO INDUSTRIES INC.

2501 West Hampton Avenue
Milwaukee, Wisconsin 53209

(1) (414) 449 2000   Fax: (1) (414) 449 5200

E-Mail:	*tom.ryan@joncoind.com*
Web Site:	*www.joncoind.com*
Description:	*Industrial sewing contractor.*
	Also provide packaging & complete warehousing.
Year Est:	*1980*
Categories:	*Distribution/Warehouse, Samples/Small Production, Uniforms, Accessories*
Specialties:	*Open for all your apparel sewing needs. All work done in-house.*
Markets:	*Menswear & Womenswear*
Machinery:	*5 Juki, 3 Consew, 3 Singer, 1 Melco Amaya, 1 Pegasus*
	2 Path Finder Cutters, 1 Kongsberg, 1 5' x 10' Laser.
Minimums:	*None*
Production Capacity:	*Varies by Item*

D'CLASE APPAREL INTERNATIONAL

Zona Franca Industrial
Gurabo
Santiago 1425
Dominican Republic
Jose Clase-President
(1) 829 947 7000   Fax: (1) 829 947 7177

E-Mail:	*cpizano@dclase.com*
Description:	*Manufacturer of footwear.*
Year Est:	*2005*
Exporting Since:	*2005*
Specialties:	*Hand sewn boat shoes, handsewn slippers and boots. Will do samples.*
Markets:	*Menswear, Womenswear & Youthwear.*
Machinery:	*Modern equipment*
Packages:	*Full Package*
Export to:	*United States, Europe*
Factory Locals:	*4 factories in Esperanza, Dominican Republic*

INDUSTRIAS TEBI, S.A. DE C. V.

Calle 5 No 16 Bodega 2
Fracc Ind Alce Blanco
Naucalpan, Estado de Mexico 53370
Mexico
Alfonso Entebi Yedid
(52) (55) 5254 8460   Fax: (52) (55) 5254 8136

E-Mail:	*ventas@tebi.com.mx*
Web Site:	*www.tebi.com.mx*
Description:	*Socks for babies and infants.*
Year Est:	*1971*
Exporting Since:	*2000*
Machinery:	*200 Single & double cylinder sock machines*
Export to:	*USA*
Minimums:	*None*
Production Capacity:	*1,000,000 pairs/monthly*

ONTARIO GLOVE MANUFACTURING CO., LTD.

5 Washburn Drive, Unit A

Kitchener, Ontario N2R 1S1
Canada

(1) (519) 886 3590   Fax: (1) (519) 886 3597

E-Mail:	*sales@ontarioglove.com*
Web Site:	*www.ontarioglove.com*
Description:	*Manufacturer & contractor of gloves of all types.*
Year Est:	*1914*
Exporting Since:	*1926*
Specialties:	*All styles of gloves, mitts, protective clothing & workwear (casual, ski, snowboard etc.).*
Markets:	*Menswear, Womenswear & Childrenswear.*

Machinery:	Sewing, Cutting, etc.
Export to:	United States, South America, Far East
Minimums:	Large Volume
Factory Locals:	Waterloo, Ontario, Canada

GRUVEN INTERNATIONAL INC.

19 Newgale Gate

Scarborough, Ontario M1X 1B6
Canada
Dave Rushton, Sales Director
(1) (416) 292 7331   Fax: (1) (416) 754 8675

E-Mail:	*drushton@gruven.com*
Web Site:	*www.gruven.com*
Description:	*Manufacturer & sewing contractor of technical outerwear, sportswear, knitwear & fleecewear.*
Year Est:	*1985*
Exporting Since:	*1985*
Categories:	*Coats/Jackets*
Specialties:	*Leading sublimated apparel specialists with artwork, printing, assembly under one roof. Complete turnaround time in 2.5 weeks for most orders.*
Markets:	*Menswear, Womenswear, Boyswear, Girlswear.*
Machinery:	*150 Single/double needle, 100 Serger*
Packages:	*All packages - screenprinting, quilting & embroidery.*
Export to:	*USA, Sweden & Japan.*
Minimums:	*250 units/style*
Factory Locals:	*Three factories in Scarborough, Ontario NAFTA certified.*

TEXTILES OPICO DBA TEXOPS

KM 31.4 Carretera a Santa Ana
San Juan Opico
La Libertad
El Salvador
Juan C. Zighelboim
() (503) 2319 0800   Fax: () (503) 2319 0812

E-Mail:	*juan.zighelboim@texops.com*
Web Site:	*www.texops.com*
Description:	*Private label contract manufacturing of active and athletic wear. Specialists in stretch synthetic fabrics with flat seams.*
Year Est:	*2008*
Exporting Since:	*2008*
Categories:	*Athletic wear, Sportswear-Wovens, Sportswear-Knits.*
Specialties:	*Specialize in knit apparel, sublimation, active, yoga, compression, fitness, cycling, running, team sports, plaquet polo shirts.*
Markets:	*Menswear, Womenswear, Boyswear, Girlswear.*
Machinery:	*200 flat seam, 265 cover stitch, 275 overlock, 250 lock stitch, 14 digital dye-sublimation printers, 4 Monti-Antonio fabric & cut part sublimation presses, 3 Lectra automated cutters, 4 Oteman Synergy Auto Spreaders, Raw Materials testing lab.*
Packages:	*Complete private label & full packages.*
Export to:	*USA 85%, Asia 5%, Canada 5%, Europe 5%,*
Agent:	*From USA - 305-503-4139 x 550*
Minimums:	*50 dozen/style*
Factory Locals:	*El Salvador*
Production Capacity:	*360,000 tops/month, 360,000 bottoms/month*

VICKY FORM, S.A. DE C.V.

Recursos Hidraulicos #2
Fracc. Industrial La Loma
Tlalnepantla, Estado de Mexico, C.P. 54060
Mexico
Kila Tochijara
(52) (55) 5333 0360   Fax: (52) (55) 5333 0361

E-Mail:	*expzaga@zaga.com*
Web Site:	*www.vickyform.com, www.zaga.com*
Description:	*Manufacturer of lingerie collections, casualwear, yoga pants, activewear, pajamas and men's underwear.*
Year Est:	*1964*
Exporting Since:	*1992*
Categories:	*Lingerie/Intimate/Underwear*
Specialties:	*Computerized pattern, marking and grading, Gerber brand sample - sample room in-house.*
Markets:	*Menswear, Womenswear, Teens, Childrenswear*
Packages:	*Full package based on program and volume*
Export to:	*U.S.A, Costa Rica, Canada*
Minimums:	*1,200 - 7,000 pieces/color*
Factory Locals:	*Tepeji Del Rio, Tulanciango*
Production Capacity:	*600,000+ units/month*

GRUPO BAMEX S.A. DE C.V.

Venustiano Carranza 477 Sur

Monterrey, N.L. 64000
Mexico
Ruben Marcos
(52) (81) 8130 7800   Fax: (52) (81) 8345 7271

E-Mail:	*rmarcos@grupobamex.com*
Web Site:	*www.mariscalmoda.com*
Description:	*Full package contractor of all types of pants & shirts for children.*
Year Est:	*1948*
Categories:	*Shirts/Tops, Uniforms, Pants*
Specialties:	*Samples available*
Markets:	*Menswear, Boyswear*
Packages:	*Sewing, cutting, patternmaking, grading/marking*
Export to:	*United States 10%*
Minimums:	*300 pcs/style*
Factory Locals:	*All work done in-house.*
	www.johnhenry.com.mx, www.grupobamex.com
Production Capacity:	*Shirts: 100,000 pcs/month, Pants: 20,000 pcs/month*

HANDWORKS

Centro Textil San Jorge local 10
Prolongacion Avenida Juan Pablo
San Salvador
El Salvador
Alessandra Castellanos - President
(503) 7886 5243   Fax: (503) 2225 9734

E-Mail:	*aoriggi@yahoo.com*
Description:	*Childrenswear manufacturer. Expert with all childrenswear styles, hand smocked girl's dresses, boy's clothing, diaper bags & bibs.*
Year Est:	*1991*
Exporting Since:	*1991*
Categories:	*Childrens Wear, Sportswear - Wovens*
Markets:	*Boyswear, Girlswear, Infantwear.*
Machinery:	*260 sewing machines. Also cutting facitily & Gerber plotter.*
Packages:	*Full packages.*
Export to:	*U.S.A. 100%*
Minimums:	*Vary - depending on product*
Factory Locals:	*El Salvador*
Production Capacity:	*3,000-5,000 dozen/week, depending on product.*

LD EL SALVADOR

Parque Industrial Zone

Franca San Salvador
El Salvador

(503) 2213 0909   Fax: (503) 2213 0912

E-Mail:	*cecile.reyes@mail.com*

Description:	*Contractor expert in all types of boyswear.*
	55,000 sq. ft. facility in El Salvador.
Categories:	*Shirts/Tops*
Specialties:	*Sourcing locations in Korea, Vietnam, Bangladesh, Cambodia &*
	Shanghai, China. J.C. Penney, Wal-Mart & Sears certified.
Markets:	*Menswear & Boyswear.*
Export to:	*U.S.A.*

VESTININA, S.A. DE C.V.
Avena #532 A - PlantaBaja

Granjas, D.F. 08400
Mexico
Abraham Daniel
(52) (55) 5654 7388   Fax: (52) (55) 5657 0091

E-Mail:	*vesti@vesti.com.mx*
Web Site:	*www.vesti.com.mx*
Description:	*Contractor of all types of childrenswear.*
Year Est:	*1985*
Exporting Since:	*1990*
Markets:	*Girlswear*
Export to:	*Canada, Costa Rica, Chile*
Production Capacity:	*35,000 pcs/month*

GLOBAL CMT CORPORATION

Zona Franca Industrial Santiago

Santiago
Dominican Republic
Francisco Rodriguez
(1) (809) 575 4777   Fax: (1) (809) 575 1232

E-Mail:	*f.rodriguez@globalcmt.com*
Web Site:	*www.globalcmt.com*
Description:	*Specialize in the production of tailored clothing as well as overcoats, uniforms and tuxedos.*
Categories:	*Uniforms, Suits/Tailored Clothing*
Markets:	*Menswear, Womenswear, Childrenswear.*
Packages:	*Full and partial packages*

GRUVEN INTERNATIONAL INC.

19 Newgale Gate

Scarborough, Ontario M1X 1B6
Canada
Dave Rushton, Sales Director
(1) (416) 292 7331   Fax: (1) (416) 754 8675

E-Mail:	*drushton@gruven.com*
Web Site:	*www.gruven.com*
Description:	*Manufacturer & sewing contractor of outerwear, knitwear & fleecewear.*
Year Est:	*1985*
Exporting Since:	*1985*
Categories:	*Active/Athletic Wear*
Specialties:	*Leading sublimated apparel specialists with artwork, printing, assembly under one roof. Complete turnaround time in 2.5 weeks for most orders.*
Markets:	*Menswear, Womenswear, Boyswear, Girlswear.*
Machinery:	*150 Single/double needle, 100 Serger*
Packages:	*All packages - screenprinting, quilting & embroidery.*
Export to:	*USA, Sweden & Japan.*
Minimums:	*250 units/style*
Factory Locals:	*Three factories in Scarborough, Ontario NAFTA certified.*

INDUSTRIAS MACYS S.A. DE C.V.

Jose Maria Izazaga 99 Piso #8
Colonia Centro
Mexico D.F., 06090
Mexico
Emilio Penhos
(52) (55) 5709 7620   Fax: (52) (55) 5709 1588

E-Mail:	*dpenhos@laurence.com.mx*
Web Site:	*www.laurence.com.mx*
Description:	*Expert resource in Mexico for fully lined jackets & more.*
Year Est:	*1986*
Exporting Since:	*1990*

Categories:	Dresses/Blouses, Shirts/Tops, Pants/Skirts
Markets:	Womenswear.
Machinery:	623 machines, all types.
Packages:	CMT & Full, Pattern/Samplemaking, Printing & CAD.
Minimums:	100 dozen/style
Factory Locals:	7 sewing plants & 2 cutting plants in & around Mexico City.

ORIGINALES SHYLA, S.A. DE C.V.

Jose Maria Izazaga No. 65 Local 17

Centro, Mexico, Distrito Federal 06080
Mexico
Lic. Benjamin Penhos Mougrabi
(52) (55) 57090018   Fax: (52) (55) 57090018

E-Mail:	bpm@originalesshyla.com
Web Site:	www.originalesshyla.com
Description:	Mexican company with more than 44 years of experience making clothes.
Year Est:	1969
Exporting Since:	2002
Specialties:	Specialize in women's raincoats and wool coats.
Markets:	Womenswear
Export to:	USA 100%
Agent:	USA: 1-877-235-4457
Minimums:	200 pcs/style
Production Capacity:	30,000 pcs/month

D'CLASE APPAREL INTERNATIONAL

Zona Franca Industrial
Gurabo
Santiago 1425
Dominican Republic
Jose Clase-President
(1) 829 947 7000   Fax: (1) 829 947 7177

E-Mail:	*cpizano@dclase.com*
Description:	*Apparel manufacturers of all styles of dresses. Laundry facilities.*
Year Est:	*1986*
Exporting Since:	*1986*
Categories:	*Pants/shorts/skirts, Uniforms*
Specialties:	*Complete testing laboratory for fabric & finished goods. Will do samples.*
Markets:	*Menswear, Womenswear & Youthwear.*
Machinery:	*Modern equipment for cutting, sewing & finishing of casual pants, uniforms, dresses.*
Packages:	*CMT, Full Packages, EDI & complete service programs.*
Export to:	*United States 98%, Canada 2%*
Minimums:	*5,000 per style/1,000 units per color/15 SKU's*
Factory Locals:	*4 factories in Esperanza, Dominican Republic*

DA SAN, S.A. DE C.V.

Km 26, Carretera a Sonsonate
Jurisdiccion de Lourdes Colon
La Libertad
El Salvador
Richard Kim
() (503) 2322 2100   Fax: () (503) 2318 1748

E-Mail:	*richard.kim@dasan.com.sv*
Description:	*Contractor pants, skirts, tops, vests, blouses & dresses.*
Year Est:	*1993*
Categories:	*Pants/Skirts, Shirts & Tops*
Markets:	*Womenswear*
Machinery:	*Over 1,400 pieces of machinery on premises.*
Packages:	*CMT & 807.*
Export to:	*U.S.A*
Factory Locals:	*El Salvador*
Production Capacity:	*100,000 units/month (tops, jackets), 35,000 units/month (bottoms) 100,000 units/month (knits).*

INDUSTRIAS FLORENZI, S.A. DE C.V.

Calle Al Matazano
Contiguo al Plantel de Salud Publica
Soyapango
El Salvador
Roberto Pineda Letona, President
() (503) 2297 0577   Fax: () (503) 2297 1223

E-Mail:	*r_pineda@navegante.com.sv*
Description:	*Contractor of dresses, sportswear & shirts.*

Year Est:	1985
Categories:	Sportswear, Uniforms
Specialties:	Patternmaking, grading, marker making, plotter service, cutting service, label printing, sewing (knitted & woven).
Markets:	Girlswear, Womenswear, Unisex.
Machinery:	180 single needle, 20 double needle, 8 multi needle, 90 safety stitch, 10 blindstitch, 15 button hole, 10 button sewing, 10 bartackers, 2 multineedle, 5 zig zag, 30 coverstitch, 15 hand irons, 3 hoffman pressers, 8 spreaders, 1 bias slitter, 2 fusing.
Packages:	807 & Full package.
Export to:	United States
Minimums:	500 pcs.
Production Capacity:	50,000 units/month

BORDALO PUNTO COM S.A. DE C.V.
Venustiano Carranza No. 34
10 de Abril,
Naucalpan, State of Mexico 53310
Mexico
Gustavo Aranda
(52) (55) 1991 4040

E-Mail:	*info@bordalo.com*
Web Site:	*www.bordalo.com*
Description:	*Embroidery contractor. Caps, emblems, shirts, uniforms & bags.*
Factory Locals:	*Mobile: 52 55 45234757*

info@fashiondex.com © The Fashiondex, Inc.

COLCHAS MEXICO S.A. DE C.V.

Km. 35-5 Manzana 823 Lote 9
Colonia San Lorenzo Riotenco
Cuautitlan Izcalli, Estado de Mexico 54713
Mexico
Daniel Saadia
(52) (55) 50615200   Fax: (52) (55) 50615208

E-Mail:	*dsaadia@colchasconcord.com*
Web Site:	*www.colchasconcord.com*
Description:	*Bedding & home textiles manufacturer, from greige goods to finished products. We can print fabrics in rotary scenes & flat screens.*
Year Est:	*1959*
Exporting Since:	*1990*
Specialties:	*Specialize in bedding, bedding accessories and home textiles. ISO 9000: 2000 certified. Approved supplier for J.C. Penny. and IKEA.*
Machinery:	*1,000 sewing machines, 50 multi-needle quilters, 30 single needle quilters, 2 printing & finishing 114" wide goods, 4 fiber-fill low-melt mix, 2 fiber-fill resin bonded machines.*
Packages:	*Complete*
Export to:	*United States 8%, Central America 4%*
Factory Locals:	*Cuautitlan Izcalli, Estado de Mexico. Also source in United States, Pakistan, Taiwan, China, Ecuador & Brazil.*
Production Capacity:	*Comforters/bed in a bag: 70,000/month, bedspreads: 200,000/month, blankets: 60,000/month, drapes/valances: 50,000/month.*

LES TEXTILES GAUVIN INC.

63 Rue Industrielle

Saint Pamphile, Quebec G0R 3X0
Canada
Normand Gauvin
(1) (418) 356 2434   Fax: (1) (418) 356 3320

E-Mail:	*info@zenima.ca*
Web Site:	*www.zenima.ca*
Description:	*Contractor specializing in sheets & throws.*
Year Est:	*1987*
Exporting Since:	*1999*
Categories:	*Intimate Apparel*
Specialties:	*All production done in-house.*
Markets:	*Menswear, Womenswear, Childrenswear & Home.*
Packages:	*Sewing, Cutting, Complete Packages, Embroidery*
Production Capacity:	*30,000 sets/month*

info@fashiondex.com © The Fashiondex, Inc.

CUALQUIER LAVADO, S.A. DE C.V.

Km.15 Carretera Tehuacan Puebla#2
Altura Desviacion a M. Cuayucatepec
Tehuacan, Puebla 75853
Mexico

Arturo Neira Francos

(52) (238) 3803700 Fax: (52) (238) 3803705

E-Mail:	*aneira@cualquierlavado.com.mx*
Web Site:	*www.cualquierlavado.com*
Description:	*Men's and women's 5 pocket blue denim jeans.*
Year Est:	*1991*
Exporting Since:	*1991*
Specialties:	*Water-less washes (ozone technology), garment dye & laser machines to replace handsanding. Fire retardant jeans.*
Markets:	*Menswear, Womenwear.*
Machinery:	*Over 1000 sewing machines, washers, dryers, embroidery, screenprinting, handsand machines etc.*
Export to:	*USA 80%, Canada 20%*
Agent:	*USA Sales VP: Sue Tyson, tel: 270-839-1555, suetyson@cualquierlavado.com*
Minimums:	*5,000 pcs/style*
Production Capacity:	*Mens Jeans: 25,000 units/week, Womens Jeans: 40,000 units/week, Work Pants: 15,000 units/week, Fashion Jeans: 20,000 units/week.*

DISMODA S.A.

Cra 30 Ave Hamburgo
Zona Franca, Bloque E.
Barranquilla
Colombia

Antonieta Russo/Cesar Caro

(57) (5) 3799777 Fax: (57) (5) 3799550

E-Mail:	*dismoda@dismoda.com*
Web Site:	*www.dismoda.com*
Description:	*Denim sportswear contractor for all markets.*
Year Est:	*1981*
Exporting Since:	*1981*
Categories:	*Dresses/Blouses, Shirts/Tops, Woven Sportwear, Pants/Shorts/Skirts, Tee shirts.*
Markets:	*Menswear, Womenswear, Childrenswear.*
Machinery:	*Over 900 sewing & finishing machines. All types.*
Packages:	*CMT, Dyeing/Finishing, Laundering/Washing.*
Export to:	*United States 100%*
Agent:	*Orlando Caro, Miami, FL (overseas source). Tel: 305-639-2486.*
Minimums:	*2,000 units/style*
Production Capacity:	*Pants: 66,000 units/month, Skirts: 15,000 units/month, Shirts: 20,000 units/month, Tees: 27,000 units/month*

PRODUCTOS WEST DE MEXICO S.A.
Calle Juan Pablos No. 519 Nte.

Torreon, Coahuila
Mexico
Fernando Mafud
(52) (871) 713 3694   Fax: (52) (871) 713 3694

E-Mail:	*newwestjeans@hotmail.com*
Description:	*Full service contractor of jeans, shirts, shorts, skirts, jackets from denim, twill, polyester & polyester blends.*
Year Est:	*1981*
Categories:	*Pants/Shorts/Skirts, Shirts/Tops*
Markets:	*Menswear, Womenswear & Childrenswear.*
Packages:	*Complete & CMT.*

PROMOTORA INTERNACIONAL DE PANTALONES, S.A. DE C.V.
Carlos Dickens No. 20 A Bajos

Polanco, Mexico, Distrito Federal 11560
Mexico
Jaime Cohen Smeke
(52) (55) 52806550   Fax: (52) (55) 52801492

E-Mail:	*jaimecohens@omsamex.com*
Description:	*Cut and sew all types of jeans.*
Exporting Since:	*1995*
Categories:	*Pants/Skirts/Shorts*
Export to:	*USA 100%*
Production Capacity:	*Underwear: 10,000dz/week, Shirts: 5,000 units/week, Trousers and Jeans: 10,000 units/week.*

SIETE LEGUAS DENIM JEANS
Calz del Tecnologico #1055

Lerdo, Durango 35150
Mexico
JJ Medina
(52) (871) 2349101   Fax: (52) (871) 7254558

E-Mail:	*jj@sieteleguas.com.mx*
Web Site:	*www.sieteleguas.com.mx*
Description:	*Full package denim jeans supplier for major brand stores. We ship worldwide.*
Year Est:	*1959*
Exporting Since:	*1980*
Specialties:	*Design, patternmaking, samples, grading/marking, embroidery, screenprinting, dyeing/finishing, washing/laundry, pack & ship.*
Markets:	*Menswear, Womenswear, Childrens & Infantwear.*
Packages:	*CMT, Sewing & Full Packages.*
Export to:	*USA 89%, Canada 2%, Dubai 1%, China 2% South America 2%, Japan 2%, Europe 2%*
Factory Locals:	*All work done in-house. Offer full "VMI" (Vendor Management Inventory) to the US.*

Production Capacity: *1.2 million/month - Jeans: 800,000 units/month,*
Skirts: 200,000 units/month, Shorts: 200,000 units/month

UNIFORMES UNION, S.A. DE C.V.

Goleta No. 37 Y 39
Fracc. Industrial Xalostoc
Ecatepec, Estado de Mexico 55390
Mexico
Carlos A. Venegas Diaz
(52) (55) 57144487   Fax: (52) (55) 57144133

E-Mail:	*uniformesunion@prodigy.net.mx*
Web Site:	*www.uniformesunion.com*
Description:	*Men & women's denim jeans in 14.5 oz. 100% cotton stoned blue denim.*
Year Est:	*1982*
Exporting Since:	*1999*
Categories:	*Shirts/Tops*
Specialties:	*Reliable Supplier Certificate*
Markets:	*Menswear, Womenswear.*
Machinery:	*100 sewing machines & equipment*
Packages:	*Full Packages*
Export to:	*USA 90%. Canada 10%*
Minimums:	*100 pcs.*
Factory Locals:	*Tlaxcala, Mexico*
Production Capacity:	*Mens Jeans: 15,000 units/month, Womens Jeans: 5,000 units/month.*

YALE DE MEXICO, S.A. DE C.V.

Calzada Javier Rojo Gomez 1330
Col. Barrio de San Miguel
Iztapalapa CP 09360
Mexico
Cristina Beltran Piza
(52) (55) 5804 4242   Fax: (52) (55) 5686 0855

E-Mail:	*cbpiza@yale.com.mx*
Web Site:	*www.yale.com.mx*
Description:	*Sewing, cutting, washing, pressing and finishing contractor.*
Year Est:	*1950*
Categories:	*Shirts/Tops, Pants/Shorts*
Markets:	*Menswear, Womenswear & Childrenswear.*
Packages:	*Full packages.*
Factory Locals:	*Above - 25,000 sq. meters*

Notes

info@fashiondex.com © The Fashiondex, Inc.

K & S INDUSTRIES, S.A.
Industrial Free Zone

San Pedro de Macoris
Dominican Republic
Junior Aza
(1) (809) 529 8080   Fax: (1) (809) 529 2535
E-Mail: *kands@claro.net.do*
Description: *Cut & sew contractor of intimate apparel, swimwear & medical items.*
Specialties: *Quick turn-around time.*
Markets: *Womenswear & Menswear.*
Packages: *Full package*
Export to: *U.S.A.*
Agent: *USA Agent: DRM Products, PO Box 645, Merrick, NY,*
David Klein, david@drmproducts.net, 516-410-4953.

LES TEXTILES GAUVIN INC.
63 Rue Industrielle

Saint Pamphile, Quebec G0R 3X0
Canada
Normand Gauvin
(1) (418) 356 2434   Fax: (1) (418) 356 3320
E-Mail: *info@zenima.ca*
Web Site: *www.zenima.ca*
Description: *Contractor of intimate apparel specializing in bathrobes.*
Year Est: *1987*
Exporting Since: *1999*
Categories: *Home Furnishings*
Specialties: *All production done in-house.*
Markets: *Menswear, Womenswear, Childrenswear & Home.*
Packages: *Sewing, Cutting, Complete Packages, Embroidery*

MANDARINTEX LTD.
17 Seamist Crescent

Toronto, Ontario M1V3K3
Canada
Philip Ip
(1) (647) 728 3254
E-Mail: *philipip@mandarintex.com*
Web Site: *www.mandarintex.com*
Description: *Cut and sew contractor.*
Categories: *Sleepwear/Robes, Samples/Small Production*
Specialties: *Specialize in loungewear, underwear, bras, briefs, boxers, robes*
and sleepwear.
Markets: *Menswear, Womenwear.*
Minimums: *400 pieces/style*

NYLONTEX INTERNACIONAL S.A.
Km. 18.5 Carretera al Mayan Golf

Villa Nueva
Guatemala
Karla Woc
(502) 6628 0700   Fax: (502) 6628 0701

E-Mail:	*kwoc@nylontexinternacional.com*
Web Site:	*www.nylontexinternacional.com*
Description:	*Sewing contractor of seamless underwear & hosiery for women & childrens underwear.*
Year Est:	*1963*
Specialties:	*Specialize in hosiery, leggings & seamless wear.*
Markets:	*Womenswear, Childrens*
Machinery:	*40 Santonni Machines*
Export to:	*Mexico, Central America, USA, Guatemala*
Production Capacity:	*Seamless Wear: 15,000 dozen/month, Hosiery: 150,000 dozen/month*

VICKY FORM, S.A. DE C.V.
Recursos Hidraulicos #2
Fracc. Industrial La Loma
Tlalnepantla, Estado de Mexico, C.P. 54060
Mexico
Kila Tochijara
(52) (55) 5333 0360   Fax: (52) (55) 5333 0361

E-Mail:	*expzaga@zaga.com*
Web Site:	*www.vickyform.com, www.zaga.com*
Description:	*Manufacturer of lingerie collections, casualwear, yoga pants, activewear, pajamas and men's underwear.*
Year Est:	*1964*
Exporting Since:	*1992*
Categories:	*Active/Athleticwear*
Specialties:	*Computerized pattern, marking and grading, Gerber brand sample - sample room in-house.*
Markets:	*Menswear, Womenswear, Teens, Childrenswear*
Packages:	*Full package based on program and volume*
Export to:	*U.S.A, Costa Rica, Canada*
Minimums:	*1,200 - 7,000 pieces/color*
Factory Locals:	*Tepeji Del Rio, Tulanciango*
Production Capacity:	*600,000+ units/month*

ALAMEDA S.A.

1a Av. La Brigada 13-30, Zona 7
Colonia San Ignacio
Mixco
Guatemala
Luis Barillas
(502) 2437 5321   Fax: (502) 2437 8287

E-Mail:	*luisb@alamedasa.com*
Web Site:	*www.alamedasa.com*
Description:	*Advanced garment production factory. In-house cutting, sewing, washing, dyeing, sandblasing & packaging.*
Specialties:	*Specialize in ladies woven and knit pants and skirts.*
Markets:	*All womens markets.*
Machinery:	*Computerized sewing machines.*
Packages:	*Full Packages.*

ANTILLES MANUFACTURING, S.A.

Calle La Canela, Nave No. 1
Zona Franca Industrial
Santiago
Dominican Republic
Ricardo J. Fondeur
(1) (809) 570 3603   Fax: (1) (809) 570 3809

E-Mail:	*recepcion@oadom.com.do*
Year Est:	*1995*
Exporting Since:	*1995*
Categories:	*Pants/Shorts*
Specialties:	*Specialize in casual pants.*
Markets:	*Menswear, Womenswear, Boyswear.*
Machinery:	*238 single, 70 merrow, 34 chain, 36 double stitch machines & many other types.*
Packages:	*Sewing only.*
Export to:	*United States, Mexico & Canada.*
Minimums:	*15,000 units/style*

D'CLASE APPAREL INTERNATIONAL

Zona Franca Industrial
Gurabo
Santiago 1425
Dominican Republic
Jose Clase-President
(1) 829 947 7000   Fax: (1) 829 947 7177

E-Mail:	*cpizano@dclase.com*
Description:	*Apparel manufacturers of casual pants, jeans. Laundry facilities.*
Year Est:	*1986*
Exporting Since:	*1986*
Categories:	*Jeans/Denimwear, Uniforms, Dresses*
Specialties:	*Complete testing laboratory for fabric & finished goods. Will do samples.*
Markets:	*Menswear, Womenswear & Youthwear.*

Machinery:	*Modern equipment for cutting, sewing & finishing of casual pants, uniforms, dresses.*
Packages:	*CMT, Full Packages, EDI & complete service programs.*
Export to:	*United States 98%, Canada 2%*
Minimums:	*5,000 per style/1,000 units per color/15 SKU's*
Factory Locals:	*4 factories in Esperanza, Dominican Republic*

DA SAN, S.A. DE C.V.

Km 26, Carretera a Sonsonate
Jurisdiccion de Lourdes Colon
La Libertad
El Salvador
Richard Kim
() (503) 2322 2100   Fax: () (503) 2318 1748

E-Mail:	*richard.kim@dasan.com.sv*
Description:	*Contractor pants, skirts, tops, vests, blouses & dresses.*
Year Est:	*1993*
Categories:	*Shirts/Tops, Dresses*
Markets:	*Womenswear*
Machinery:	*Over 1,400 pieces of machinery on premises.*
Packages:	*CMT & 807.*
Export to:	*U.S.A*
Factory Locals:	*El Salvador*
Production Capacity:	*100,000 units/month (tops, jackets), 35,000 units/month (bottoms) 100,000 units/month (knits).*

GRUPO BAMEX S.A. DE C.V.

Venustiano Carranza 477 Sur

Monterrey, N.L. 64000
Mexico
Ruben Marcos
(52) (81) 8130 7800   Fax: (52) (81) 8345 7271

E-Mail:	*rmarcos@grupobamex.com*
Web Site:	*www.mariscalmoda.com*
Description:	*Full package contractor of dress and casual pants.*
Year Est:	*1948*
Categories:	*Shirts/Tops, Uniforms*
Specialties:	*Samples available*
Markets:	*Menswear, Boyswear*
Packages:	*Sewing, cutting, patternmaking, grading/marking*
Export to:	*United States 10%*
Minimums:	*300 pcs/style*
Factory Locals:	*All work done in-house. www.johnhenry.com.mx, www.grupobamex.com*
Production Capacity:	*Shirts: 100,000 pcs/month, Pants: 20,000 pcs/month*

INDUSTRIAS MACYS S.A. DE C.V.

Jose Maria Izazaga 99 Piso #8
Colonia Centro
Mexico D.F., 06090
Mexico
Emilio Penhos
(52) (55) 5709 7620   Fax: (52) (55) 5709 1588

E-Mail:	*dpenhos@laurence.com.mx*
Web Site:	*www.laurence.com.mx*
Description:	*Expert resource in Mexico for fully lined & unlined skirts.*
Year Est:	*1986*
Exporting Since:	*1990*
Categories:	*Dresses/Blouses, Shirts/Tops, Coats/Jackets*
Markets:	*Womenswear.*
Machinery:	*623 machines, all types.*
Packages:	*CMT & Full, Pattern/Samplemaking, Printing & CAD.*
Minimums:	*100 dozen/style*
Factory Locals:	*7 sewing plants & 2 cutting plants in & around Mexico City.*

PERFECTION SHIRT INC.

P.O.Box 190
101 Perfection Avenue
Courcelles (Quebec) G0M 1C0
Canada
Rock Doucet
(1) (418) 483 5227   Fax: (1) (418) 483 5827

E-Mail:	*sales@perfectionshirt.com*
Web Site:	*www.perfectionshirt.com*
Description:	*Manufacturer of uniforms & dress & sport shirts and pants.*
Year Est:	*1947*
Categories:	*Uniforms, Shirts*
Markets:	*Menswear, Womenswear.*
Export to:	*USA 5%*
Production Capacity:	*60,000 shirts/month, 10,000 pants/month*

PHILIPPO MANUFACTURING CORP.

3177 Fleury East

Montreal, Quebec H1H2R2
Canada
Gaetano Orsina
(1) (514) 389 4321   Fax: (1) (514) 389 1491

E-Mail:	*gates@qc.aibn.com*
Description:	*CMT of fully constructed wool, linen or poly/cotton womens suits, pants, skirts & shorts.*
Year Est:	*1976*
Categories:	*Pants/Shorts/Skirts*
Markets:	*Womens*
Export to:	*U.S.A.*

Minimums:	50 pcs/style
Production Capacity:	3,000 suits/week

PRODUCTOS WEST DE MEXICO S.A.

Calle Juan Pablos No. 519 Nte.

Torreon, Coahuila
Mexico
Fernando Mafud
(52) (871) 713 3694   Fax: (52) (871) 713 3694

E-Mail:	newwestjeans@hotmail.com
Description:	Full service contractor of jeans, shirts, shorts, skirts, jackets from denim, twill, polyester & polyester blends.
Year Est:	1981
Categories:	Jeans/Denimwear, Shirts/Tops
Markets:	Menswear, Womenswear & Childrenswear.
Packages:	Complete & CMT.

PROMOTORA INTERNACIONAL DE PANTALONES, S.A. DE C.V.

Carlos Dickens No. 20 A Bajos

Polanco, Mexico, Distrito Federal 11560
Mexico
Jaime Cohen Smeke
(52) (55) 52806550   Fax: (52) (55) 52801492

E-Mail:	jaimecohens@omsamex.com
Description:	Cut and sew all types of trousers and jeans.
Exporting Since:	1995
Export to:	USA 100%
Production Capacity:	Underwear: 10,000dz/week, Shirts: 5,000 units/week, Trousers and Jeans: 10,000 units/week.

ROCEDES S.A.

Zona Franca Las Mercedes Bldg.#29
Km 12 1/2 Carretera Norte
Managua
Nicaragua
Scott Vaughn
(505) 2263 2032   Fax: (505) 2263 2033

E-Mail:	svaughn@rocedes.com.ni
Web Site:	www.rocedes.com.ni
Description:	Contractor of casual wear, work wear and uniforms.
Year Est:	1993
Categories:	Uniforms
Markets:	Menswear, Womenswear, Boyswear, Girlswear.
Machinery:	698 Plain sewers, 195 Bartacker, 34 Button Hole, 283 Overlock, 53 Bander, 51 Compos.
Export to:	United States 100%
Factory Locals:	Managua, Nicaragua
Production Capacity:	600,000 pieces/month

YALE DE MEXICO, S.A. DE C.V.

Calzada Javier Rojo Gomez 1330
Col. Barrio de San Miguel
Iztapalapa CP 09360
Mexico
Cristina Beltran Piza
(52) (55) 5804 4242   Fax: (52) (55) 5686 0855

E-Mail:	*cbpiza@yale.com.mx*
Web Site:	*www.yale.com.mx*
Description:	*Sewing, cutting, washing, pressing and finishing contractor.*
Year Est:	*1950*
Categories:	*Shirts/Tops, Jeans/Denimwear*
Markets:	*Menswear, Womenswear & Childrenswear.*
Packages:	*Full packages.*
Factory Locals:	*Above - 25,000 sq. meters*

DOUBLETEX
9785 Jeanne Mance

Montreal, Quebec H3L3B6
Canada
Richard Zuckerman
(1) (514) 382 1770   Fax: (1) (514) 382 9587

E-Mail:	*sales@doubletex.com*
Web Site:	*www.doubletex.com*
Description:	*Toll Free#1-800-311-1770. All types of quilting.*
Year Est:	*Over 90 years in business.*
Categories:	*Quilting Contractors, Finshing/Coating Contractors*
Specialties:	*Carry fiberfill battings.*
Markets:	*Popular to better mens, womens, childrens & active.*
Minimums:	*None*

Notes

info@fashiondex.com © The Fashiondex, Inc.

MANDARINTEX LTD.

17 Seamist Crescent

Toronto, Ontario M1V3K3
Canada
Philip Ip
(1) (647) 728 3254

E-Mail:	*philipip@mandarintex.com*
Web Site:	*www.mandarintex.com*
Description:	*Cut and sew contractor.*
Categories:	*Sleepwear/Robes, Lingerie/Intimate/Underwear*
Specialties:	*Specialize in loungewear, underwear, bras, briefs, boxers, robes and sleepwear.*
Markets:	*Menswear, Womenwear.*
Minimums:	*400 pieces/style*

STAR CONCEPT APPAREL LTD.

54 East 6th Avenue

Vancouver, B.C. V5T1J4
Canada

(1) (604) 879 9018   Fax: (1) (604) 879 9328

E-Mail:	*info@starconceptapparel.com*
Web Site:	*www.starconceptapparel.com*
Description:	*Contractor for all types of garments using fabrics such as cotton fleece, French terry, polar fleece, stretch nylon and more.*
Categories:	*Tee Shirts*
Specialties:	*Specialize in basic tee shirts to running jackets.*
Markets:	*Menswear, Womenswear & Childrenswear.*
Machinery:	*Single needle, 4 and 5 thread sergers, cover stitches, waistband machines, button hole and button machines, piping cutters and more.*

Notes

info@fashiondex.com © The Fashiondex, Inc.

3 MT ENTERPRISES
Zona Franca Industrial#1

San Pedro de Macaris
Dominican Republic

(1) (809) 246 3501   Fax: (1) (809) 246 3502

E-Mail:	*selmufdi@grupo3mt.com*
Web Site:	*www.grupo3mt.com*
Description:	*Contractor of knit shirts and sportswear.*
	Full package specialist.
Specialties:	*Specialize in tee shirts, hooded shirts, fleece styles & knit pants.*
	In house screen printing & embroidery.
Markets:	*Womenswear, Menswear, Childrenswear.*
Packages:	*807 & full package.*
Export to:	*USA 100%*
Agent:	*US Office: Miami Sourcing/Grupo 3MT, Miami Beach, Fl.*
	Tony Fernandez 305 301 0986-tonyfernz10@gmail.com
Factory Locals:	*Factory group includes knit fabric production.*
Production Capacity:	*3,000 doz/week*

CONFECCIONES INTERNACIONALES S.A. DE C.V.
Zona Libre Tegucigalpa
Colonia Kennedy, Quinta Entrada
Tegucigalpa
Honduras
Enrique Facusse
(504) 2230 5518   Fax: (504) 2230 5422

E-Mail:	*sales@confecciones.com*
Web Site:	*www.confecciones.com*
Description:	*Integrated full package manufacturer specializing in knit tops,*
	tee shirts, polo sport shirts & fleece products.
Year Est:	*1993*
Categories:	*Activewear, Tee-Shirts, Shirts/Tops, Underwear.*
Specialties:	*Also sell knit fabric (jersey, pique, fleece, others).*
Markets:	*Menswear, Womenswear & Childrenswear.*
Machinery:	*Over 950 machines from Juki, Union special, Brother, Yamato &*
	automated equipment from Atlanta Attachment.
Packages:	*Full packages*
Export to:	*U.S.A.*
Agent:	*In USA tel# 786-837-0215 x 1231*
	E-Fax 305-675-3121
Factory Locals:	*Tegucigalpa, Honduras*

DA SAN, S.A. DE C.V.

Km 26, Carretera a Sonsonate
Jurisdiccion de Lourdes Colon
La Libertad
El Salvador
Richard Kim
() (503) 2322 2100   Fax: () (503) 2318 1748

E-Mail:	*richard.kim@dasan.com.sv*
Description:	*Contractor pants, skirts, tops, vests, blouses & dresses.*
Year Est:	*1993*
Categories:	*Pants/Skirts, Dresses*
Markets:	*Womenswear*
Machinery:	*Over 1,400 pieces of machinery on premises.*
Packages:	*CMT & 807.*
Export to:	*U.S.A*
Factory Locals:	*El Salvador*
Production Capacity:	*100,000 units/month (tops, jackets), 35,000 units/month (bottoms) 100,000 units/month (knits).*

GRUPO BAMEX S.A. DE C.V.

Venustiano Carranza 477 Sur

Monterrey, N.L. 64000
Mexico
Ruben Marcos
(52) (81) 8130 7800   Fax: (52) (81) 8345 7271

E-Mail:	*rmarcos@grupobamex.com*
Web Site:	*www.mariscalmoda.com*
Description:	*Full package contractor of dress and casual shirts.*
Year Est:	*1948*
Categories:	*Pants, Uniforms*
Specialties:	*Samples available*
Markets:	*Menswear, Boyswear*
Packages:	*Sewing, cutting, patternmaking, grading/marking*
Export to:	*United States 10%*
Minimums:	*300 pcs/style*
Factory Locals:	*All work done in-house. www.johnhenry.com.mx, www.grupobamex.com*
Production Capacity:	*Shirts: 100,000 pcs/month, Pants: 20,000 pcs/month*

INDUSTRIAS MACYS S.A. DE C.V.

Jose Maria Izazaga 99 Piso #8
Colonia Centro
Mexico D.F., 06090
Mexico
Emilio Penhos
(52) (55) 5709 7620   Fax: (52) (55) 5709 1588

E-Mail:	*dpenhos@laurence.com.mx*
Web Site:	*www.laurence.com.mx*
Description:	*Expert resource in Mexico for blouses, shirts & tops.*
Year Est:	*1986*

Exporting Since:	1990
Categories:	Dresses/Blouses, Shirts/Tops, Coats/Jackets, Pants/Shorts/Skirts
Markets:	Womenswear.
Machinery:	623 machines, all types.
Packages:	CMT & Full, Pattern/Samplemaking, Printing & CAD.
Minimums:	100 dozen/style
Factory Locals:	7 sewing plants & 2 cutting plants in & around Mexico City.

KATTAN GROUP

800 mts. Carretera a la Jutosa
Inhdelva Free Trade Zone
Choloma, Cortes
Honduras
Gabriel Kattan
(504) 2617 0150   Fax: (504) 2617 0155

E-Mail:	gabriel.kattan@kattangroup.com
Web Site:	www.kattangroup.com
Description:	Full service contractor, with screenprinting, embroidery, washing, handsand, sandblast, finishing, quilting, stitching capabilities & more.
Year Est:	1920
Exporting Since:	1984
Categories:	Uniforms
Specialties:	Main focus is woven tops, both dress and sport shirts as well as uniform work wear.
Markets:	Menswear, Womenswear
Machinery:	5,000 single needle, 1,000 double needle, 1,000 coverstitch, 1,000 coverstitch, 500 pressing, 20 embroidery, 8 MHM screenprinting, 12 300-lb. washers, 10 400-lb. dryers.
Packages:	806, 807, CMT & Full service & complete packages.
Export to:	United States, Europe
Agent:	US Office: 12181 W. Linebaugh Avenue, Tampa, Fl. Tel#813-925-0001.
Minimums:	1200 units per color
Factory Locals:	Own 23 factories in the Free Trade Zone
Production Capacity:	Knits: 960,000 units/week, Woven bottoms: 120,000 units/week, Woven tops: 120,000 units/week.

LD EL SALVADOR

Parque Industrial Zone

Franca San Salvador
El Salvador

(503) 2213 0909   Fax: (503) 2213 0912

E-Mail:	cecile.reyes@mail.com
Description:	Contractor expert in all types of men's dress, sport & polo shirts. 55,000 sq. ft. facility in El Salvador.
Categories:	Childrens Wear
Specialties:	Sourcing locations in Korea, Vietnam, Bangladesh, Cambodia & Shanghai, China. J.C. Penney, Wal-Mart & Sears certified.

Markets: Menswear & Boyswear.
Export to: U.S.A.

PERFECTION SHIRT INC.
P.O.Box 190
101 Perfection Avenue
Courcelles (Quebec) G0M 1C0
Canada
Rock Doucet
(1) (418) 483 5227   Fax: (1) (418) 483 5827
E-Mail: sales@perfectionshirt.com
Web Site: www.perfectionshirt.com
Description: Manufacturer of dress & sport shirts. Also, corporate shirts for
chain store, restaurant or company executives & employees.
Year Est: 1947
Categories: Uniforms, Pants
Markets: Menswear, Womenswear.
Export to: USA 5%
Production Capacity: 60,000 shirts/month, 10,000 pants/month

PRODUCTOS WEST DE MEXICO S.A.
Calle Juan Pablos No. 519 Nte.

Torreon, Coahuila
Mexico
Fernando Mafud
(52) (871) 713 3694   Fax: (52) (871) 713 3694
E-Mail: newwestjeans@hotmail.com
Description: Full service contractor of jeans, shirts, shorts, skirts, jackets from
denim, twill, polyester & polyester blends.
Year Est: 1981
Categories: Jeans/Denimwear, Pants/Shorts/Skirts
Markets: Menswear, Womenswear & Childrenswear.
Packages: Complete & CMT.

S.M.C., S.A.
Zona Franca Industrial De La Vega

La Vega
Dominican Republic
Julio Ortiz, President
(1) (809) 242 6565, 242 6566   Fax: (1) (809) 242 6567
E-Mail: smcdr@yahoo.com
Description: Woven shirts, blouses and uniforms
Year Est: 1987
Exporting Since: 1987
Categories: Uniforms
Specialties: Uniform shirts.
Markets: Menswear, Womenswear, Childrenswear.
Machinery: 250 sewing machines & special machines for shirts.
Packages: CM, CMT & Full packages

Export to:	U.S.A. 100%
Minimums:	300 dozen/style
Factory Locals:	Free zone La Vega, Dominican Republic
Production Capacity:	6,000 doz/month

UNIFORMES UNION, S.A. DE C.V.

Goleta No. 37 Y 39
Fracc. Industrial Xalostoc
Ecatepec, Estado de Mexico 55390
Mexico
Carlos A. Venegas Diaz
(52) (55) 57144487   Fax: (52) (55) 57144133

E-Mail:	uniformesunion@prodigy.net.mx
Web Site:	www.uniformesunion.com
Description:	Men's shirts with short and long sleeves manufactured in woven and knit fabrics. Dress, oxford, work & golf shirts.
Year Est:	1982
Exporting Since:	1999
Categories:	Jeans/Denimwear
Specialties:	Reliable Supplier Certificate
Markets:	Menswear
Machinery:	200 sewing machines & equipment
Packages:	Full Packages
Export to:	USA 90%. Canada 10%
Minimums:	1,000 pcs.
Factory Locals:	Texcoco, Mexico
Production Capacity:	Woven Shirts: 30,000 pcs/month, Knit Shirts: 10,000 pcs/month

YALE DE MEXICO, S.A. DE C.V.

Calzada Javier Rojo Gomez 1330
Col. Barrio de San Miguel
Iztapalapa CP 09360
Mexico
Cristina Beltran Piza
(52) (55) 5804 4242   Fax: (52) (55) 5686 0855

E-Mail:	cbpiza@yale.com.mx
Web Site:	www.yale.com.mx
Description:	Sewing, cutting, washing, pressing and finishing contractor.
Year Est:	1950
Categories:	Jeans/Denimwear, Pants/Shorts
Markets:	Menswear, Womenswear & Childrenswear.
Packages:	Full packages.
Factory Locals:	Above - 25,000 sq. meters

info@fashiondex.com © The Fashiondex, Inc.

MANDARINTEX LTD.
17 Seamist Crescent

Toronto, Ontario M1V3K3
Canada
Philip Ip
(1) (647) 728 3254

E-Mail:	*philipip@mandarintex.com*
Web Site:	*www.mandarintex.com*
Description:	*Cut and sew contractor.*
Categories:	*Sample Room/Small Production, Lingerie/Intimate/Underwear*
Specialties:	*Specialize in loungewear, underwear, bras, briefs, boxers, robes and sleepwear.*
Markets:	*Menswear, Womenwear.*
Minimums:	*400 pieces/style*

info@fashiondex.com © The Fashiondex, Inc.

3 MT ENTERPRISES
Zona Franca Industrial#1

San Pedro de Macaris
Dominican Republic

(1) (809) 246 3501   Fax: (1) (809) 246 3502

E-Mail:	*selmufdi@grupo3mt.com*
Web Site:	*www.grupo3mt.com*
Description:	*Contractor of knit shirts and sportswear.* *Full package specialist.*
Specialties:	*Specialize in tee shirts, hooded shirts, fleece styles & knit pants.* *In house screen printing & embroidery.*
Markets:	*Womenswear, Menswear, Childrenswear.*
Packages:	*807 & full package.*
Export to:	*USA 100%*
Agent:	*US Office: Miami Sourcing/Grupo 3MT, Miami Beach, Fl.* *Tony Fernandez 305 301 0986-tonyfernz10@gmail.com*
Factory Locals:	*Factory group includes knit fabric production.*
Production Capacity:	*3,000 doz/week*

J. M. J. FASHIONS INC.
365 Bannatyne Avenue

Winnipeg, Manitoba R3A 0E5
Canada
Roman Witkowski
(1) (204) 942 0252   Fax: (1) (204) 943 5083

E-Mail:	*romanw@jmjingenuity.com*
Web Site:	*www.jmjingenuity.com*
Description:	*Manufacturer and contractor of ladies sportswear coordinates plus uniforms for banks, real estate agencies, airlines and more.*
Year Est:	*1933 - Family owned*
Exporting Since:	*1993*
Categories:	*Sportswear Wovens/Uniforms*
Markets:	*Womenswear*
Machinery:	*27 single needle, 1 double needle, 11 seam serger, 2 blind stitch, 2 cover stitch, 1 tacker, 5 button hole, 1 grommet, 4 button machine, 4 lock stitch.*
Packages:	*Cut & Sew, Patternmaking, Complete Packages available.*
Export to:	*United States*
Factory Locals:	*All work is done in-house*
Production Capacity:	*4,000 pieces/monthly*

PRIDE MANUFACTURING S. DE R. L.

Zip Honduras
Edificio No.2
Choloma, Cortes
Honduras
Buda Escoto
(504) 2620 0450   Fax: (504) 2669 3624

E-Mail:	*buda.escoto@grupokarims.com*
Web Site:	*www.grupokarims.com*
Description:	*Manufacturer of all types of knit tops, tee shirts, placket shirts, sweatshirts, shorts & elastic pants.*
Year Est:	*1991*
Exporting Since:	*1991*
Specialties:	*Sample room, fabric testing, cutting room, embroidery as well as warehouse and distribution facilities.*
Markets:	*All apparel markets.*
Machinery:	*Over 1,500 machines, including: overlock, coverstitch, single needle, flat lock & more. Also embroidery equipment, & top-of-the-line cutting machinery.*
Packages:	*Full & CMT packages.*
Export to:	*USA*
Minimums:	*100 dozen/order, 2,500 dozen/program*
Factory Locals:	*Factories in Honduras with affilliates in Mexico, Miami, Pakistan, China & Guatemala.*
Production Capacity:	*Knit tops: 15,000 doz/wk, Woven tops: 1,500 doz/wk & Woven bottoms: 2,000 doz/wk.*

TEXTILES OPICO DBA TEXOPS

KM 31.4 Carretera a Santa Ana
San Juan Opico
La Libertad
El Salvador
Juan C. Zighelboim
() (503) 2319 0800   Fax: () (503) 2319 0812

E-Mail:	*juan.zighelboim@texops.com*
Web Site:	*www.texops.com*
Description:	*Private label contract manufacturing of active and athletic wear. Specialists in stretch synthetic fabrics with flat seams.*
Year Est:	*2008*
Exporting Since:	*2008*
Categories:	*Athletic wear, Sportswear-Wovens, Sportswear-Knits.*
Specialties:	*Specialize in knit apparel, sublimation, active, yoga, compression, fitness, cycling, running, team sports, plaquet polo shirts.*
Markets:	*Menswear, Womenswear, Boyswear, Girlswear.*
Machinery:	*200 flat seam, 265 cover stitch, 275 overlock, 250 lock stitch, 14 digital dye-sublimation printers, 4 Monti-Antonio fabric & cut part sublimation presses, 3 Lectra automated cutters, 4 Oteman Synergy Auto Spreaders, Raw Materials testing lab.*
Packages:	*Complete private label & full packages.*
Export to:	*USA 85%, Asia 5%, Canada 5%, Europe 5%,*
Agent:	*From USA - 305-503-4139 x 550*

Minimums:	*50 dozen/style*
Factory Locals:	*El Salvador*
Production Capacity:	*360,000 tops/month, 360,000 bottoms/month*

VICKY FORM, S.A. DE C.V.

Recursos Hidraulicos #2
Fracc. Industrial La Loma
Tlalnepantla, Estado de Mexico, C.P. 54060
Mexico
Kila Tochijara
(52) (55) 5333 0360   Fax: (52) (55) 5333 0361

E-Mail:	*expzaga@zaga.com*
Web Site:	*www.vickyform.com, www.zaga.com*
Description:	*Manufacturer of lingerie collections, casualwear, yoga pants, activewear, pajamas and men's underwear.*
Year Est:	*1964*
Exporting Since:	*1992*
Categories:	*Lingerie/Intimate/Underwear, Active/Athleticwear*
Specialties:	*Computerized pattern, marking and grading, Gerber brand sample - sample room in-house.*
Markets:	*Menswear, Womenswear, Teens, Childrenswear*
Packages:	*Full package based on program and volume*
Export to:	*U.S.A, Costa Rica, Canada*
Minimums:	*1,200 - 7,000 pieces/color*
Factory Locals:	*Tepeji Del Rio, Tulanciango*
Production Capacity:	*600,000+ units/month*

Notes

info@fashiondex.com © The Fashiondex, Inc.

DISMODA S.A.

Cra 30 Ave Hamburgo
Zona Franca, Bloque E.
Barranquilla
Colombia
Antonieta Russo/Cesar Caro
(57) (5) 3799777 Fax: (57) (5) 3799550

E-Mail:	*dismoda@dismoda.com*
Web Site:	*www.dismoda.com*
Description:	*Woven sportswear contractor for all markets.*
Year Est:	*1981*
Exporting Since:	*1981*
Categories:	*Dresses/Blouses, Shirts/Tops, Tee Shirts, Jeans/Denimwear, Pants/Shorts/Skirts*
Markets:	*Menswear, Womenswear, Childrenswear.*
Machinery:	*Over 900 sewing & finishing machines. All types.*
Packages:	*CMT, Dyeing/Finishing, Laundering/Washing.*
Export to:	*United States 100%*
Agent:	*Orlando Caro, Miami, FL (overseas source). Tel: 305-639-2486.*
Minimums:	*2,000 units/style*
Production Capacity:	*Pants: 66,000 units/month, Skirts: 15,000 units/month, Shirts: 20,000 units/month, Tees: 27,000 units/month*

INDUSTRIAS FLORENZI, S.A. DE C.V.

Calle Al Matazano
Contiguo al Plantel de Salud Publica
Soyapango
El Salvador
Roberto Pineda Letona, President
() (503) 2297 0577 Fax: () (503) 2297 1223

E-Mail:	*r_pineda@navegante.com.sv*
Description:	*Contractor of all kinds of sportswear & shirts.*
Year Est:	*1985*
Categories:	*Dresses/Blouses, Uniforms*
Specialties:	*Patternmaking, grading, marker making, plotter service, cutting service, label printing, sewing (knitted & woven).*
Markets:	*Girlswear, Womenswear, Unisex.*
Machinery:	*180 single needle, 20 double needle, 8 multi needle, 90 safety stitch, 10 blindstitch, 15 button hole, 10 button sewing, 10 bartackers, 2 multineedle, 5 zig zag, 30 coverstitch, 15 hand irons, 3 hoffman pressers, 8 spreaders, 1 bias slitter, 2 fusing.*
Packages:	*807 & Full package.*
Export to:	*United States*
Minimums:	*500 pcs.*
Production Capacity:	*50,000 units/month*

J. M. J. FASHIONS INC.

365 Bannatyne Avenue

Winnipeg, Manitoba R3A 0E5
Canada
Roman Witkowski
(1) (204) 942 0252   Fax: (1) (204) 943 5083

E-Mail:	*romanw@jmjingenuity.com*
Web Site:	*www.jmjingenuity.com*
Description:	*Manufacturer and contractor of ladies sportswear coordinates plus uniforms for banks, real estate agencies, airlines and more.*
Year Est:	*1933 - Family owned*
Exporting Since:	*1993*
Categories:	*Sportswear Knits/Uniforms*
Markets:	*Womenswear*
Machinery:	*27 single needle, 1 double needle, 11 seam serger, 2 blind stitch, 2 cover stitch, 1 tacker, 5 button hole, 1 grommet, 4 button machine, 4 lock stitch.*
Packages:	*Cut & Sew, Patternmaking, Complete Packages available.*
Export to:	*United States*
Factory Locals:	*All work is done in-house*
Production Capacity:	*4,000 pieces/monthly*

PRIDE MANUFACTURING S. DE R. L.

Zip Honduras
Edificio No.2
Choloma, Cortes
Honduras
Buda Escoto
(504) 2620 0450   Fax: (504) 2669 3624

E-Mail:	*buda.escoto@grupokarims.com*
Web Site:	*www.grupokarims.com*
Description:	*Manufacturer of all types of woven products: dress pants, dress shirts, cargo pants, uniform shirts, skirts, labcoats & denim shirts.*
Year Est:	*1991*
Exporting Since:	*1991*
Specialties:	*Sample room, fabric testing, cutting room, embroidery as well as warehouse and distribution facilities.*
Markets:	*All apparel markets.*
Machinery:	*Over 1,500 machines, including: overlock, coverstitch, single needle, flat lock & more. Also embroidery equipment, & top-of-the-line cutting machinery.*
Packages:	*Full & CMT packages.*
Export to:	*USA*
Minimums:	*100 dozen/order, 2,500 dozen/program*
Factory Locals:	*Factories in Honduras with affilliates in Mexico, Miami, Pakistan, China & Guatemala.*
Production Capacity:	*Knit tops: 15,000 doz/wk, Woven tops: 1,500 doz/wk & Woven bottoms: 2,000 doz/wk.*

GLOBAL CMT CORPORATION
Zona Franca Industrial Santiago

Santiago
Dominican Republic
Francisco Rodriguez
(1) (809) 575 4777   Fax: (1) (809) 575 1232

E-Mail:	*f.rodriguez@globalcmt.com*
Web Site:	*www.globalcmt.com*
Description:	*Specialize in the production of tailored clothing as well as overcoats, uniforms and tuxedos.*
Categories:	*Uniforms, Coats/Jackets*
Markets:	*Menswear, Womenswear, Childrenswear.*
Packages:	*Full and partial packages*

BORDA SURI SRL
Calle Chaco No. 747 (Sopocachi)

La Paz
Bolivia
Enrique Borda
(591) (22) 413663   Fax: (591) (22) 415916

E-Mail:	*alpac@suri-bo.com*
Web Site:	*www.suri-bo.com*
Description:	*Manufacturers of apparel made of alpaca, sheep yarn and llama yarn.*
Year Est:	*1977*
Exporting Since:	*1979*
Specialties:	*Pullovers, cardigans, jackets, overcoats, vests, scarves, shawls & gloves in 100% alpaca yarn.*
Markets:	*Menswear, Womenswear & Childrenswear.*
Machinery:	*Weaving & sewing machinery. Individual styles finished by hand.*
Export to:	*U.S.A., Japan, Denmark*
Minimums:	*300 pieces/style*
Production Capacity:	*300-800 pieces/month - depending on style.*

CSR INTERNATIONAL INC.

150 rue du Couvent

St. Romain, Quebec, G0Y 1L0
Canada
Jean-Luc Fortin
(1) (418) 486 7481   Fax: (1) (418) 486 7903

E-Mail:	*jlfortin@csr-intl.com*
Web Site:	*www.groupecsr.com*
Description:	*CMT & complete package contractor of women's & children's swimwear & activewear.*
Year Est:	*1972*
Exporting Since:	*1996*
Markets:	*Womenswear, Childrenswear.*
Machinery:	*Sergers, single & double needle, bartack, multi needle, cover stitch, button, flatlock & zig zag machinery.*
Packages:	*CMT & complete packages.*
Export to:	*United States*
Minimums:	*500 units/style*

K & S INDUSTRIES, S.A.

Industrial Free Zone

San Pedro de Macoris
Dominican Republic
Junior Aza
(1) (809) 529 8080   Fax: (1) (809) 529 2535

E-Mail:	*kands@claro.net.do*
Description:	*Cut & sew contractor of intimate apparel, swimwear & medical items.*
Specialties:	*Quick turn-around time.*
Markets:	*Womenswear & Menswear.*
Packages:	*Full package*
Export to:	*U.S.A.*
Agent:	*USA Agent: DRM Products, PO Box 645, Merrick, NY, David Klein, david@drmproducts.net, 516-410-4953.*

Notes

CONFECCIONES INTERNACIONALES S.A. DE C.V.

Zona Libre Tegucigalpa
Colonia Kennedy, Quinta Entrada
Tegucigalpa
Honduras
Enrique Facusse
(504) 2230 5518   Fax: (504) 2230 5422

E-Mail:	*sales@confecciones.com*
Web Site:	*www.confecciones.com*
Description:	*Integrated full package manufacturer specializing in knit tops, tee shirts, polo sport shirts & fleece products.*
Year Est:	*1993*
Categories:	*Activewear, Tee-Shirts, Shirts/Tops, Underwear.*
Specialties:	*Also sell knit fabric (jersey, pique, fleece, others).*
Markets:	*Menswear, Womenswear & Childrenswear.*
Machinery:	*Over 950 machines from Juki, Union special, Brother, Yamato & automated equipment from Atlanta Attachment.*
Packages:	*Full packages*
Export to:	*U.S.A.*
Agent:	*In USA tel# 786-837-0215 x 1231 E-Fax 305-675-3121*
Factory Locals:	*Tegucigalpa, Honduras*

DISMODA S.A.

Cra 30 Ave Hamburgo
Zona Franca, Bloque E.
Barranquilla
Colombia
Antonieta Russo/Cesar Caro
(57) (5) 3799777   Fax: (57) (5) 3799550

E-Mail:	*dismoda@dismoda.com*
Web Site:	*www.dismoda.com*
Description:	*Tee shirt manufacturer for all markets.*
Year Est:	*1981*
Exporting Since:	*1981*
Categories:	*Dresses/Blouses, Shirts/Tops, Woven Sportwear, Jeans/Denimwear, Pants/Shorts/Skirts*
Markets:	*Menswear, Womenswear, Childrenswear.*
Machinery:	*Over 900 sewing & finishing machines. All types.*
Packages:	*CMT, Dyeing/Finishing, Laundering/Washing.*
Export to:	*United States 100%*
Agent:	*Orlando Caro, Miami, FL (overseas source). Tel: 305-639-2486.*
Minimums:	*2,000 units/style*
Production Capacity:	*Pants: 66,000 units/month, Skirts: 15,000 units/month, Shirts: 20,000 units/month, Tees: 27,000 units/month*

NOVA CREATION

Km 13.5 Carretera a El Salvador
Puerta Parads, Sta.
Catarina Pinula
Guatemala
Jose Gisbert
(502) 6646 5880

E-Mail:	*j.gisbert@novacreation.net*
Description:	*Full-package manufacturer of t-shirts, polos, tank tops, hoodies, onsies and more.*
Specialties:	*Tech Package, dyeing & finishing, pattern design & cutting, sewing, trims, printing & finishing in-house, packaging.*
Packages:	*Full Packages*

STAR CONCEPT APPAREL LTD.

54 East 6th Avenue

Vancouver, B.C. V5T1J4
Canada

(1) (604) 879 9018   Fax: (1) (604) 879 9328

E-Mail:	*info@starconceptapparel.com*
Web Site:	*www.starconceptapparel.com*
Description:	*Contractor for all types of garments using fabrics such as cotton fleece, French terry, polar fleece, stretch nylon and more.*
Categories:	*Sample Rooms/Small Production*
Specialties:	*Specialize in basic tee shirts to running jackets.*
Markets:	*Menswear, Womenswear & Childrenswear.*
Machinery:	*Single needle, 4 and 5 thread sergers, cover stitches, waistband machines, button hole and button machines, piping cutters and more.*

D'CLASE APPAREL INTERNATIONAL

Zona Franca Industrial
Gurabo
Santiago 1425
Dominican Republic
Jose Clase-President
(1) 829 947 7000   Fax: (1) 829 947 7177

E-Mail:	*cpizano@dclase.com*
Description:	*Manufacturer of uniforms, coveralls, lab coats.*
	Laundry facilities.
Year Est:	*1992*
Exporting Since:	*1992*
Specialties:	*Screen Printing - Multi color print, high density, puff, foil print,*
	athletic print, rock, suede, frog, four color process, distress & more.
Markets:	*Menswear, Womenswear & Youthwear.*
Machinery:	*Modern equipment for cutting, sewing, printing and finishing.*
Packages:	*CMT, Full Package*
Export to:	*United States*
Minimums:	*500 dz on sewing/1,000 units on screen printing*
Factory Locals:	*4 factories in Esperanza, Dominican Republic*

GLOBAL CMT CORPORATION

Zona Franca Industrial Santiago

Santiago
Dominican Republic
Francisco Rodriguez
(1) (809) 575 4777   Fax: (1) (809) 575 1232

E-Mail:	*f.rodriguez@globalcmt.com*
Web Site:	*www.globalcmt.com*
Description:	*Specialize in the production of tailored clothing as well as*
	overcoats, uniforms and tuxedos.
Categories:	*Suits/Tailored Clothing, Coats/Jackets*
Markets:	*Menswear, Womenswear, Childrenswear.*
Packages:	*Full and partial packages*

GRUPO BAMEX S.A. DE C.V.

Venustiano Carranza 477 Sur

Monterrey, N.L. 64000
Mexico
Ruben Marcos
(52) (81) 8130 7800   Fax: (52) (81) 8345 7271

E-Mail:	*rmarcos@grupobamex.com*
Web Site:	*www.mariscalmoda.com*
Description:	*Full package contractor of office & industrial uniforms.*
Year Est:	*1948*
Categories:	*Shirts/Tops, Pants*
Specialties:	*Samples available*
Markets:	*Menswear, Boyswear*
Packages:	*Sewing, cutting, patternmaking, grading/marking*

Export to:	*United States 10%*
Minimums:	*300 pcs/style*
Factory Locals:	*All work done in-house.*
	www.johnhenry.com.mx, www.grupobamex.com
Production Capacity:	*Shirts: 100,000 pcs/month, Pants: 20,000 pcs/month*

INDUSTRIAS FLORENZI, S.A. DE C.V.
Calle Al Matazano
Contiguo al Plantel de Salud Publica
Soyapango
El Salvador
Roberto Pineda Letona, President
() (503) 2297 0577   Fax: () (503) 2297 1223

E-Mail:	*r_pineda@navegante.com.sv*
Description:	*Contractor of uniforms. Scrubs and coats for doctors & nurses.*
Year Est:	*1985*
Categories:	*Dresses/Blouses, Sportswear*
Specialties:	*Patternmaking, grading, marker making, plotter service, cutting service, label printing, sewing (knitted & woven).*
Markets:	*Girlswear, Womenswear, Unisex.*
Machinery:	*180 single needle, 20 double needle, 8 multi needle, 90 safety stitch, 10 blindstitch, 15 button hole, 10 button sewing, 10 bartackers, 2 multineedle, 5 zig zag, 30 coverstitch, 15 hand irons, 3 hoffman pressers, 8 spreaders, 1 bias slitter, 2 fusing.*
Packages:	*807 & Full package.*
Export to:	*United States*
Minimums:	*500 pcs.*
Production Capacity:	*50,000 units/month*

J. M. J. FASHIONS INC.
365 Bannatyne Avenue

Winnipeg, Manitoba R3A 0E5
Canada
Roman Witkowski
(1) (204) 942 0252   Fax: (1) (204) 943 5083

E-Mail:	*romanw@jmjingenuity.com*
Web Site:	*www.jmjingenuity.com*
Description:	*Manufacturer and contractor of ladies sportswear coordinates plus uniforms for banks, real estate agencies, airlines and more.*
Year Est:	*1933 - Family owned*
Exporting Since:	*1993*
Categories:	*Sportswear Wovens/Sportswear Knits*
Markets:	*Womenswear*
Machinery:	*27 single needle, 1 double needle, 11 seam serger, 2 blind stitch, 2 cover stitch, 1 tacker, 5 button hole, 1 grommet, 4 button machine, 4 lock stitch.*
Packages:	*Cut & Sew, Patternmaking, Complete Packages available.*
Export to:	*United States*
Factory Locals:	*All work is done in-house*
Production Capacity:	*4,000 pieces/monthly*

KATTAN GROUP

800 mts. Carretera a la Jutosa
Inhdelva Free Trade Zone
Choloma, Cortes
Honduras
Gabriel Kattan
(504) 2617 0150   Fax: (504) 2617 0155

E-Mail:	*gabriel.kattan@kattangroup.com*
Web Site:	*www.kattangroup.com*
Description:	*Full service contractor, with screenprinting, embroidery, washing, handsand, sandblast, finishing, quilting, stitching capabilities & more.*
Year Est:	*1920*
Exporting Since:	*1984*
Categories:	*Shirts/Tops*
Specialties:	*Work wear such as scrubs, uniforms and hospitality wear.*
Markets:	*Menswear, Womenswear*
Machinery:	*5,000 single needle, 1,000 double needle, 1,000 coverstitch, 1,000 coverstitch, 500 pressing, 20 embroidery, 8 MHM screenprinting, 12 300-lb. washers, 10 400-lb. dryers.*
Packages:	*806, 807, CMT & Full service & complete packages.*
Export to:	*United States, Europe*
Agent:	*US Office: 12181 W. Linebaugh Avenue, Tampa, Fl. Tel#813-925-0001.*
Minimums:	*1200 units per color*
Factory Locals:	*Own 23 factories in the Free Trade Zone*
Production Capacity:	*Knits: 960,000 units/week, Woven bottoms: 120,000 units/week, Woven tops: 120,000 units/week.*

PERFECTION SHIRT INC.

P.O.Box 190
101 Perfection Avenue
Courcelles (Quebec) G0M 1C0
Canada
Rock Doucet
(1) (418) 483 5227   Fax: (1) (418) 483 5827

E-Mail:	*sales@perfectionshirt.com*
Web Site:	*www.perfectionshirt.com*
Description:	*Manufacturer of uniforms & dress & sport shirts. Also, corporate shirts for chain store, restaurant or company executives & employees.*
Year Est:	*1947*
Categories:	*Shirts/Tops, Pants*
Markets:	*Menswear, Womenswear.*
Export to:	*USA 5%*
Production Capacity:	*60,000 shirts/month, 10,000 pants/month*

PRODUCTORA CLINIMEX INDUSTRIAL, S.A. DE C. V.

Carr Panamericana Km. 545
Jesus Gomez Portugal
Aguascalientes 20909
Mexico
Mario Oranday
(52) (449) 9730304, 9730302

E-Mail:	*orandaym@agssite.com.mx*
Description:	*Manufacturer of all kinds of disposable garments/uniforms specializing in disposable coveralls.*
Year Est:	*1989*
Export to:	*USA 80% & South America 15% & Germany 5%*
Production Capacity:	*300,000 pcs/month*

ROCEDES S.A.

Zona Franca Las Mercedes Bldg.#29
Km 12 1/2 Carretera Norte
Managua
Nicaragua
Scott Vaughn
(505) 2263 2032   Fax: (505) 2263 2033

E-Mail:	*svaughn@rocedes.com.ni*
Web Site:	*www.rocedes.com.ni*
Description:	*Contractor of casual wear, work wear and uniforms.*
Year Est:	*1993*
Categories:	*Pants/Shorts/Skirts*
Markets:	*Menswear, Womenswear, Boyswear, Girlswear.*
Machinery:	*698 Plain sewers, 195 Bartacker, 34 Button Hole, 283 Overlock, 53 Bander, 51 Compos.*
Export to:	*United States 100%*
Factory Locals:	*Managua, Nicaragua*
Production Capacity:	*600,000 pieces/month*

S.M.C., S.A.

Zona Franca Industrial De La Vega

La Vega
Dominican Republic
Julio Ortiz, President
(1) (809) 242 6565, 242 6566   Fax: (1) (809) 242 6567

E-Mail:	*smcdr@yahoo.com*
Description:	*Woven shirts, blouses and uniforms*
Year Est:	*1987*
Exporting Since:	*1987*
Categories:	*Blouses/Shirts/Tops*
Specialties:	*Uniform shirts.*
Markets:	*Menswear, Womenswear, Childrenswear.*
Machinery:	*250 sewing machines & special machines for shirts.*
Packages:	*CM, CMT & Full packages*
Export to:	*U.S.A. 100%*
Minimums:	*300 dozen/style*

Factory Locals:	Free zone La Vega, Dominican Republic
Production Capacity:	6,000 doz/month

VALLEN PROVEEDORA DE SEGURIDAD INDUSTRIAL DEL GOLFO

Blvd. A. Lopez Mateos No. 4000
Universidad Poniente
Tampico, Tamaulipas 89336
Mexico
Jorge Mina Kuri
(52) (833) 2301700   Fax: (52) (833) 2301701

E-Mail:	jmina@vallenproveedora.com.mx
Web Site:	www.vallenproveedora.com.mx
Description:	All types of safety & surgical clothing.
Specialties:	Specialize in protective coveralls and uniforms.
Export to:	USA 35%, Panama 15%, Guatemala 20%, Peru 15%, Colombia 15%
Production Capacity:	20,000 pcs/month

info@fashiondex.com © The Fashiondex, Inc.

ROBOCUTS

1625 Chabanel West
Suite 729
Montreal, Quebec H4N 2S7
Canada
Dave Fernandez
(1) (514) 388 8001   Fax: (1) (514) 388 7783

E-Mail:	*sales@robocuts.com*
Web Site:	*www.robocuts.com*
Description:	*Canada's largest automated cutting service.*
Specialties:	*Services include grading, marking, automated cutting, fusing and sewing.*

Notes

info@fashiondex.com © The Fashiondex, Inc.

EZC DYE HOUSE
Free Zone #1

San Pedro de Macoris
Dominican Republic
Jamie Nelson
(U.S.A.) (954) 732 4134

E-Mail:	*jnpcgoods@aol.com*
Description:	*Garment dying & tie dying for large quantities on finished garments from swimwear to active wear. We will pass CTL, MTL requirements.*
Specialties:	*Specialize in quick turnaround. Also offer finishing, complete (hang tags, poly bags, hangers, boxes) if needed.*
Minimums:	*Tie dye/5,000 pcs.*
Factory Locals:	*Free container shipping from our warehouse in Miami to the Dominican Republic & back.*

info@fashiondex.com © The Fashiondex, Inc.

DOUBLETEX
9785 Jeanne Mance

Montreal, Quebec H3L3B6
Canada
Richard Zuckerman
(1) (514) 382 1770   Fax: (1) (514) 382 9587

E-Mail:	*sales@doubletex.com*
Web Site:	*www.doubletex.com*
Description:	*Toll Free#1-800-311-1770. All types of coating, finishing, washer finishes & fabric dyeing.*
Year Est:	*Over 90 years in business.*
Categories:	*Quilting Contractors*
Specialties:	*Laminating*
Markets:	*All.*
Minimums:	*None*

Notes

MODE WORKS

1395 Marine Drive
P.O. Box 27022
Vancouver, British Columbia V7T 2X8
Canada
Alina Unglert
(1) (604) 562 4921

E-Mail:	alina@modeworks.ca
Web Site:	www.modeworks.ca
Description:	Pattern drafting & grading and marking services with Gerber technology.
Year Est:	1997
Categories:	Patternmaking, Grading/Marking
Specialties:	Technical illustration, merchandizing & design services. Consultation for contemporary & streetwear markets. Use Karat Cad Designer.

MODE WORKS

1395 Marine Drive
P.O. Box 27022
Vancouver, British Columbia V7T 2X8
Canada
Alina Unglert
(1) (604) 562 4921

E-Mail:	*alina@modeworks.ca*
Web Site:	*www.modeworks.ca*
Description:	*Pattern drafting & grading and marking services with Gerber technology.*
Year Est:	*1997*
Categories:	*Patternmaking, Grading/Marking*
Specialties:	*Technical illustration, merchandizing & design services. Consultation for contemporary & streetwear markets. Use Karat Cad Designer.*

PURE BLANKZ ORGANIC FASHION INC.

572 Dahlia Crescent

Pickering, Ontario L1W 3G5
Canada
Adila Cokar
(1) 647 248 8326   Fax: (1) 888 807 5508

E-Mail:	*adila@pureblankz.com*
Web Site:	*www.pureblankz.com*
Description:	*Complete garment sourcing, product management, factory selection, price negotiation, sourcing, marketing, trend research, tech packages.*
Specialties:	*Manufacture goods in an eco-friendly & sustainable way. We can help you develop custom and private label products.*
Markets:	*Menswear, Womenswear, Childrenswear, Accessories, Home*
Packages:	*Full service*
Factory Locals:	*All our factories are ISO 9001-2000 certified & GOTS certified.*

Notes

info@fashiondex.com © The Fashiondex, Inc.

Bolivia

BORDA SURI SRL
Calle Chaco No. 747 (Sopocachi)

La Paz
Bolivia
Enrique Borda
(591) (22) 413663   Fax: (591) (22) 415916

E-Mail:	*alpac@suri-bo.com*
Web Site:	*www.suri-bo.com*
Description:	*Manufacturers of apparel made of alpaca, sheep yarn and llama yarn.*
Year Est:	*1977*
Exporting Since:	*1979*
Categories:	*Sweaters/Knitwear*
Specialties:	*Pullovers, cardigans, jackets, overcoats, vests, scarves, shawls & gloves in 100% alpaca yarn.*
Markets:	*Menswear, Womenswear & Childrenswear.*
Machinery:	*Weaving & sewing machinery. Individual styles finished by hand.*
Export to:	*U.S.A., Japan, Denmark*
Minimums:	*300 pieces/style*
Production Capacity:	*300-800 pieces/month - depending on style.*

Canada

CSR INTERNATIONAL INC.
150 rue du Couvent

St. Romain, Quebec, G0Y 1L0
Canada
Jean-Luc Fortin
(1) (418) 486 7481   Fax: (1) (418) 486 7903

E-Mail:	*jlfortin@csr-intl.com*
Web Site:	*www.groupecsr.com*
Description:	*CMT & complete package contractor of women's & children's swimwear & activewear.*
Year Est:	*1972*
Exporting Since:	*1996*
Categories:	*Swimwear/Dancewear*
Markets:	*Womenswear, Childrenswear.*
Machinery:	*Sergers, single & double needle, bartack, multi needle, cover stitch, button, flatlock & zig zag machinery.*
Packages:	*CMT & complete packages.*
Export to:	*United States*
Minimums:	*500 units/style*

DOUBLETEX

9785 Jeanne Mance

Montreal, Quebec H3L3B6
Canada
Richard Zuckerman
(1) (514) 382 1770   Fax: (1) (514) 382 9587

E-Mail:	*sales@doubletex.com*
Web Site:	*www.doubletex.com*
Description:	*1-800-311-1770. All types of coating, finishing, washer finishes and fabric dyeing. Also, bonding, laminating & all types of quilting.*
Year Est:	*Over 90 years in business.*
Categories:	*Quilting Contractors, Finshing/Coating Contractors.*
Specialties:	*Water proofing, showerproofing & coating. Carry fiberfill battings for quilting contract work.*
Markets:	*All.*
Minimums:	*None*

GRUVEN INTERNATIONAL INC.

19 Newgale Gate

Scarborough, Ontario M1X 1B6
Canada
Dave Rushton, Sales Director
(1) (416) 292 7331   Fax: (1) (416) 754 8675

E-Mail:	*drushton@gruven.com*
Web Site:	*www.gruven.com*
Description:	*Manufacturer & sewing contractor of outerwear, knitwear & fleecewear.*
Year Est:	*1985*
Exporting Since:	*1985*
Categories:	*Coats/Jackets, Active/Athletic Wear*
Specialties:	*Leading sublimated apparel specialists with artwork, printing, assembly under one roof. Complete turnaround time in 2.5 weeks for most orders.*
Markets:	*Menswear, Womenswear, Boyswear, Girlswear.*
Machinery:	*150 Single/double needle, 100 Serger*
Packages:	*All packages - screenprinting, quilting & embroidery.*
Export to:	*USA, Sweden & Japan.*
Minimums:	*250 units/style*
Factory Locals:	*Three factories in Scarborough, Ontario NAFTA certified.*

J. M. J. FASHIONS INC.

365 Bannatyne Avenue

Winnipeg, Manitoba R3A 0E5
Canada
Roman Witkowski
(1) (204) 942 0252   Fax: (1) (204) 943 5083

E-Mail:	*romanw@jmjingenuity.com*
Web Site:	*www.jmjingenuity.com*
Description:	*Manufacturer and contractor of ladies sportswear coordinates plus*

uniforms for banks, real estate agencies, airlines and more.

Year Est:	1933 - Family owned
Exporting Since:	1993
Categories:	Sportswear Knits/Sportswear Wovens, Uniforms
Markets:	Womenswear
Machinery:	27 single needle, 1 double needle, 11 seam serger, 2 blind stitch, 2 cover stitch, 1 tacker, 5 button hole, 1 grommet, 4 button machine, 4 lock stitch.
Packages:	Cut & Sew, Patternmaking, Complete Packages available.
Export to:	United States
Factory Locals:	All work is done in-house
Production Capacity:	4,000 pieces/monthly

LES TEXTILES GAUVIN INC.
63 Rue Industrielle

Saint Pamphile, Quebec G0R 3X0
Canada
Normand Gauvin
(1) (418) 356 2434   Fax: (1) (418) 356 3320

E-Mail:	info@zenima.ca
Web Site:	www.zenima.ca
Description:	Contractor specializing in sheets, throws & bathrobes.
Year Est:	1987
Exporting Since:	1999
Categories:	Intimate Apparel, Home Furnishings
Specialties:	All production done in-house.
Markets:	Menswear, Womenswear, Childrenswear & Home.
Packages:	Sewing, Cutting, Complete Packages, Embroidery
Production Capacity:	30,000 sets/month

MANDARINTEX LTD.
17 Seamist Crescent

Toronto, Ontario M1V3K3
Canada
Philip Ip
(1) (647) 728 3254

E-Mail:	philipip@mandarintex.com
Web Site:	www.mandarintex.com
Description:	Cut and sew contractor.
Categories:	Sample Room/Small Production, Lingerie/Intimate/Underwear, Sleepwear & Robes
Specialties:	Specialize in loungewear, underwear, bras, briefs, boxers, robes and sleepwear.
Markets:	Menswear, Womenwear.
Minimums:	400 pieces/style

MODE WORKS

1395 Marine Drive
P.O. Box 27022
Vancouver, British Columbia V7T 2X8
Canada
Alina Unglert
(1) (604) 562 4921

E-Mail:	*alina@modeworks.ca*
Web Site:	*www.modeworks.ca*
Description:	*Pattern drafting & grading and marking services with Gerber technology.*
Year Est:	*1997*
Categories:	*Patternmaking, Grading/Marking*
Specialties:	*Technical illustration, merchandizing & design services. Consultation for contemporary & streetwear markets. Use Karat Cad Designer.*

ONTARIO GLOVE MANUFACTURING CO., LTD.

5 Washburn Drive, Unit A

Kitchener, Ontario N2R 1S1
Canada

(1) (519) 886 3590   Fax: (1) (519) 886 3597

E-Mail:	*sales@ontarioglove.com*
Web Site:	*www.ontarioglove.com*
Description:	*Manufacturer & contractor of gloves of all types.*
Year Est:	*1914*
Exporting Since:	*1926*
Categories:	*Accessories*
Specialties:	*All styles of gloves, mitts, protective clothing & workwear (casual, ski, snowboard etc.).*
Markets:	*Menswear, Womenswear & Childrenswear.*
Machinery:	*Sewing, Cutting, etc.*
Export to:	*United States, South America, Far East*
Minimums:	*Large Volume*
Factory Locals:	*Waterloo, Ontario, Canada*

PERFECTION SHIRT INC.

P.O. Box 190
101 Perfection Avenue
Courcelles (Quebec) G0M 1C0
Canada
Rock Doucet
(1) (418) 483 5227   Fax: (1) (418) 483 5827

E-Mail:	*sales@perfectionshirt.com*
Web Site:	*www.perfectionshirt.com*
Description:	*Manufacturer of uniforms & dress & sport shirts. Also, corporate shirts for chain store, restaurant or company executives & employees.*
Year Est:	*1947*
Categories:	*Uniforms, Shirts/Tops, Pants*
Markets:	*Menswear, Womenswear.*

Export to:	USA 5%
Production Capacity:	60,000 shirts/month, 10,000 pants/month

PHILIPPO MANUFACTURING CORP.

3177 Fleury East

Montreal, Quebec H1H2R2
Canada
Gaetano Orsina
(1) (514) 389 4321   Fax: (1) (514) 389 1491

E-Mail:	gates@qc.aibn.com
Description:	CMT of fully constructed wool, linen or poly/cotton womens suits, pants, skirts & shorts.
Year Est:	1976
Categories:	Pants/Shorts/Skirts
Markets:	Womens
Export to:	U.S.A.
Minimums:	50 pcs/style
Production Capacity:	3,000 suits/week

PURE BLANKZ ORGANIC FASHION INC.

572 Dahlia Crescent

Pickering, Ontario L1W 3G5
Canada
Adila Cokar
(1) 647 248 8326   Fax: (1) 888 807 5508

E-Mail:	adila@pureblankz.com
Web Site:	www.pureblankz.com
Description:	Complete garment sourcing, product management, factory selection, price negotiation, sourcing, marketing, trend research, tech packages.
Categories:	Production Sourcing/Factory Agents
Specialties:	Manufacture goods in an eco-friendly & sustainable way. We can help you develop custom and private label products.
Markets:	Menswear, Womenswear, Childrenswear, Accessories, Home
Packages:	Full service
Factory Locals:	All our factories are ISO 9001-2000 certified & GOTS certified.

ROBOCUTS

1625 Chabanel West
Suite 729
Montreal, Quebec H4N 2S7
Canada
Dave Fernandez
(1) (514) 388 8001   Fax: (1) (514) 388 7783

E-Mail:	sales@robocuts.com
Web Site:	www.robocuts.com
Description:	Canada's largest automated cutting service.
Specialties:	Services include grading, marking, automated cutting, fusing and sewing.

STAR CONCEPT APPAREL LTD.
54 East 6th Avenue

Vancouver, B.C. V5T1J4
Canada

(1) (604) 879 9018   Fax: (1) (604) 879 9328

E-Mail:	*info@starconceptapparel.com*
Web Site:	*www.starconceptapparel.com*
Description:	*Contractor for all types of garments using fabrics such as cotton fleece, French terry, polar fleece, stretch nylon and more.*
Categories:	*Tee Shirts, Sample Rooms/Small Production*
Specialties:	*Specialize in basic tee shirts to running jackets.*
Markets:	*Menswear, Womenswear & Childrenswear.*
Machinery:	*Single needle, 4 and 5 thread sergers, cover stitches, waistband machines, button hole and button machines, piping cutters and more.*

Colombia

DISMODA S.A.
Cra 30 Ave Hamburgo
Zona Franca, Bloque E.
Barranquilla
Colombia
Antonieta Russo/Cesar Caro
(57) (5) 3799777   Fax: (57) (5) 3799550

E-Mail:	*dismoda@dismoda.com*
Web Site:	*www.dismoda.com*
Description:	*Sportswear, casual wear & formal wear contractor for all markets.*
Year Est:	*1981*
Exporting Since:	*1981*
Categories:	*Dresses/Blouses, Shirts/Tops, Woven Sportwear, Jeans/Denimwear, Pants/Shorts/Skirts, Tee Shirts.*
Markets:	*Menswear, Womenswear, Childrenswear.*
Machinery:	*Over 900 sewing & finishing machines. All types.*
Packages:	*CMT, Dyeing/Finishing, Laundering/Washing.*
Export to:	*United States 100%*
Agent:	*Orlando Caro, Miami, FL (overseas source). Tel: 305-639-2486.*
Minimums:	*2,000 units/style*
Production Capacity:	*Pants: 66,000 units/month, Skirts: 15,000 units/month, Shirts: 20,000 units/month, Tees: 27,000 units/month*

Dominican Republic

3 MT ENTERPRISES
Zona Franca Industrial#1

San Pedro de Macaris
Dominican Republic

(1) (809) 246 3501   Fax: (1) (809) 246 3502
E-Mail:	*selmufdi@grupo3mt.com*
Web Site:	*www.grupo3mt.com*
Description:	*Contractor of knit shirts and sportswear.*
	Full package specialist.
Specialties:	*Specialize in tee shirts, hooded shirts, fleece styles & knit pants.*
	In house screen printing & embroidery.
Markets:	*Womenswear, Menswear, Childrenswear.*
Packages:	*807 & full package.*
Export to:	*USA 100%*
Agent:	*US Office: Miami Sourcing/Grupo 3MT, Miami Beach, Fl.*
	Tony Fernandez 305 301 0986-tonyfernz10@gmail.com
Factory Locals:	*Factory group includes knit fabric production.*
Production Capacity:	*3,000 doz/week*

ANTILLES MANUFACTURING, S.A.
Calle La Canela, Nave No. 1
Zona Franca Industrial
Santiago
Dominican Republic
Ricardo J. Fondeur
(1) (809) 570 3603   Fax: (1) (809) 570 3809
E-Mail:	*recepcion@oadom.com.do*
Year Est:	*1995*
Exporting Since:	*1995*
Categories:	*Pants/Shorts*
Specialties:	*Specialize in casual pants.*
Markets:	*Menswear, Womenswear, Boyswear.*
Machinery:	*238 single, 70 merrow, 34 chain, 36 double*
	stitch machines & many other types.
Packages:	*Sewing only.*
Export to:	*United States, Mexico & Canada.*
Minimums:	*15,000 units/style*

D'CLASE APPAREL INTERNATIONAL
Zona Franca Industrial
Gurabo
Santiago 1425
Dominican Republic
Jose Clase-President
(1) 829 947 7000   Fax: (1) 829 947 7177
E-Mail:	*cpizano@dclase.com*
Description:	*Apparel manufacturers of casual pants, uniforms & dresses.*
	Laundry facilities.
Year Est:	*1986*

Exporting Since:	1986
Categories:	Pants/shorts/Skirts, Uniforms, Dresses
Specialties:	Complete testing laboratory for fabric & finished goods. Will do samples.
Markets:	Menswear, Womenswear & Youthwear.
Machinery:	Modern equipment for cutting, sewing & finishing of casual pants, uniforms & dresses.
Packages:	CMT, Full Packages, EDI & complete service programs.
Export to:	United States 98%, Canada 2%
Minimums:	5,000 per style/1,000 units per color/15 SKU's
Factory Locals:	4 factories in Esperanza, Dominican Republic

EZC DYE HOUSE
Free Zone #1

San Pedro de Macoris
Dominican Republic
Jamie Nelson
(U.S.A.) (954) 732 4134

E-Mail:	jnpcgoods@aol.com
Description:	Garment dying & tie dying for large quantities on finished garments from swimwear to active wear. We will pass CTL, MTL requirements.
Categories:	Dyeing Contractors
Specialties:	Specialize in quick turnaround. Also offer finishing, complete (hang tags, poly bags, hangers, boxes) if needed.
Minimums:	Tie dye/5,000 pcs.
Factory Locals:	Free container shipping from our warehouse in Miami to the Dominican Republic & back.

GLOBAL CMT CORPORATION
Zona Franca Industrial Santiago

Santiago
Dominican Republic
Francisco Rodriguez
(1) (809) 575 4777   Fax: (1) (809) 575 1232

E-Mail:	f.rodriguez@globalcmt.com
Web Site:	www.globalcmt.com
Description:	Specialize in the production of tailored clothing as well as overcoats, uniforms and tuxedos.
Categories:	Uniforms, Suits/Tailored Clothing, Coats/Jackets
Markets:	Menswear, Womenswear, Childrenswear.
Packages:	Full and partial packages

K & S INDUSTRIES, S.A.
Industrial Free Zone

San Pedro de Macoris
Dominican Republic
Junior Aza
(1) (809) 529 8080   Fax: (1) (809) 529 2535
- **E-Mail:** *kands@claro.net.do*
- **Description:** *Cut & sew contractor of intimate apparel, swimwear & medical items.*
- **Specialties:** *Quick turn-around time.*
- **Markets:** *Womenswear & Menswear.*
- **Packages:** *Full package*
- **Export to:** *U.S.A.*
- **Agent:** *USA Agent: DRM Products, PO Box 645, Merrick, NY,*
  David Klein, david@drmproducts.net, 516-410-4953.

S.M.C., S.A.
Zona Franca Industrial De La Vega

La Vega
Dominican Republic
Julio Ortiz, President
(1) (809) 242 6565, 242 6566   Fax: (1) (809) 242 6567
- **E-Mail:** *smcdr@yahoo.com*
- **Description:** *Woven shirts, blouses and uniforms*
- **Year Est:** *1987*
- **Exporting Since:** *1987*
- **Categories:** *Blouses/Shirts/Tops, Uniforms*
- **Specialties:** *Uniform shirts.*
- **Markets:** *Menswear, Womenswear, Childrenswear.*
- **Machinery:** *250 sewing machines & special machines for shirts.*
- **Packages:** *CM, CMT & Full packages*
- **Export to:** *U.S.A. 100%*
- **Minimums:** *300 dozen/style*
- **Factory Locals:** *Free zone La Vega, Dominican Republic*
- **Production Capacity:** *6,000 doz/month*

El Salvador

DA SAN, S.A. DE C.V.
Km 26, Carretera a Sonsonate
Jurisdiccion de Lourdes Colon
La Libertad
El Salvador
Richard Kim
() (503) 2322 2100   Fax: () (503) 2318 1748
- **E-Mail:** *richard.kim@dasan.com.sv*
- **Description:** *Contractor pants, skirts, tops, vests, blouses & dresses.*
- **Year Est:** *1993*
- **Categories:** *Shirts/Tops, Pants/Skirts, Dresses*
- **Markets:** *Womenswear*

Machinery:	*Over 1,400 pieces of machinery on premises.*
Packages:	*CMT & 807.*
Export to:	*U.S.A*
Factory Locals:	*El Salvador*
Production Capacity:	*100,000 units/month (tops, jackets), 35,000 units/month (bottoms) 100,000 units/month (knits).*

HANDWORKS

Centro Textil San Jorge local 10
Prolongacion Avenida Juan Pablo
San Salvador
El Salvador
Alessandra Castellanos
(503) 7886 5243   Fax: (503) 2225 9734

E-Mail:	*aoriggi@yahoo.com*
Description:	*Childrenswear manufacturer. Expert with all childrenswear styles, hand smocked girl's dresses, boy's clothing, diaper bags & bibs.*
Year Est:	*1991*
Exporting Since:	*1991*
Categories:	*Childrens Wear*
Markets:	*Menswear, Womenswear, Childrenswear.*
Machinery:	*260 sewing machines. Also cutting facitily & Gerber plotter.*
Packages:	*Full packages.*
Export to:	*U.S.A. 100%*
Minimums:	*Vary - depending on product*
Factory Locals:	*El Salvador*
Production Capacity:	*3,000-5,000 dozen/week, depending on product.*

INDUSTRIAS FLORENZI, S.A. DE C.V.

Calle Al Matazano
Contiguo al Plantel de Salud Publica
Soyapango
El Salvador
Roberto Pineda Letona, President
() (503) 2297 0577   Fax: () (503) 2297 1223

E-Mail:	*r_pineda@navegante.com.sv*
Description:	*Contractor of dresses, sportswear, shirts and uniforms.*
Year Est:	*1985*
Categories:	*Dresses/Blouses, Sportswear, Shirts, Uniforms*
Specialties:	*Patternmaking, grading, marker making, plotter service, cutting service, label printing, sewing (knitted & woven).*
Markets:	*Girlswear, Womenswear, Unisex.*
Machinery:	*180 single needle, 20 double needle, 8 multi needle, 90 safety stitch, 10 blindstitch, 15 button hole, 10 button sewing, 10 bartackers, 2 multineedle, 5 zig zag, 30 coverstitch, 15 hand irons, 3 hoffman pressers, 8 spreaders, 1 bias slitter, 2 fusing.*
Packages:	*807 & Full package.*
Export to:	*United States*
Minimums:	*500 pcs.*
Production Capacity:	*50,000 units/month*

LD EL SALVADOR
Parque Industrial Zone

Franca San Salvador
El Salvador

(503) 2213 0909   Fax: (503) 2213 0912

E-Mail: *cecile.reyes@mail.com*
Description: *Contractor expert in all types of boyswear & men's dress, sport & polo shirts. 55,000 sq. ft. facility in El Salvador.*
Categories: *Shirts/Tops, Childrens Wear*
Specialties: *Sourcing locations in Korea, Vietnam, Bangladesh, Cambodia & Shanghai, China. J.C. Penney, Wal-Mart & Sears certified.*
Markets: *Menswear & Boyswear.*
Export to: *U.S.A.*

TEXTILES OPICO DBA TEXOPS
KM 31.4 Carretera a Santa Ana
San Juan Opico
La Libertad
El Salvador
Juan C. Zighelboim
() (503) 2319 0800   Fax: () (503) 2319 0812

E-Mail: *juan.zighelboim@texops.com*
Web Site: *www.texops.com*
Description: *Private label contract manufacturing of active and athletic wear. Specialists in stretch synthetic fabrics with flat seams.*
Year Est: *2008*
Exporting Since: *2008*
Categories: *Athletic wear, Sportswear-Wovens, Sportswear-Knits.*
Specialties: *Specialize in knit apparel, sublimation, active, yoga, compression, fitness, cycling, running, team sports, plaquet polo shirts.*
Markets: *Menswear, Womenswear, Boyswear, Girlswear.*
Machinery: *200 flat seam, 265 cover stitch, 275 overlock, 250 lock stitch, 14 digital dye-sublimation printers, 4 Monti-Antonio fabric & cut part sublimation presses, 3 Lectra automated cutters, 4 Oteman Synergy Auto Spreaders, Raw Materials testing lab.*
Packages: *Complete private label & full packages.*
Export to: *USA 85%, Asia 5%, Canada 5%, Europe 5%,*
Agent: *From USA - 305-503-4139 x 550*
Minimums: *50 dozen/style*
Factory Locals: *El Salvador*
Production Capacity: *360,000 tops/month, 360,000 bottoms/month*

Guatemala

ALAMEDA S.A.

1a Av. La Brigada 13-30, Zona 7
Colonia San Ignacio
Mixco
Guatemala
Luis Barillas
(502) 2437 5321   Fax: (502) 2437 8287

E-Mail:	*luisb@alamedasa.com*
Web Site:	*www.alamedasa.com*
Description:	*Advanced garment production factory. In-house cutting, sewing, washing, dyeing, sandblasing & packaging.*
Categories:	*Pants/Shorts/Skirts*
Specialties:	*Specialize in ladies woven and knit pants and skirts.*
Markets:	*All womens markets.*
Machinery:	*Computerized sewing machines.*
Packages:	*Full Packages.*

NOVA CREATION

Km 13.5 Carretera a El Salvador
Puerta Parads, Sta.
Catarina Pinula
Guatemala
Jose Gisbert
(502) 6646 5880

E-Mail:	*j.gisbert@novacreation.net*
Description:	*Full-package manufacturer of t-shirts, polos, tank tops, hoodies, onsies and more.*
Categories:	*Tee Shirts/Sweat Shirts*
Specialties:	*Tech Package, dyeing & finishing, pattern design & cutting, sewing, trims, printing & finishing in-house, packaging.*
Packages:	*Full Packages*

NYLONTEX INTERNACIONAL S.A.

Km. 18.5 Carretera al Mayan Golf

Villa Nueva
Guatemala
Karla Woc
(502) 6628 0700   Fax: (502) 6628 0701

E-Mail:	*kwoc@nylontexinternacional.com*
Web Site:	*www.nylontexinternacional.com*
Description:	*Sewing contractor of seamless underwear & hosiery for women & childrens underwear.*
Year Est:	*1963*
Specialties:	*Specialize in hosiery, leggings & seamless wear.*
Markets:	*Womenswear, Childrens*
Machinery:	*40 Santonni Machines*
Export to:	*Mexico, Central America, USA, Guatemala*
Production Capacity:	*Seamless Wear: 15,000 dozen/month, Hosiery: 150,000 dozen/month*

Honduras

CONFECCIONES INTERNACIONALES S.A. DE C.V.

Zona Libre Tegucigalpa
Colonia Kennedy, Quinta Entrada
Tegucigalpa
Honduras
Enrique Facusse
(504) 2230 5518   Fax: (504) 2230 5422

E-Mail:	*sales@confecciones.com*
Web Site:	*www.confecciones.com*
Description:	*Integrated full package manufacturer specializing in knit tops, tee shirts, polo sport shirts & fleece products.*
Year Est:	*1993*
Categories:	*Activewear, Tee-Shirts, Shirts/Tops, Underwear.*
Specialties:	*Also sell knit fabric (jersey, pique, fleece, others).*
Markets:	*Menswear, Womenswear & Childrenswear.*
Machinery:	*Over 950 machines from Juki, Union special, Brother, Yamato & automated equipment from Atlanta Attachment.*
Packages:	*Full packages*
Export to:	*U.S.A.*
Agent:	*In USA tel# 786-837-0215 x 1231 E-Fax 305-675-3121*
Factory Locals:	*Tegucigalpa, Honduras*

KATTAN GROUP

800 mts. Carretera a la Jutosa
Inhdelva Free Trade Zone
Choloma, Cortes
Honduras
Gabriel Kattan
(504) 2617 0150   Fax: (504) 2617 0155

E-Mail:	*gabriel.kattan@kattangroup.com*
Web Site:	*www.kattangroup.com*
Description:	*Full service contractor, with screenprinting, embroidery, washing, handsand, sandblast, finishing, quilting, stitching capabilities & more.*
Year Est:	*1920*
Exporting Since:	*1984*
Categories:	*Shirts/Tops, Uniform*
Specialties:	*Main focus is woven tops, both dress and sport shirts as well as uniform work wear.*
Markets:	*Menswear, Womenswear*
Machinery:	*5,000 single needle, 1,000 double needle, 1,000 coverstitch, 1,000 coverstitch, 500 pressing, 20 embroidery, 8 MHM screenprinting, 12 300-lb. washers, 10 400-lb. dryers.*
Packages:	*806, 807, CMT & Full service & complete packages.*
Export to:	*United States, Europe*
Agent:	*US Office: 12181 W. Linebaugh Avenue, Tampa, Fl. Tel#813-925-0001.*
Minimums:	*1200 units per color*
Factory Locals:	*Own 23 factories in the Free Trade Zone*
Production Capacity:	*Knits: 960,000 units/week, Woven bottoms: 120,000 units/week, Woven tops: 120,000 units/week.*

PRIDE MANUFACTURING S. DE R. L.

Zip Honduras
Edificio No.2
Choloma, Cortes
Honduras
Buda Escoto
(504) 2620 0450   Fax: (504) 2669 3624

E-Mail:	*buda.escoto@grupokarims.com*
Web Site:	*www.grupokarims.com*
Description:	*Manufacturer of all types of knit & woven sportswear.*
Year Est:	*1991*
Exporting Since:	*1991*
Specialties:	*Sample room, fabric testing, cutting room, embroidery as well as warehouse and distribution facilities.*
Markets:	*All apparel markets.*
Machinery:	*Over 1,500 machines, including: overlock, coverstitch, single needle, flat lock & more. Also embroidery equipment, & top-of-the-line cutting machinery.*
Packages:	*Full & CMT packages.*
Export to:	*USA*
Minimums:	*100 dozen/order, 2,500 dozen/program*
Factory Locals:	*Factories in Honduras with affilliates in Mexico, Miami, Pakistan, China & Guatemala.*
Production Capacity:	*Knit tops: 15,000 doz/wk, Woven tops: 1,500 doz/wk & Woven bottoms: 2,000 doz/wk.*

Mexico

BORDALO PUNTO COM S.A. DE C.V.

Venustiano Carranza No. 34
10 de Abril,
Naucalpan, State of Mexico 53310
Mexico
Gustavo Aranda
(52) (55) 1991 4040

E-Mail:	*info@bordalo.com*
Web Site:	*www.bordalo.com*
Description:	*Embroidery contractor. Caps, emblems, shirts, uniforms & bags.*
Categories:	*Embroidery Contractor*
Factory Locals:	*Mobile: 52 55 45234757*

COLCHAS MEXICO S.A. DE C.V.

Km. 35-5 Manzana 823 Lote 9
Colonia San Lorenzo Riotenco
Cuautitlan Izcalli, Estado de Mexico 54713
Mexico
Daniel Saadia
(52) (55) 50615200   Fax: (52) (55) 50615208

E-Mail:	*dsaadia@colchasconcord.com*
Web Site:	*www.colchasconcord.com*
Description:	*Bedding & home textiles manufacturer, from greige goods to finished*

products. We can print fabrics in rotary scenes & flat screens.

Year Est:	1959
Exporting Since:	1990
Categories:	Home Furnishings
Specialties:	Specialize in bedding, bedding accessories and home textiles. ISO 9000: 2000 certified. Approved supplier for J.C. Penny. and IKEA.
Machinery:	1,000 sewing machines, 50 multi-needle quilters, 30 single needle quilters, 2 printing & finishing 114" wide goods, 4 fiber-fill low-melt mix, 2 fiber-fill resin bonded machines.
Packages:	Complete
Export to:	United States 8%, Central America 4%
Factory Locals:	Cuautitlan Izacalli, Estado de Mexico. Also source in United States, Pakistan, Taiwan, China, Ecuador & Brazil.
Production Capacity:	Comforters/bed in a bag: 70,000/month, bedspreads: 200,000/month, blankets: 60,000/month, drapes/valances: 50,000/month.

CUALQUIER LAVADO, S.A. DE C.V.

Km.15 Carretera Tehuacan Puebla#2
Altura Desviacion a M. Cuayucatepec
Tehuacan, Puebla 75853
Mexico
Arturo Neira Francos
(52) (238) 3803700   Fax: (52) (238) 3803705

E-Mail:	aneira@cualquierlavado.com.mx
Web Site:	www.cualquierlavado.com
Description:	Men's and women's 5 pocket blue denim jeans.
Year Est:	1991
Exporting Since:	1991
Categories:	Jeans/Denimwear
Specialties:	Water-less washes (ozone technology), garment dye & laser machines to replace handsanding. Fire retardant jeans.
Markets:	Menswear, Womenwear.
Machinery:	Over 1000 sewing machines, washers, dryers, embroidery, screenprinting, handsand machines etc.
Export to:	USA 80%, Canada 20%
Agent:	USA Sales VP: Sue Tyson, tel: 270-839-1555, suetyson@cualquierlavado.com
Minimums:	5,000 pcs/style
Production Capacity:	Mens Jeans: 25,000 units/week, Womens Jeans: 40,000 units/week, Work Pants: 15,000 units/week, Fashion Jeans: 20,000 units/week.

GRUPO BAMEX S.A. DE C.V.

Venustiano Carranza 477 Sur

Monterrey, N.L. 64000
Mexico
Ruben Marcos
(52) (81) 8130 7800   Fax: (52) (81) 8345 7271

E-Mail:	rmarcos@grupobamex.com
Web Site:	www.mariscalmoda.com
Description:	Full package contractor of all types of pants, shirts & uniforms.

Year Est:	1948
Categories:	Shirts/Tops, Uniforms, Pants, Childrenswear
Specialties:	Samples available
Markets:	Menswear, Boyswear
Packages:	Sewing, cutting, patternmaking, grading/marking
Export to:	United States 10%
Minimums:	300 pcs/style
Factory Locals:	All work done in-house.
	www.johnhenry.com.mx, www.grupobamex.com
Production Capacity:	Shirts: 100,000 pcs/month, Pants: 20,000 pcs/month

INDUSTRIAS MACYS S.A. DE C.V.

Jose Maria Izazaga 99 Piso #8
Colonia Centro
Mexico D.F., 06090
Mexico
Emilio Penhos
(52) (55) 5709 7620   Fax: (52) (55) 5709 1588

E-Mail:	dpenhos@laurence.com.mx
Web Site:	www.laurence.com.mx
Description:	Expert resource in Mexico for blouses/tops & fully lined jackets & skirts.
Year Est:	1986
Exporting Since:	1990
Categories:	Dresses/Blouses, Shirts/Tops, Pants/Skirts, Coats/Jackets
Markets:	Womenswear.
Machinery:	623 machines, all types.
Packages:	CMT & Full, Pattern/Samplemaking, Printing & CAD.
Minimums:	100 dozen/style
Factory Locals:	7 sewing plants & 2 cutting plants in & around Mexico City.

INDUSTRIAS TEBI, S.A. DE C. V.

Calle 5 No 16 Bodega 2
Fracc Ind Alce Blanco
Naucalpan, Estado de Mexico 53370
Mexico
Alfonso Entebi Yedid
(52) (55) 5254 8460   Fax: (52) (55) 5254 8136

E-Mail:	ventas@tebi.com.mx
Web Site:	www.tebi.com.mx
Description:	Socks for babies and infants.
Year Est:	1971
Exporting Since:	2000
Categories:	Accessories
Machinery:	200 Single & double cylinder sock machines
Export to:	USA
Minimums:	None
Production Capacity:	1,000,000 pairs/monthly

ORIGINALES SHYLA, S.A. DE C.V.

Jose Maria Izazaga No. 65 Local 17

Centro, Mexico, Distrito Federal 06080
Mexico
Lic. Benjamin Penhos Mougrabi
(52) (55) 57090018   Fax: (52) (55) 57090018

E-Mail:	*bpm@originalesshyla.com*
Web Site:	*www.originalesshyla.com*
Description:	*Mexican company with more than 44 years of experience making clothes.*
Year Est:	*1969*
Exporting Since:	*2002*
Categories:	*Coats/Jackets*
Specialties:	*Specialize in women's raincoats and wool coats.*
Markets:	*Womenswear*
Export to:	*USA 100%*
Agent:	*USA: 1-877-235-4457*
Minimums:	*200 pcs/style*
Production Capacity:	*30,000 pcs/month*

PRODUCTORA CLINIMEX INDUSTRIAL, S.A. DE C. V.

Carr Panamericana Km. 545
Jesus Gomez Portugal
Aguascalientes 20909
Mexico
Mario Oranday
(52) (449) 9730304, 9730302

E-Mail:	*orandaym@agssite.com.mx*
Description:	*Manufacturer of all kinds of disposable garments/uniforms specializing in disposable coveralls.*
Year Est:	*1989*
Categories:	*Uniforms*
Export to:	*USA 80% & South America 15% & Germany 5%*
Production Capacity:	*300,000 pcs/month*

PRODUCTOS WEST DE MEXICO S.A.

Calle Juan Pablos No. 519 Nte.

Torreon, Coahuila
Mexico
Fernando Mafud
(52) (871) 713 3694   Fax: (52) (871) 713 3694

E-Mail:	*newwestjeans@hotmail.com*
Description:	*Full service contractor of jeans, shirts, shorts, skirts, jackets from denim, twill, polyester & polyester blends.*
Year Est:	*1981*
Categories:	*Jeans/Denimwear, Pants/Shorts/Skirts, Shirts/Tops*
Markets:	*Menswear, Womenswear & Childrenswear.*
Packages:	*Complete & CMT.*

PROMOTORA INTERNACIONAL DE PANTALONES, S.A. DE C.V.

Carlos Dickens No. 20 A Bajos

Polanco, Mexico, Distrito Federal 11560
Mexico
Jaime Cohen Smeke
(52) (55) 52806550   Fax: (52) (55) 52801492

E-Mail:	*jaimecohens@omsamex.com*
Description:	*Cut and sew all types of pants and jeans for women.*
Exporting Since:	*1995*
Categories:	*Jeans, Pants/Skirts/Shorts*
Export to:	*USA 100%*
Production Capacity:	*Underwear: 10,000dz/week, Shirts: 5,000 units/week, Trousers and Jeans: 10,000 units/week.*

SIETE LEGUAS DENIM JEANS

Calz del Tecnologico #1055

Lerdo, Durango 35150
Mexico
JJ Medina
(52) (871) 2349101   Fax: (52) (871) 7254558

E-Mail:	*jj@sieteleguas.com.mx*
Web Site:	*www.sieteleguas.com.mx*
Description:	*Full package denim jeans supplier for major brand stores. We ship worldwide.*
Year Est:	*1959*
Exporting Since:	*1980*
Categories:	*Jeans/Denimwear*
Specialties:	*Design, patternmaking, samples, grading/marking, embroidery, screenprinting, dyeing/finishing, washing/laundry, pack & ship.*
Markets:	*Menswear, Womenswear, Childrens & Infantwear.*
Packages:	*CMT, Sewing & Full Packages.*
Export to:	*USA 89%, Canada 2%, Dubai 1%, China 2% South America 2%, Japan 2%, Europe 2%*
Factory Locals:	*All work done in-house. Offer full "VMI" (Vendor Management Inventory) to the US.*
Production Capacity:	*1.2 million/month - Jeans: 800,000 units/month, Skirts: 200,000 units/month, Shorts: 200,000 units/month*

UNIFORMES UNION, S.A. DE C.V.

Goleta No. 37 Y 39
Fracc. Industrial Xalostoc
Ecatepec, Estado de Mexico 55390
Mexico
Carlos A. Venegas Diaz
(52) (55) 57144487   Fax: (52) (55) 57144133

E-Mail:	*uniformesunion@prodigy.net.mx*
Web Site:	*www.uniformesunion.com*
Description:	*Men & women's denim jeans in 14.5 oz. 100% cotton stoned blue denim & men's dress shirts, oxford shirts, work & golf shirts.*

Year Est:	*1982*
Exporting Since:	*1999*
Categories:	*Jeans/Denimwear, Shirts/Tops*
Specialties:	*Reliable Supplier Certificate*
Markets:	*Menswear, Womenswear.*
Machinery:	*100 sewing machines & equipment*
Packages:	*Full Packages*
Export to:	*USA 90%. Canada 10%*
Minimums:	*Shirts: 1,000 pcs., Jeans: 100 pcs.*
Factory Locals:	*Texcoco & Tlaxcala, Mexico*
Production Capacity:	*Mens Jeans: 15,000 units/month, Womens Jeans: 5,000 units/month.*
	Woven Shirts: 30,000 pcs/month, Knit Shirts: 10,000 pcs/month.

VALLEN PROVEEDORA DE SEGURIDAD INDUSTRIAL DEL GOLFO

Blvd. A. Lopez Mateos No. 4000
Universidad Poniente
Tampico, Tamaulipas 89336
Mexico
Jorge Mina Kuri
(52) (833) 2301700   Fax: (52) (833) 2301701

E-Mail:	*jmina@vallenproveedora.com.mx*
Web Site:	*www.vallenproveedora.com.mx*
Description:	*All types of safety & surgical clothing.*
Categories:	*Uniforms*
Specialties:	*Specialize in protective coveralls and uniforms.*
Export to:	*USA 35%, Panama 15%, Guatemala 20%, Peru 15%,*
	Colombia 15%
Production Capacity:	*20,000 pcs/month*

VESTININA, S.A. DE C.V.

Avena #532 A - PlantaBaja

Granjas, D.F. 08400
Mexico
Abraham Daniel
(52) (55) 5654 7388   Fax: (52) (55) 5657 0091

E-Mail:	*vesti@vesti.com.mx*
Web Site:	*www.vesti.com.mx*
Description:	*Contractor of all types of childrenswear.*
Year Est:	*1985*
Exporting Since:	*1990*
Categories:	*Childrens Wear*
Markets:	*Girlswear*
Export to:	*Canada, Costa Rica, Chile*
Production Capacity:	*35,000 pcs/month*

VICKY FORM, S.A. DE C.V.

Recursos Hidraulicos #2
Fracc. Industrial La Loma
Tlalnepantla, Estado de Mexico, C.P. 54060
Mexico
Kila Tochijara
(52) (55) 5333 0360   Fax: (52) (55) 5333 0361

E-Mail:	*expzaga@zaga.com*
Web Site:	*www.vickyform.com, www.zaga.com*
Description:	*Manufacturer of lingerie collections, casualwear, yoga pants, activewear, pajamas and men's underwear.*
Year Est:	*1964*
Exporting Since:	*1992*
Categories:	*Lingerie/Intimate/Underwear, Active/Athleticwear*
Specialties:	*Computerized pattern, marking and grading, Gerber brand sample - sample room in-house.*
Markets:	*Menswear, Womenswear, Teens, Childrenswear*
Packages:	*Full package based on program and volume*
Export to:	*U.S.A, Costa Rica, Canada*
Minimums:	*1,200 - 7,000 pieces/color*
Factory Locals:	*Tepeji Del Rio, Tulanciango*
Production Capacity:	*600,000+ units/month*

YALE DE MEXICO, S.A. DE C.V.

Calzada Javier Rojo Gomez 1330
Col. Barrio de San Miguel
Iztapalapa CP 09360
Mexico
Cristina Beltran Piza
(52) (55) 5804 4242   Fax: (52) (55) 5686 0855

E-Mail:	*cbpiza@yale.com.mx*
Web Site:	*www.yale.com.mx*
Description:	*Sewing, cutting, washing, pressing and finishing contractor.*
Year Est:	*1950*
Categories:	*Shirts/Tops, Jeans/Denimwear, Pants/Shorts*
Markets:	*Menswear, Womenswear & Childrenswear.*
Packages:	*Full packages.*
Factory Locals:	*Above - 25,000 sq. meters*

Nicaragua

ROCEDES S.A.

Zona Franca Las Mercedes Bldg.#29
Km 12 1/2 Carretera Norte
Managua
Nicaragua
Scott Vaughn
(505) 2263 2032   Fax: (505) 2263 2033

E-Mail:	*svaughn@rocedes.com.ni*
Web Site:	*www.rocedes.com.ni*
Description:	*Contractor of casual wear, work wear and uniforms.*

Year Est:	1993
Categories:	Pants/Shorts/Skirts, Uniforms
Markets:	Menswear, Womenswear, Boyswear, Girlswear.
Machinery:	698 Plain sewers, 195 Bartacker, 34 Button Hole, 283 Overlock, 53 Bander, 51 Compos.
Export to:	United States 100%
Factory Locals:	Managua, Nicaragua
Production Capacity:	600,000 pieces/month

Notes

Company Index

Company Index

Company Index

Notes

---

3 MT ENTERPRISES
selmufdi@grupo3mt.com
Dominican Republic • (1) (809) 246 3501
www.grupo3mt.com

3D INDUSTRIES
sales@3d-ind.com
U.S.A. • (1) (949) 588 5884
www.3d-ind.com

5 KIDS EMBROIDERY GROUP LLC
philm@5kidsembroidery.com
U.S.A. • (1) (732) 774 5331
www.5kidsembroidery.com

A PROMOS USA DBA THE IMAGEMAKER & AARROW PROMOTIONS
sales@imagemakerus.com
U.S.A. • (1) (516) 377 0186
www.apromosusa.com

A RIFKIN COMPANY
jbachkosky@arifkin.com
U.S.A. • (1) (570) 825 9551
www.rifkinsewing.com

A&S CLOTHING
asclothing@tds.net
U.S.A. • (1) (706) 632 2133

A+ LAUNDRY
linens@aol.com
U.S.A. • (1) (516) 371 2100

AA WORLD CLASS EMBROIDERY & EMBELLISHMENT CO.
bena@aaworld.com
U.S.A. • (1) (201) 313 0022
www.aaworld.com

AAA PATTERNS & MARKING SERVICES
patterns@aaapatternsmarking.com
U.S.A. • (1) (334) 445 4870
www.aaapatternsmarking.com

ABSOLUTELY! DESIGN SERVICE
nlittman@mindspring.com
U.S.A. • (1) (212) 769 0548
www.batlledesign.com

ABSTRACT GRAPHICS
art@customapparelzone.com
U.S.A. • (1) (610) 746 4933
www.customapparelzone.com

ACCURATE FLANNEL BAG COMPANY
service@accuratebags.com
U.S.A. • (1) (973) 720 1800
www.accuratebags.com

ACCURATE SERVICES, INC.
suetex@accurateservice.com
U.S.A. • (1) (508) 674 5773
www.accurateservice.com

ACE BINDING CO.,INC.
larry@acebinding.com
U.S.A. • (1) (410) 525 0700
www.acebinding.com

ACTIVE APPAREL INC.
sales@activeapparel.net
U.S.A. • (1) (951) 361 0060
www.activeapparel.net

ADVANCE PLEATING & BUTTON CO.
U.S.A. • (1) (415) 648 3111

AETNA SHIRT/ON CALL MEDICAL COATS
customerservice@medicalcoats.com
U.S.A. • (1) (410) 574 2657
www.medicalcoats.com

AFAP
sales@afapfashion.com
U.S.A. • (1) (626) 330 6376
www.afapfashion.com

AIKEN INDUSTRIES, INC.
carysarah@aol.com
U.S.A. • (1) (803) 648 5467
www.aikenind.com

AIM GARMENTS
info@aimgarments.com
U.S.A. • (1) 443 745 1502
www.aimgarments.com

AIR WAVES, INC.
cs@airwavesinc.com
U.S.A. • (1) (740) 548 1200
www.airwavesstore.com

ALAMEDA S.A.
luisb@alamedasa.com
Guatemala • (502) 2437 5321
www.alamedasa.com

ALL AMERICAN EMBROIDERY
aae2000@aol.com
U.S.A. • (1) (412) 922 8999

ALL AMERICAN WASH CO.
alexkahen@allamericanwashco.com
U.S.A. • (1) (323) 265 2626

ALL U, INC.
sales@allu.com
U.S.A. • (1) (518) 438 2558
www.allu.com

ALLIED TRANSPORT SYSTEM
teresa@atsnyc.com
U.S.A. • (1) (718) 977 9448
www.atsnyc.com

ALMORE DYE HOUSE, INC.
adh@almoredyehouse.com
U.S.A. • (1) (818) 506 5444
www.almoredyehouse.com

ALVARADO DYE & KNITTING MILL
sales@alvaradomills.com
U.S.A. • (1) (510) 324 8892
www.alvaradomill.wix.com/oursdesign

Telephone, E-mail and WWW Index

AMERICA'S BEST CLEANERS	chriswhite@americasbestcleaners.com	U.S.A. • (1) (415) 857 2378 www.americasbestcleaners.com
AMERICAN ICON SCREEN PRINTING	katrina@americaniconmerch.com	U.S.A. • (1) (845) 561 1299 www.americaniconshirts.com
AMERICAN SEWING DYNAMICS, INC.	sales@americansewingdynamics.com	U.S.A. • (1) (773) 394 9544 www.americansewingdynamics.com
AMERICAN STITCHCO INC.	stitchco@stitchco.com	U.S.A. • (1) 888 903 0049 www.stitchco.com
AMERICAN TEXTILE & APPAREL INC.	luis.mejia@ata-usa.com	U.S.A. • (1) (954) 734 9988 www.ata-usa.com
ANDARI FASHION INC.	info@andari.com	U.S.A. • (1) (626) 575 2759 www.andari.com
ANTAKY QUILTING COMPANY	sales@antakyquilting.com	U.S.A. • (1) (323) 233 2500 www.antakyquilting.com
ANTILLEAN MARINE SHIPPING CORP.	antillean@antillean.com	U.S.A. • (1) (305) 633 6361 www.antillean.com
ANTILLES MANUFACTURING, S.A.	recepcion@oadom.com.do	Dominican Republic • (1) (809) 570 3603
APPAREL AGENCY, THE	info@theapparelagency.com	U.S.A. • (1) (312) 265 0900 www.theapparelagency.com
APPAREL MARK SERVICES	barbbctx@yahoo.com	U.S.A. • (1) (915) 833 2643
APPAREL PRINTING DIV OF KENMAR SHIRTS	kareng@apparelprinting.com	U.S.A. • (1) (718) 824 3880 www.apparelprinting.com
APPAREL PRODUCTION INC.	teddyapparelprod@aol.com	U.S.A. • (1) (212) 278 8362 www.apparelproductionny.com
APPAREL SOLUTIONS CORP.	john@usapparelsolutions.com	U.S.A. • (1) (212) 868 1700 www.usapparelsolutions.com
ARI SHIPPING CORP.	ilan@arishipping.com	U.S.A. • (1) (516) 371 7770 www.arishipping.com
ARTEX KNITTING MILLS INC.	sales@artexknit.com	U.S.A. • (1) (856) 456 2800 www.artexknit.com
ARTWEAR EMBROIDERY, INC.	artwear@artwearinc.com	U.S.A. • (1) (336) 992 2166 www.artwearinc.com
ATLANTA SEWING & PATTERN-MAKING SERVICE	info@asapsewingservice.com	U.S.A. • (1) (770) 952 9211 www.asapsewingservice.com
AVALON COUTURE & TEXTILE, LTD.	service@avaloncouture.com	U.S.A. • (1) 877 832 2227 www.avaloncouture.com
AVB DESIGNS	vonbromssen@mac.com	U.S.A. • (1) (650) 346 1533 www.avbdesigns.com
AVITEX	avi@avitex.com	U.S.A. • (1) (973) 242 2410 www.celioavitex.com
AXIS MOON DESIGN AND PRODUCTION	ellenkreager@gmail.com	U.S.A. • (1) (214) 395 1277 www.axismoon.com
B.M.A.C.	bmacservice@aol.com	U.S.A. • (1) (212) 736 5380 www.bmacnewyork.com
BERGEN SCREEN PRINTING	uday@bergenscreen.com	U.S.A. • (1) (973) 595 1222 www.bergenscreen.com
BIANCA GROUP LTD	biancainc@aol.com	U.S.A. • (1) (212) 768 3011
BIG FRONT UNIFORMS	info@bigfront.com	U.S.A. • (1) (323) 227 4222 www.bigfrontuniforms.com
BIG PRINTING T-SHIRT COMPANY	bigprinting@gmail.com	U.S.A. • (1) (510) 638 2782 www.bigprintingshirts.com
BJ CON-SEW	bjconsew@triadbiz.rr.com	U.S.A. • (1) (336) 629 4550 www.bjconsew.com

BLANKET BOSS	blanketboss@aol.com	U.S.A. • (1) (845) 477 4774 www.theblanketboss.com
BLOOM FASHION USA	sales@bloomfashionusa.com	U.S.A. • (1) (703) 323 6793 www.bloomfashionusa.com
BLUE CREATIONS OF CA INC.	info@bluecreationsinc.com	U.S.A. • (1) (310) 816 3100 www.bluecreationsinc.com
BONNAZ EMBROIDERY CO.	embroideryusa@msn.com	U.S.A. • (1) (201) 552 94 94
BORDA SURI SRL	alpac@suri-bo.com	Bolivia • (591) (22) 413663 www.suri-bo.com
BORDALO PUNTO COM S.A. DE C.V.	info@bordalo.com	Mexico • (52) (55) 1991 4040 www.bordalo.com
BOULDER PATH DESIGNS	info@boulderpathdesigns.com	U.S.A. • (1) (541) 296 4470 www.boulderpathdesigns.com
BRANDED EMBLEM	dannys@campdavid.com	U.S.A. • (1) (913) 648 7920 www.campdavid.com
BRIARCLIFF APPAREL TECHNOLOGIES LTD.	fashionprofessor@hotmail.com	U.S.A. • (1) (212) 840 7666
C.R.C. DESIGN SERVICES	carlos.c@comcast.net	U.S.A. • (1) (508) 644 3166
CALEDONIAN DYE WORKS, INC.		U.S.A. • (1) (215) 739 2322
CALIFORNIA APPAREL SERVICE	tom@californiaapparelservice.com	U.S.A. • (1) (714) 222 1970 www.californiaapparelservice.com
CALIFORNIA RAIN	info@californiarainla.com	U.S.A. • (1) (213) 623 6061 www.californiarainla.com
CANDILEJAS CLOTHING CO.		U.S.A. • (1) (213) 489 2855
CARMICHAEL INTERNATIONAL SERVICE	sales@carmnet.com	U.S.A. • (1) (213) 353 0800 www.carmnet.com
CAROL PETERS INC. (CPI)	carolcpi512@aol.com	U.S.A. • (1) (347) 256 7804
CAROLACE EMBROIDERY CO., INC.	info@carolace.com	U.S.A. • (1) (201) 945 2151 www.carolace.com
CAROLINA COTTON WORKS, INC.	bryan@carolinacotton.com	U.S.A. • (1) (864) 488 2824 www.carolinacotton.com
CATAWBA CREATIONS	catawbacreations@msn.com	U.S.A. • (1) (828) 397 7088
CHANGES/INT'L WAREHOUSING & DISTRIBUTION	changes440@aol.com	U.S.A. • (1) (305) 828 6811
CHATHAM KNITTING MILLS, INC.	mattharris2006@gmail.com	U.S.A. • (1) (434) 432 4701 x11
CHERIE BIXLER	cheriebixler@verizon.net	U.S.A. • (1) (201) 944 2886 www.cheriebixler.com
CHESTER LINE CORP.	soungkim@chesterline.com	U.S.A. • (1) (562) 944 2777 www.chesterline.com
CHINAMINE USA	info@chinamineusa.com	U.S.A. • (1) (212) 575 1525 www.chinamineusa.com
CO2 TEXTILES	melodylevy@co2textiles.com	U.S.A. • (1) (212) 269 2222
COLCHAS MEXICO S.A. DE C.V.	dsaadia@colchasconcord.com	Mexico • (52) (55) 50615200 www.colchasconcord.com
COLLECTIVE APPAREL	contact@collectiveapparel.us	U.S.A. • (1) 310 770 1093 www.collectiveapparel.us
COLORADO CONTRACT CUT & SEW	jane@coloradocut.com	U.S.A. • (1) (303) 733 5376 www.coloradocut.com

COLORSTAR CORP.		U.S.A. • (1) (610) 837 2400
	colorstar@aol.com	www.colorstaronline.com
COLORWORKS INC.		U.S.A. • (1) (845) 647 0300
	dyestudio@colorworksalley.com	www.colorworksalley.com
CONFECCIONES INTERNACIONALES S.A. DE C.V.		Honduras • (504) 2230 5518
	sales@confecciones.com	www.confecciones.com
COTTON & ELSE INC.		U.S.A. • (1) (954) 677 8010
	cottonet@bellsouth.net	www.cottonandelse.net
COVILLE INC.		U.S.A. • (1) (336) 759 0115
	kwilliams@covilleinc.com	www.covilleinc.com
CRAFTEX REWORK INC.		U.S.A. • (1) (252) 239 0123
	boneal@craftexinc.com	
CRAIG INDUSTRIES		U.S.A. • (1) (843) 326 5561
	craig.ind@craigindustries.net	
CRAVATTA MANUFACTUERS		U.S.A. • (1) (856) 302 1151
	info@cravattamfg.com	www.cravattamfg.com
CREATE-A-MARKER, INC.		U.S.A. • (1) (212) 730 5615
	cad@createamarkernyc.com	www.createamarkernyc.com
CREATIVE BUSINESS HOUSE		U.S.A. • (1) (646) 543 1831
	info@creativebusinesshouse.com	www.creativebusinesshouse.com
CREATIVE EMBROIDERY CORP.		U.S.A. • (1) (973) 497 5700
	sdiam43091@aol.com	
CREATIVE OUTLET, INC.		U.S.A. • (1) (252) 808 3898
	sscrubs@yahoo.com	www.creativeoutlet.info
CREATIVE PATTERN AND SAMPLE		U.S.A. • (1) (213) 233 0253
	contact@creativepatternandsample.com	www.creativepatternandsample.com
CROOKED BROOK		U.S.A. • (1) (315) 733 1992
	info@crookedbrook.com	www.crookedbrook.com
CSR INTERNATIONAL INC.		Canada • (1) (418) 486 7481
	jlfortin@csr-intl.com	www.groupecsr.com
CUALQUIER LAVADO, S.A. DE C.V.		Mexico • (52) (238) 3803700
	aneira@cualquierlavado.com.mx	www.cualquierlavado.com
CUSTOM APPAREL PROCESSING		U.S.A. • (1) (508) 675 2962
CUSTOM CHENILLE EMBROIDERY		U.S.A. • (1) (214) 343 0888
	kgilmer@chenille.com	www.chenille.com
CUSTOM-SEWING-SERVICES		U.S.A. • (1) (516) 499 7304
	customsewingservices@yahoo.com	
CYCLE FASHION PATTERN INC.		U.S.A. • (1) (212) 216 9668
		www.cyclefashionpattern.com
D'CLASE APPAREL INTERNATIONAL		Dominican Republic • (1) 829 947 7000
	cpizano@dclase.com	
DA SAN, S.A. DE C.V.		El Salvador • () (503) 2322 2100
	richard.kim@dasan.com.sv	
DALMA DRESS MFG CO INC		U.S.A. • (1) (212) 391 8296
DARWOOD MANUFACTURING CO.		U.S.A. • (1) (229) 294 4932
	darwood@bellsouth.net	www.darwoodmfg.com
DAVE PRESSLEY DESIGN		U.S.A. • (1) 917 771 9557
	jewelman65@gmail.com	www.djphandmade.com
DELUXE SCREEN PRINTING		U.S.A. • (1) (213) 765 0838
	deluxe@deluxescreenprinting.net	www.deluxescreenprinting.net
DEPENDABLE DISTRIBUTION CENTERS		U.S.A. • (1) (323) 526 2200 ext. 2086
	jp.durrer@dependableinc.com	www.godependable.com
DEPENDABLE GLOBAL EXPRESS		U.S.A. • (1) (310) 669 8888
	brad.dechter@dhx.com	www.dgxglobal.com

DEPENDABLE LOGISTICS SERVICES	jp.durrer@dependableinc.com	U.S.A. • (1) (323) 526 2200 www.godependable.com
DESIGN PRINCIPLES LLC, THE	hollis@thedesignprinciples.com	U.S.A. • (1) 727 488 8162 www.thedesignprinciples.com
DIDI OF CALIFORNIA		U.S.A. • (1) (323) 256 4514
DISMODA S.A.	dismoda@dismoda.com	Colombia • (57) (5) 3799777 www.dismoda.com
DOUBLETEX	sales@doubletex.com	Canada • (1) (514) 382 1770 www.doubletex.com
DREAMBAGS INC	sales@dreambags.com	U.S.A. • (1) (773) 394 3136 www.dreambags.com
DURO INDUSTRIES	boulis_bryan@durolink.com	U.S.A. • (1) (508) 675 0101 www.duroindustries.com
DYE FX	carolperri@verizon.net	U.S.A. • (1) 718 596 4611
DYE IT UP	sales@dyeitup.com	U.S.A. • (1) (267) 288 5545 www.dyeitup.com
DYEHOUSE, INC., THE	prb21439@aol.com	U.S.A. • (1) (601) 776 3777
DYENAMIX INC.	info@dyenamix.com	U.S.A. • (1) (212) 941 6642 www.dyenamix.com
DYNASHAPE INTIMA CORPORATION	stewart@dynashapeintima.com	U.S.A. • (1) (626) 289 8418 www.dynashapeintima.com
DYNOTEX INC.	dynotexinc@gmail.com	U.S.A. • (1) (917) 532 9068 www.dynotex.com
E.T. MANUFACTURING CO.	info@etmanufacturing.com	U.S.A. • (1) (770) 867 8152 www.etmanufacturing.com
EAGLE DYERS	vjsavta@aol.com	U.S.A. • (1) 212 947 2712
EAST BAY GARMENT CUTTING & SEWING SERVICE	annielam6688@gmail.com	U.S.A. • (1) (510) 261 6688
EAST COAST EMBOSSING	info@sunbritedyeco.com	U.S.A. • (1) (973) 777 9830
EATONTEX RESOURCES LTD.	sales@eatontexresources.com	U.S.A. • (1) 212 221 1473 www.eatontexresources.com
ELEGANT EMBROIDERY/MELON INK SCREEN PRINT	nancy@elegantembroidery.com	U.S.A. • (1) (847) 540 8003 www.elegantembroidery.com
EMBROIDERED CORPORATE IMAGE	rla@eci-embroidery.com	U.S.A. • (1) (208) 772 4044 www.eci-embroidery.com
EMBROIDERY CONCEPTS	kevin@1clickshirts.com	U.S.A. • (1) 724 225 3644 www.1clickshirts.com
EMBROIDERY ONE CORPORATION	emb1@pacbell.net	U.S.A. • (1) (213) 572 0280 www.embroidery-one.com
ESTEPHANIAN ORIGINALS INC.	mark@eodye.com	U.S.A. • (1) (626) 358 7265 www.eodye.com
EXACTA	contactus@exactagarment.com	U.S.A. • (1) (973) 259 0104 www.exactagarment.com
EXPLOSION SPORTSWEAR/ IMAGE SOURCE	info@explosionsportswear.com	U.S.A. • (1) (602) 243 2728 www.explosionsportswear.com
EZC DYE HOUSE	jnpcgoods@aol.com	Dominican Republic • (U.S.A.) (954) 732 4134
F & M HAT CO., INC.	customerservice@fmhat.com	U.S.A. • (1) (717) 336 5505 www.fmhat.com
FABRI-QUILT INC.	jhlinam@msn.com	U.S.A. • (1) (816) 421 2000 www.fabri-quilt.com

Company	Email	Contact
FABRICLEAN	info@nycclean.com	U.S.A. • (1) (888) 692 2532 www.nycclean.com
FACTORY 212, THE	angela@thefactory212.com	U.S.A. • (1) (212) 944 6900 www.thefactory212.com
FAIR TRADE KNITTERS	sales@fairtradeknitters.com	U.S.A. • (1) (609) 610 4018 www.fairtradeknitters.com
FANTASY DESIGNS	dgleck@fantasydesigns.net	U.S.A. • (1) (949) 635 9591 www.fantasydesigns.net
FASHION SOURCES, INC.	fashsource@aol.com	U.S.A. • (1) (215) 699 6801
FASHIONS UNLIMITED, INC.	fashionsu@verizon.net	U.S.A. • (1) (410) 783 1584 www.fashionsu.net
FIBERLOK, INC.	info@fiberlok.com	U.S.A. • (1) (970) 221 1200 www.fiberlok.com
FIDUCCIA CUSTOM SHIRTS	walter@fiducciacustomshirts.com	U.S.A. • (1) (201) 507 0644 www.fiducciacustomshirts.com
FINE LINE, INC.	info@finelineinc.com	U.S.A. • (1) (818) 361 8103 www.finelineinc.com
FINE PRODUCTS/FP SERVICES INC.	jay@fineproducts.net	U.S.A. • (1) (845) 651 4020 www.fpservicesapparel.com
FLEXSYSTEMS USA INC.	sales@flexsystems.com	U.S.A. • (1) (619) 401 1858 www.flexsystems.com
FLOOR-READY SERVICES, INC.	contact@floorready.com	U.S.A. • (1) (828) 651 8504 www.floorready.com
FORMART CORPORATION	bellini_formart@hotmail.com	U.S.A. • (1) (212) 819 1819 www.formartcorp.com
FRENCH CURVE DESIGNS	hmadrid@frenchcurvedesigns.com	U.S.A. • (1) 972 571 1196 www.frenchcurvedesigns.com
FRSTEAM BY WEST COVINA CLEANERS	westcovina@frsteam.com	U.S.A. • (1) (626) 960 1911 www.frsteamwc.com
G & M SERVICES	gary@gmser.com	U.S.A. • (1) (214) 358 0041 www.gmser.com
G.S. FASHION	ssimonn@aol.com	U.S.A. • (1) (323) 581 0764
GARMENT INDUSTRY DEVELOPMENT CORP/GIDC	award@gidc.org	U.S.A. • (1) (212) 842 9343 www.gidc.org
GELTMAN INDUSTRIES	info@geltman.com	U.S.A. • (1) (213) 622 2015 www.geltman.com
GEMBA GROUP, INC.	joavila@gembagroup.com	U.S.A. • (1) (956) 607 0890
GENESIS IMPORTS	akimbel@aol.com	U.S.A. • (1) (512) 292 4000 www.genesismexico.com
GIL SEWING CORPORATION	gilsewing@sbcglobal.net	U.S.A. • (1) (773) 545 0990 www.gilsewing.com
GIMASPORT	sales@gimasport.com	U.S.A. • (1) (860) 296 4441 www.gimasport.com
GLOBAL CMT CORPORATION	f.rodriguez@globalcmt.com	Dominican Republic • (1) (809) 575 4777 www.globalcmt.com
GLOBE-TEX	robert@globe-tex.com	U.S.A. • (1) (914) 560 8422 www.globe-tex.com
GOLDEN EGG CORPORATION	calvinlin123@gmail.com	U.S.A. • (1) (626) 279 2779
GRANITE KNITWEAR/DBA CAL CRU	calcru@mindspring.com	U.S.A. • (1) (704) 279 5526 www.calcru.com
GRECO APPAREL	joe@grecoapparel.com	U.S.A. • (1) (215) 628 2557 www.grecoapparel.com

GRIFFIN MANUFACTURING CO., INC. sales@griffinmanufacturing.com		U.S.A. • (1) (508) 677 0048 www.griffinmanufacturing.com
GRUPO BAMEX S.A. DE C.V. rmarcos@grupobamex.com		Mexico • (52) (81) 8130 7800 www.mariscalmoda.com
GRUVEN INTERNATIONAL INC. drushton@gruven.com		Canada • (1) (416) 292 7331 www.gruven.com
GWEN'S CREATIVE SEWING gebaker@roadrunner.com		U.S.A. • (1) (910) 276 2121
H.T.T. HEADWEAR LTD. contact@httapparel.com		U.S.A. • (1) (951) 304 0400 www.httapparel.com
HAGINS INDUSTRIES, INC. haginsinds@bellsouth.net		U.S.A. • (1) (910) 628 6777
HAMILTON EMBROIDERY CO. fblaso@cs.com		U.S.A. • (1) (201) 867 4084
HANDWORKS aoriggi@yahoo.com		El Salvador • (503) 7886 5243
HANES DYE & FINISHING COMPANY hfcsales@hanesindustries.com		U.S.A. • (1) (336) 725 1391 www.hanesfinishing.com
HARDRIVE PRODUCTIONS, INC. hdrivemike@aol.com		U.S.A. • (1) (407) 872 3030 www.hardriveinc.com
HARODITE INDUSTRIES, INC. tbridges@harodite.com		U.S.A. • (1) (864) 834 9066 www.harodite.com
HARPER INDUSTRIES, INC. tsf@harcrest.com		U.S.A. • (1) (510) 655 5143 www.harcrest.com
HARRIS PILLOW SUPPLY INC. john@harrispillow.com		U.S.A. • (1) 800 845 8240 www.harrispillow.com
HEATHER MENZIES PATTERN DESIGN heather@nypatternmaker.com		U.S.A. • (1) (516) 375 3807 www.nypatternmaker.com
HEIDI-HO, INC. heidiho@kinex.net		U.S.A. • (1) (434) 736 8763
HELMSMAN QUALITY & TECHNOLOGY SERVICES LTD. jeff.singleton@hqts.com		U.S.A. • (1) (212) 757 2400 www.hqts.com
HEMINGWAY APPAREL MFG., INC. jmarsh@hemingwayapparel.com		U.S.A. • (1) (843) 558 3482 www.hemingwayapparel.com
HENDERSON ADVERTIZING hendersonart@ameritech.net		U.S.A. • (1) (217) 544 9419 www.henderson-advertising.com
HENSCHEL HAT CO. usahat@aol.com		U.S.A. • (1) (314) 421 0009 www.henschelhats.com
HICKORY BRANDS INC. josh@hickorybrands.com		U.S.A. • (1) (828) 322 2600 www.tenseconds.com
HOSPI-TEL MANUFACTURING COMPANY info@hospitel.com		U.S.A. • (1) (973) 678 7100 www.hospitel.com
ID4U JACKETS WITH IDENTITY daryl@id4u-jackets.com		U.S.A. • (1) 888 968 4348 www.id4u-jackets.com
IDEA LLC. tomdemuth@ideallc.com		U.S.A. • (1) (843) 744 2727 www.ideallc.com
IN STYLE USA, INC. instyleusa@instyleusa.net		U.S.A. • (1) (212) 631 0278
IN.STYLE EXCHANGE™ info@instyleexchange.com		U.S.A. • (1) (817) 886 9222 www.instyleexchange.com
INDU FASHIONS shashi@indufashions.com		U.S.A. • (1) (619) 336 4638 www.indufashions.com
INDUSTRIAS FLORENZI, S.A. DE C.V. r_pineda@navegante.com.sv		El Salvador • () (503) 2297 0577
INDUSTRIAS MACYS S.A. DE C.V. dpenhos@laurence.com.mx		Mexico • (52) (55) 5709 7620 www.laurence.com.mx

INDUSTRIAS TEBI, S.A. DE C. V.	ventas@tebi.com.mx	Mexico • (52) (55) 5254 8460 www.tebi.com.mx
INTEDGE INDUSTRIES INC.	sales@intedge.com	U.S.A. • (1) (864) 969 9601 www.intedge.com
INTERNATIONAL FULFILLMENT, INC.	tristan@jessicainternational.com	U.S.A. • (1) (305) 825 1040 www.jessicainternational.com
J. M. J. FASHIONS INC.	romanw@jmjingenuity.com	Canada • (1) (204) 942 0252 www.jmjingenuity.com
J.B.'S PRIVATE LABEL	jackiembender@aol.com	U.S.A. • (1) (213) 747 1922 www.dunadesigns.com
J.L.S.C./SYDNEY BUSH	michaelraske@msn.com	U.S.A. • (1) (718) 742 9629
J.P. SPORTSWEAR/AARON CORP.	jppaul2@pacbell.net	U.S.A. • (1) (323) 235 5959 www.jpsportswear.net
JADE APPAREL	jadey989@aol.com	U.S.A. • (1) (215) 922 3953
JJ PATTERN INC.	myjjpatternnyc@gmail.com	U.S.A. • (1) (212) 391 8089 www.jjpatternnyc.com
JOCASSEE DESIGNS INC.	julie@jocasseedesigns.com	U.S.A. • (1) (864) 433 1113 www.jocasseedesigns.com
JONCO INDUSTRIES INC.	tom.ryan@joncoind.com	U.S.A. • (1) (414) 449 2000 www.joncoind.com
JORO, INC.	joro@joroinc.comcastbiz.net	U.S.A. • (1) (770) 867 7364
JULIE HUTTON, INC.	julie@juliehuttoninc.com	U.S.A. • (1) (212) 532 5126 www.juliehuttoninc.com
JUN'S PATTERN	jennykwon64@gmail.com	U.S.A. • (1) (212) 221 6130
JUST JEN	jennifer@justjen.com	U.S.A. • (1) 310 539 6000 www.justjen.com
K & S INDUSTRIES, S.A.	kands@claro.net.do	Dominican Republic • (1) (809) 529 8080
KAM MANUFACTURING INC.	ollie@kammfg.com	U.S.A. • (1) (419) 238 6037 www.kammfg.com
KATRINA PATTERNS		U.S.A. • (1) (212) 563 7332 www.katrinapatterns.com
KATTAN GROUP	gabriel.kattan@kattangroup.com	Honduras • (504) 2617 0150 www.kattangroup.com
KEMESTRY	elj1978@aol.com	U.S.A. • (1) (954) 922 2802 www.kemestryonline.com
KRISTABEN	dinhyang@hotmail.com	U.S.A. • (1) (214) 760 9796 www.kristaben.com
L.I. CUTTING	info@licutting.com	U.S.A. • (1) (516) 826 6138 www.licutting.com
L.S.W. CUTTING & SEWING SERVICE	lswcuttingandsewing@hotmail.com	U.S.A. • (1) (510) 891 9246
LACOA INC	hector@lacoa.com	U.S.A. • (1) (973) 754 1000 www.lacoa.com
LACORP/LEBANON APPAREL CORP.	jeoff@lacorpusa.com	U.S.A. • (1) (276) 889 3656 www.lacorpusa.com
LAMCOM, INC.	lamcom1@aol.com	U.S.A. • (1) (212) 868 6910 www.lamcominc.com
LANDZEG INC.	landzeg@gmail.com	U.S.A. • (1) (212) 575 0746
LATITUDES	info@latitudespdx.com	U.S.A. • (1) (503) 248 2060 www.latitudespdx.com

LAUNDRY SPECIALTIES LLC	richard@laundryspecialties.com	U.S.A. • (1) (610) 351 3860 www.laundryspecialties.com
LD EL SALVADOR	cecile.reyes@mail.com	El Salvador • (503) 2213 0909
LEAHPATRA KNITTING	leahpatra@leahpatra.com	U.S.A. • (1) 310 951 9095 www.leahpatra.com
LEFT IN STITCHES INC.	info@leftinstitches.com	U.S.A. • (1) (707) 822 3041 www.leftinstitches.com
LEONORA FASHIONS, INC.	mike@leonorafashions.com	U.S.A. • (1) (305) 885 8148 www.leonorafashions.com
LES TEXTILES GAUVIN INC.	info@zenima.ca	Canada • (1) (418) 356 2434 www.zenima.ca
LIBERTY GRAPHICS	sales@lgtees.com	U.S.A. • (1) (207) 589 4596 www.lgtees.com
LLU INC.	lluinc@hotmail.com	U.S.A. • (1) (718) 271 3228
LOGISTICS ON THE WEST	info@logisticsonthewest.com	U.S.A. • (1) (732) 418 0800 www.logisticsonthewest.com
LOGOS FASHION SERVICE	info@logosfashionservice.com	U.S.A. • (1) (703) 879 8827 www.logosfashionservice.com
LORI ANN DESIGN	lori@lorianndesign.com	U.S.A. • (1) (707) 845 5043 www.lorianndesign.com
M. FRANABAR INC. CORRECTIONS & REWORKS	info@mfranabar.com	U.S.A. • (1) (718) 499 5190 www.mfranabar.com
M.S.R. CUSTOM MADE SHIRTS	msrcostumshirt@verizon.net	U.S.A. • (1) (201) 941 7970 www.msrcustomshirtmakers.com
MAGNATEX APPAREL SERVICES	magnatex@cox.net	U.S.A. • (1) (949) 551 9624
MANDARINTEX LTD.	philipip@mandarintex.com	Canada • (1) (647) 728 3254 www.mandarintex.com
MANUFACTURING IN CHINA	manufacturinginchina@rcn.com	U.S.A. • (1) (212) 255 5597 www.imexchinaltd.com
MANZELLA PRODUCTIONS	info@manzella.com	U.S.A. • (1) (716) 681 8880 www.manzella.com
MARGARET'S CLEANERS	generalmail@margarets.com	U.S.A. • (1) (858) 454 2375 www.margarets.com
MARK D.A., INC.	pbartual@msn.com	U.S.A. • (1) 212 868 3081
MARKER EXPRESS INC.	maryann@markerxpress.com	U.S.A. • (1) (707) 259 5201 www.markerxpress.com
MCBEE MANUFACTURING COMPANY	vinci@shtc.net	U.S.A. • (1) (843) 335 8234 www.vinciclothiers.com
ME'LANSON PATTERNS	thepatternmaker14@gmail.com	U.S.A. • (1) (702) 742 3082 www.coroflot.com/marfig
MEHERA SHAW TEXTILES PVT LTD.	info@meherashaw.com	U.S.A. • (1) (919) 969 2572 www.meherashaw.com
MERIDIAN SHIPPING CO. INC.	mershico@cs.com	U.S.A. • (1) (718) 995 3598
METRO DYEING SERVICES, LTD	cs@nyfashioncenter.com	U.S.A. • (1) 212 391 1001 www.metrodyeing.com
METRO TEXTILE INC.	zee@mtcsourcing.com	U.S.A. • (1) 214 352 0219 www.mtcsourcing.com
METRO TRIMMING CORP.	metrotrimming@gmail.com	U.S.A. • (1) (212) 564 7966 www.metrotrimmingcorp.com
MIAMI STYLE INC.	sofia@miamistyle.com	U.S.A. • (1) (305) 805 1168 www.miamistyle.com

443

MICHAEL CALDERONE, INC.		U.S.A. • (1) (212) 465 1093
	mcpatterns@aol.com	www.mcpatternservice.com
MODE WORKS		Canada • (1) (604) 562 4921
	alina@modeworks.ca	www.modeworks.ca
MOKITA		U.S.A. • (1) (917) 664 4864
	info@mokitaglobal.com	www.mokitaglobal.com
MONALISA FASHIONS INC.		U.S.A. • (1) (610) 770 0806
	monalisamfg@gmail.com	www.monalisamfg.com
MOONLITE GRAPHICS CO., INC.		U.S.A. • (1) (508) 676 6674
	moonlite79@verizon.net	
NEO-CONCEPT (NY) CORPORATION		U.S.A. • (1) (212) 242 6808
	glenda@neo-concept.com	www.neo-concept.com
NETWORK BROKERS INTERNATIONAL		U.S.A. • (1) (516) 825 6623
	info@networkbrokers.com	www.networkbrokers.com
NEW CONCEPTS OF NEW YORK LLC		U.S.A. • (1) (212) 695 4999
	sales@newconceptsllc.com	www.newconceptsllc.com
NEW ICM, LP		U.S.A. • (1) (979) 578 0543
	rcwhitson@newicm.com	www.newicm.com
NEW YORK BINDING COMPANY		U.S.A. • (1) 718 729 2454
NORTHRIDGE MILLS INC.		U.S.A. • (1) (818) 361 7373
	rocio@northridgemills.com	
NOVA CREATION		Guatemala • (502) 6646 5880
	j.gisbert@novacreation.net	
NOVELTY POM POM COMPANY		U.S.A. • (1) (212) 391 9175
NU YALE		U.S.A. • (1) (812) 285 7400
	mike@nuyale.com	www.nuyale.com
NY STUDIO LLC		U.S.A. • (1) (212) 244 1269
	robert@nystudiollc.com	www.nystudiollc.com
NYLONTEX INTERNACIONAL S.A.		Guatemala • (502) 6628 0700
	kwoc@nylontexinternacional.com	www.nylontexinternacional.com
OCASA		U.S.A. • (1) (212) 758 0101
	customer.service@ocasa.com	www.ocasa.com
OCEAN AIR LOGISTICS		U.S.A. • (1) (305) 599 0966
	sales@oceanairlogistics.com	www.oceanairlogistics.com
ONTARIO GLOVE MANUFACTURING CO., LTD.		Canada • (1) (519) 886 3590
	sales@ontarioglove.com	www.ontarioglove.com
OREGON SCREEN IMPRESSIONS		U.S.A. • (1) (503) 231 0181
	tiffanyf@oregonscreen.com	www.oregonscreen.com
ORIGINALES SHYLA, S.A. DE C.V.		Mexico • (52) (55) 57090018
	bpm@originalesshyla.com	www.originalesshyla.com
PARAMOUNT APPAREL INTERNATIONAL		U.S.A. • (1) (573) 732 4411
	sales@paramountapparel.com	www.paramountapparel.com
PARIS ACCESSORIES		U.S.A. • (1) (212) 868 0500
	info@parisacc.com	
PATTERN DESIGN UNLIMITED, INC.		U.S.A. • (1) (717) 336 0500
	pdu@patterndesign.com	www.patterndesign.com
PATTERN GRADING & MARKER SERVICES		U.S.A. • (1) (954) 441 4432
	regina@pattern-maker.com	www.pattern-maker.com
PATTERN GRADING & MARKING BY ANDREW GLONINGER		U.S.A. • (1) (610) 356 1777
	andrew@gradingandmarking.com	www.gradingandmarking.com
PENN & FLETCHER, INC.		U.S.A. • (1) (212) 239 6868
	pennandfletcher@aol.com	www.pennandfletcher.com
PERFECTION SHIRT INC.		Canada • (1) (418) 483 5227
	sales@perfectionshirt.com	www.perfectionshirt.com

PERFORMANCE DESIGN STUDIO	info@performancedesignstudio.com	U.S.A. • (1) (619) 623 7692 www.performancedesignstudio.com
PHILIPPO MANUFACTURING CORP.	gates@qc.aibn.com	Canada • (1) (514) 389 4321
POL SYSTEMS	mdkeith@suddenlink.net	U.S.A. • (1) 870 562 2901 www.polsystems.net
POPULAR PATTERN CO.	ssinger1@aol.com	U.S.A. • (1) (212) 947 2902
PORTCHESTER, USA	portchester_usa@verizon.net	U.S.A. • (1) (718) 937 4200 www.portchesterusa.com
PRECISION WAREHOUSING & DISTRIBUTION	rob@precisioninc.com	U.S.A. • (1) (714) 690 9344 www.precisioninc.com
PRIDE MANUFACTURING S. DE R. L.	buda.escoto@grupokarims.com	Honduras • (504) 2620 0450 www.grupokarims.com
PRIMAL SCREEN	catie@primalscreenprinting.com	U.S.A. • (1) (330) 677 1766 www.primalscreenprinting.com
PRIMO COAT COMPANY	alan@alandavidnyc.com	U.S.A. • (1) (718) 349 2070
PRIORITY MANUFACTURING	richard@customuniforms.com	U.S.A. • (1) (305) 576 3000 www.customuniforms.com
PRO WASH	ykoo@aol.com	U.S.A. • (1) (323) 756 6000
PRODUCTORA CLINIMEX INDUSTRIAL, S.A. DE C. V.	orandaym@agssite.com.mx	Mexico • (52) (449) 9730304, 9730302
PRODUCTOS WEST DE MEXICO S.A.	newwestjeans@hotmail.com	Mexico • (52) (871) 713 3694
PROMOTORA INTERNACIONAL DE PANTALONES, S.A. DE C.V.	jaimecohens@omsamex.com	Mexico • (52) (55) 52806550
PROSTER FASHION	prosterlock23@gmail.com	U.S.A. • (1) (212) 730 8503
PURE BLANKZ ORGANIC FASHION INC.	adila@pureblankz.com	Canada • (1) 647 248 8326 www.pureblankz.com
QUALITY CORRECTIONS & INSPECTIONS	stacey_burket@qualitycorrections.com	U.S.A. • (1) (814) 696 3737 www.qualitycorrections.com
QUETICO LOGISTICS LLC	nick@queticollc.com	U.S.A. • (1) (909) 628 6200 www.queticollc.com
QUICK FUSING INC.	quickfuse5@aol.com	U.S.A. • (1) (212) 967 0311 www.apparelexpert.com
QUINTIN CO.	info@quintinco.com	U.S.A. • (1) (323) 221 9202 www.quintinco.com
R & N HEADWEAR		U.S.A. • (1) (718) 522 6990
RAINBOW STYLE	info@rainbowpattern.com	U.S.A. • (1) (212) 290 0209 www.rainbowpattern.com
RAYLON CORPORATION	jpollak@rayloncorp.com	U.S.A. • (1) (212) 221 3633
RAYTEX INDUSTRIES	jhellegers@raytexindustries.com	U.S.A. • (1) (516) 584 1111 www.raytexindustries.com
RED FISH BLUE FISH DYE WORKS INC.	jeff@rfbfdyeworks.com	U.S.A. • (1) (603) 692 3900 www.rfbfdyeworks.com
REGAL ORIGINALS, INC.	rodger@regaloriginals.com	U.S.A. • (1) (201) 569 2144 www.regaloriginals.com
RENATO'S CUTTING SERVICE		U.S.A. • (1) (213) 489 0944
REST IN BEAUTY, INC.	restinbeauty@bellsouth.net	U.S.A. • (1) (803) 245 5126 www.restinbeauty.com

ROBKO LLC		U.S.A. • (1) (610) 746 4933
	art@customapparelzone.com	www.customapparelzone.com
ROBOCUTS		Canada • (1) (514) 388 8001
	sales@robocuts.com	www.robocuts.com
ROCEDES S.A.		Nicaragua • (505) 2263 2032
	svaughn@rocedes.com.ni	www.rocedes.com.ni
ROOCHI TRADERS INC.		U.S.A. • (1) (323) 722 5592
	mickey@roochi.com	www.cottonheritage.com
ROUND HOUSE MANUFACTURING		U.S.A. • (1) (405) 273 0510
	info@round-house.com	www.round-house.com
ROYAL APPAREL INC.		U.S.A. • (1) (631) 213 8299
	sales@royalapparel.net	www.royalapparel.net
ROYAL BLUE INTERNATIONAL		U.S.A. • (1) (310) 888 0156
	samikahen@aol.com	
S. KANOUNI DESIGN & PATTERN STUDIO		U.S.A. • (1) (213) 627 2281
	skfashion@att.net	
S.M.C., S.A.		Dominican Republic • (1) (809) 242 6565, 242 6566
	smcdr@yahoo.com	
SAN FRANCISCO PLEATING CO.		U.S.A. • (1) (415) 982 3003
	rustysfpleating@comcast.net	
SARAH LYNN SPORTSWEAR, INC.		U.S.A. • (1) (610) 770 1702
	rkoury@slsportswear.com	www.slsportswear.com
SCHOTT BROTHERS, INC.		U.S.A. • (1) (908) 527 0011
	schott@schottnyc.com	www.schottnyc.com
SCOTTEX GLOBAL SOURCING LLC		U.S.A. • (1) (215) 540 1244
	bradley@scottexglobal.com	www.scottexglobal.com
SEMEL'S EMBROIDERY, INC.		U.S.A. • (1) (973) 473 3959
	embroideri@aol.com	www.semelsembroidery.com
SEW PRECISE COMPANY		U.S.A. • (1) (773) 481 1400
	info@sewprecise.com	www.sewprecise.com
SEWN PRODUCT SERVICES		U.S.A. • (1) (206) 467 5459
	contact@sewnproductservices.com	www.sewnproductservices.com
SHEHU		U.S.A. • (1) (267) 496 5208
	bela@shehu.net	www.shehu.net
SHURCO MANUFACTURING INC.		U.S.A. • (1) (773) 907 8400
	sy924@sbcglobal.net	
SIETE LEGUAS DENIM JEANS		Mexico • (52) (871) 2349101
	jj@sieteleguas.com.mx	www.sieteleguas.com.mx
SILK CITY FIBERS		U.S.A. • (1) 800 899 7455
	scfserv@aol.com	www.silkcityfibers.com
SILK CITY SALES INTERNATIONAL		U.S.A. • (1) (212) 382 2235
	maureen@silkcitysales.com	
SKY BLUE SEWING		U.S.A. • (1) (415) 777 9978
	skyblueswg@sbcglobal.net	
SNAPCO MANUFACTURING CORPORATION	ray.snapco@gmail.com	U.S.A. • (1) (973) 282 0300
		www.snapco.com
SOARING EAGLE OUTERWEAR, INC.		U.S.A. • (1) (701) 838 2110
	seagle@srt.com	
SOLID STONE FABRICS		U.S.A. • (1) (276) 634 0115
	dstone@solidstonefabrics.com	www.solidstonefabrics.com
SOMIYA INC.		U.S.A. • (1) (212) 302 3089
	somiyainc@yahoo.com	
SOURCE-I		U.S.A. • (1) (727) 725 2981
	wwilson@source-i.com	www.source-i.com
SPOILED ROTTEN U.S.A.		U.S.A. • (1) (718) 993 7006
	eberoff@yahoo.com	

SQUEEGEE PRINTERS	squeegee@together.net	U.S.A. • (1) (802) 266 3426
STAR CONCEPT APPAREL LTD.	info@starconceptapparel.com	Canada • (1) (604) 879 9018 www.starconceptapparel.com
STAR EMBROIDERY	dwiley921@gmail.com	U.S.A. • (1) (973) 481 4300 www.star-embroidery.com
STERLINGWEAR OF BOSTON, INC.	dfredella@sterlingwear.com	U.S.A. • (1) (617) 567 6465 www.sterlingwear.com
STILE ASSOCIATES LTD	isaacg@stileintl.com	U.S.A. • (1) (516) 394 2166 www.stileintl.com
STITCH DESIGNERS	marketing@dbswebsite.com	U.S.A. • (1) (502) 637 8619 www.stitchdesigners.com
STUCKI EMBROIDERY	mail@stuckiembroidery.com	U.S.A. • (1) (845) 657 2308 www.stuckiembroidery.com
STUDIO NTK LLC	studiontk@gmail.com	U.S.A. • (1) (317) 886 7327 www.studiontk.com
STUDIO ONE LEATHER DESIGN INC.	arthur@studio1leather.com	U.S.A. • (1) (212) 760 1701
STYLE COUNCIL, THE	marissa@stylecouncil.com	U.S.A. • (1) (212) 564 9380 www.stylecouncil.com
STYLE SOURCE INC.	geoff@style-source.com	U.S.A. • (1) (910) 399 2288 www.style-source.com
SUNBRITE DYE COMPANY	info@sunbritedyeco.com	U.S.A. • (1) (973) 777 9830
SUNCOAST TRENDS CORP.		U.S.A. • (1) (727) 321 4948
SUNDOG PRODUCTIONS	j.sague@sunpup.com	U.S.A. • (1) (703) 978 0041 www.sunpup.com
SUPERIOR PATTERN SERVICES	superior_patterns@yahoo.com	U.S.A. • (1) (305) 805 1540 www.superiorpatterns.com
SUPERTEX LIBERTY INDUSTRIES INC.	info@supertex-inc.com	U.S.A. • (1) (336) 622 1000 www.supertex-inc.com
SWAN DYEING	swansales@swandyeandprint.com	U.S.A. • (1) (508) 674 4611 www.swandyeandprint.com
SWEATER BRAND INC.	info@sweaterbrand.com	U.S.A. • (1) (718) 797 0505
SWEENIE MANUFACTURING CORPORATION	diane@sweeniemanufacturing.com	U.S.A. • (1) (646) 825 5027 www.sweeniemanufacturing.com
TAG STUDIO PATTERN DESIGN SERVICE	tagpatrn@gmail.com	U.S.A. • (1) (415) 664 2408 www.tagstudio.biz
TANNERY DIRECT	asampson@tannerydirect.com	U.S.A. • (1) (212) 465 1503
TAYLORED SERVICES INC.	ckearns@tpservices.com	U.S.A. • (1) (732) 248 7900 www.tayloredservices.com
TECHS BY TERRY	terrmaloney@aol.com	U.S.A. • (1) (718) 440 7185
TESTFABRICS, INC.	info@testfabrics.com	U.S.A. • (1) (570) 603 0432 www.testfabrics.com
TEX PRINT USA, LLC	ginettam@texprintusa.com	U.S.A. • (1) (201) 773 6531 www.texprintusa.com
TEXTILE ARTS MARKETING INC,.	ken@textileartsmarketing.com	U.S.A. • (1) (914) 837 3588 www.textileartsmarketing.com
TEXTILES OPICO DBA TEXOPS	juan.zighelboim@texops.com	El Salvador • () (503) 2319 0800 www.texops.com
TODD RUTKIN	jan@toddrutkin.com	U.S.A. • (1) (323) 584 9225 www.toddrutkin.com

Company	Email	Contact
TOPPS SAFETY APPAREL INC.	info@toppssafetyapparel.com	U.S.A. • (1) (574) 223 4311 www.toppssafetyapparel.com
TOUCH OF LACE, INC.	sales@touchoflace.com	U.S.A. • (1) (201) 943 1082 www.touchoflace.com
TOUCHDOWN FREIGHT COMPANY	touch@touchdownco.com	U.S.A. • (1) (310) 973 7112
TRANN TECHNOLOGIES INC.	sales@tranntech.com	U.S.A. • (1) (888) 668 6700 www.tranntech.com
TRINITY SPORTS INC.	info@trinitysportsinc.com	U.S.A. • (1) (323) 277 9288 www.trinitysportsinc.com
TRUE MEASURE INC.	melida@truemeasureinc.com	U.S.A. • (1) (323) 213 3184 www.truemeasureinc.com
TURFER ATHLETIC	ggoldberg@turfer.com	U.S.A. • (1) (401) 427 1369 www.turfer.com
UNIFORMES UNION, S.A. DE C.V.	uniformesunion@prodigy.net.mx	Mexico • (52) (55) 57144487 www.uniformesunion.com
UNIQUE SCREEN PRINTING, INC.	Jose@uniquescreenprinting.com	U.S.A. • (1) (908) 925 3773 www.uniquescreenprintings.com
UNWRAPPED, INC.	skatz@unwrappedinc.com	U.S.A. • (1) (978) 441 0242 www.unwrappedinc.com
UPLIFTING SALES, INC.	jp@jpbrogan.com	U.S.A. • (1) (917) 913 2284
USA BEADING/FARAJ INC.	farajinc@aol.com	U.S.A. • (1) (201) 313 4480 www.farajinc.com
V.A. PRIVATE LABEL	info@vaprivatelabel.com	U.S.A. • (1) (215) 496 0408 www.vaprivatelabel.com
VALLEN PROVEEDORA DE SEGURIDAD INDUSTRIAL DEL GOLFO	jmina@vallenproveedora.com.mx	Mexico • (52) (833) 2301700 www.vallenproveedora.com.mx
VAPOR APPAREL	sales@sourcesubstrates.com	U.S.A. • (1) (843) 747 4200 www.vaporapparel.com
VESTIGE DESIGN	info@vestigedesign.com	U.S.A. • (1) (212) 944 4389 www.vestigedesign.com
VESTININA, S.A. DE C.V.	vesti@vesti.com.mx	Mexico • (52) (55) 5654 7388 www.vesti.com.mx
VICKY FORM, S.A. DE C.V.	expzaga@zaga.com	Mexico • (52) (55) 5333 0360 www.vickyform.com, www.zaga.com
VISHAL ENTERPRISES	vishal@vishalent.com	U.S.A. • (1) (212) 629 0880 www.vishalent.com
VISIONAIRE PLEATING LLC.	john@visionairepleating.com	U.S.A. • (1) 917 520 4100 www.visionairepleating.com
VOGUE TOO PLEATING STITCHING AND EMBROIDERY	larry@voguetoo.com	U.S.A. • (1) (212) 354 8976 www.voguetoo.com
W.Y. SHUGART	tshugart@wyshugart.com	U.S.A. • (1) (256) 845 1251 www.wyshugart.com
WAITEX INTERNATIONAL	candice@waitex.com	U.S.A. • (1) (212) 967 8100 www.waitex.com
WEBER & DOEBRICH	wedoembroidery@gmail.com	U.S.A. • (1) (201) 867 1540
WELLS HOSIERY MILLS, INC.	info@wellshosiery.com	U.S.A. • (1) (336) 633 4881 www.wellshosiery.com
WERKSTATT	tina@werkstattny.com	U.S.A. • (1) (646) 414 4545 www.werkstattny.com
WGCI	wgci@wgciusa.com	U.S.A. • (1) (323) 583 9832 www.wgciusa.com
WILLIAM THE PATTERNMAKER	williamsmithline@yahoo.com	U.S.A. • (1) 646 824 2280 www.williamthepatternmaker.com

WINGOLD EMBROIDERY LLC		U.S.A. • (1) (201) 945 2727
	tfigliolino@aol.com	www.wingoldembroidery.com
WORLD CLASS SHIPPING		U.S.A. • (1) (516) 568 8861
	billjr@worldclassshipping.com	www.worldclassshipping.com
WORLD SOURCE		U.S.A. • (1) (212) 594 9129
	info@worldsourcenyc.com	
YALE DE MEXICO, S.A. DE C.V.		Mexico • (52) (55) 5804 4242
	cbpiza@yale.com.mx	www.yale.com.mx
YOONIMEX INC. DBA/U.S. EMBROIDERY		U.S.A. • (1) (562) 906 2100
	info@us-embroidery.com	www.us-embroidery.com
Z.W. DESIGNS, INC.		U.S.A. • (1) (770) 513 0906
	zwd@zwdesigns.com	www.zwdesigns.com

Advertisers

Directories

Sourcing Made Simpler/On-line Access

Sourcing Made Simpler/On-line Access Online access to over 2,000 nationwide suppliers of all types of fabrics, trims, notions, forecast services, swatch design studios, CAD services & much more for the apparel industry. **"one click"** to contact suppliers via email and or website. 1 year subscription.

Listings include:
Company address, phone, fax, and email; Sales manager names; Products they sell or manufacture and/or services they provide; If goods are domestic or imported and where they import from; Minimum quantities for production; Price points; Markets they cater to; and more.

Fabric and trim manufacturers, converters, jobbers, agents, mills and reps listed. Over 65 categories serve all your industry sourcing needs.

Ref: 001 $ 99.⁰⁰ 1 year subscription

order online: www.fashiondex.com/store or by phone 212 647 0051

Apparel Production Made Simpler/On-line Access
American Edition

Up-to-date directory committed to solving your production sourcing and contracting needs in the Americas. Hundreds of contractors open for production, includes sewing, CMT & finishing contractors, & production services from the U.S. Listings include: contact info; specialty areas; package capabilities; machinery; minimums; and more!

"one click" to contact suppliers via email and or website. 1 year subscription.

Reference: 002 $ 99.⁰⁰ 1 year subscription

order online: www.fashiondex.com/store or by phone 212 647 0051

Sourcing

The Apparel Industry Sourcebook

Comprehensive directory for apparel manufacturers, designers, merchandisers, trim and fabric buyers and production sourcing departments in the men's, women's, children's and accessory markets.

A complete and up-to-date sourcebook listing over 2,000 nationwide suppliers of all fabrics, trims, notions, forecast services, swatch studios, CAD services and more for the apparel industry.

Listings include:
Company address, phone, fax, and email; Sales manager names; Products they sell or manufacture and/or services they provide; If goods are domestic or imported and where they import from; Minimum quantities for production; Price points; Markets they cater to; and more.

Fabric and trim manufacturers, converters, jobbers, agents, mills and reps listed. Over 65 categories serve all your industry sourcing needs.

Reference 101 $ 135.⁰⁰   Ref 001 $ 99.⁰⁰/Online*

The Small Design Company's Guide to Wholesale Fabrics and Trims

The perfect sourcebook for companies requiring smaller yardage quantities of production fabric.

This concise directory lists over 400 fabric suppliers selling low minimum (500 yards or less) of a fabric, to the fashion trade. Also listed are suppliers and jobbers of no minimum and in-stock goods.

Listings are grouped by fabric category, and each listing includes company address, phone, fax, email and website address. Also listed is the sales manager name, the fabric qualities they sell, price points, minimum yardage quantities for production, and more!

The sourcebook begins with an excellent introduction chapter which instructs the how-tos' when one is shopping the wholesale fabric market!

Specifically created for start-up companies, small design houses, and home sewing businesses.

Reference 106   On Sale! 65.⁰⁰

order online: www.fashiondex.com/store or by phone 212 647 0051

Directories

The Apparel Production Sourcebook American Edition

Up-to-date directory committed to solving your production sourcing and contracting needs in the Americas. Hundreds of contractors open for production, includes sewing, CMT & finishing contractors, & production services from the U.S. Listings include: contact info; specialty areas; package capabilities; machinery; minimums; and more!

Excellent tool for all production sourcing departments.

Reference: 102 $ 125.⁰⁰

Directory of Brand Name Apparel Manufacturers and Importers

Up-to-date directory lists brand name and private label manufacturers and importers of women's, men's, and children's wear and accessories. Developed and targeted for retail store and catalogue buyers to shop the apparel and accessory markets easily.

Over 1,800 brand name labels listed, broken down by type of apparel classification. No cross-referencing. Listings include: labels; line types; types of retailers sold; showroom/sales rep locations; whether products are domestic/import; price points; and RN numbers.

Reference: 104 $ 135.⁰⁰

order online: www.fashiondex.com/store or by phone 212 647 0051

Sourcing

Crisis in the 21st Century Garment Industry

Last man standing may well be an accurate description of the steps that we must take to survive the current downturn. Everything depends on how fast the players understand that the rules of survival have changed.

Reference 226 $ 45.00

Birnbaum's Global Guide to Material Sourcing

You can no longer depend on how you sourced materials a few years ago, those methods are already antiquated. Is your company on the leading edge, or are you falling behind?

Reference 230 $ 45.00

Birnbaum's Global Guide to Winning the Great Garment War

The premier book on garment costing and sourcing, and the ultimate book for all garment industry professionals.

Reference 201 $ 35.00

Best Seller!

Sourcing A,B,C'S

We published this 16 page booklet to assist all new designers and entrepreneurs sourcing apparel production for the first time.

You have an idea for a new garment, apparel concept, clothing line or product that doesn't exist at retail... or.... You are a designer planning to start out on your own... or.... Your existing locally-made product line has grown and you need to outsource production...

If any of the these scenarios are the case and you are traveling to a trade show or sourcing event to research how to produce this new idea/garment/product line, then this booklet is for you.

Reference 190 $ 6.99

Technical

Apparel Design and Production Handbook- A Technical Reference

Invaluable reference book for fashion designers, merchandisers, technical designers, production managers, apparel-making factories, patternmakers, and all industry executives working in the men's, women's and children's markets today.

Chapters include:
•How to measure the body for apparel production.
•Standard body measurements for regular and special sizes of men's, women's and children's wear.
•How to measure garments for apparel production.
•Standard garment specifications and flats for basic styles.
•Grading charts for all markets and sizes.
•Blank costing and specification sheets.
•Croquis drawings for design, illustration, tracing and more.

Reference: IOS $ 95.⁰⁰

The Vendor Compliance Handbook
with Forms and Data Templates 2nd Edition

This book outlines everything a designer or a garment manufacturer needs to know about producing a compliant garment from start to finish.

This in-depth handbook explains all standards and guidelines of all production phases, so that garments are delivered compliant and disconcerting incidents, such as chargebacks and late deliveries, are avoided.

A must-have for every garment production department!

Reference: 228 $ 60.⁰⁰

How to Start a Fashion Company

Straight forward step-by-step guide for designers and entrepreneurs wanting to start their own line. Book contains all the necessary fashion terms you need to know to start a line; basic information on Making Prototypes, Costing, Marketing, and Production.

Reference: 230 $ 45.⁰⁰

Stitch Sample Kit

A comprehensive guide, providing both technical and creative solutions for garment construction. The Stitch Sample Kit contains over 80 mounted swatches of current stitches and techniques used within the garment industry today. You will find the Stitch Sample Kit both informative and inspirational.

- Stitches are organized by type; thread is color-coded
- Swatches are pre-mounted
- Includes required specs, ISO #'s and approximate US cost, where applicable

Reference: 231 $ 150.⁰⁰

Fabric Swatch Kit

A well-organized fabric collection featuring over 175 swatches for the fashion and textile industries. Informative and concise, this overview includes all commonly-used fabrics and their uses. Swatches are organized by fabric category, and fabric types are arranged alphabetically in each category. Simple-to-understand construction details and a technical glossary of terms complete this must-have reference. Additionally, one gets the opportunity to learn each fabric type as they mount each swatch to its corresponding definition. Loads of extra blank pages are included so you can add your own swatches as well, and build an entire fabric library. Perfect for everyone in the fashion design and textile trades.

Reference: 602 $ 85.⁰⁰

order online: www.fashiondex.com/store or by phone 212 647 0051

A Picture Speaks A Thousand Words

This book demonstrates the use of computer–aided design to create clearly detailed technical information for factories through the stages of design, development and manufacture, using graphic illustration wherever possible.

The specification is a critical document to be shared by all involved in the buying, selling, design and manufacture of the product. A style can be amended many times before the start of production, and specifications created by CAD can be quickly amended in minutes and circulated to everyone involved.

The book takes the reader through a variety of specifications step by step and explains the reasoning behind creating each page; a complete detailed specification may have up to 20 pages depending on the style and construction detail. This book is a practical, hands-on approach to the subject written with many years experience in the industry. The message is that good graphics is an international language, which helps to avoid misunderstandings; details that are in text can be lost in translation.

A recent quote from a source in China states that the most common issue between buyers and suppliers is the lack of communication and unclear specifications for products that leads to mistakes and that Quality Control is your most effective tool to getting the correct product when your specifications/expectations are clear.

This book is a definitive approach to specification writing for the clothing and related industries, demonstrating the advantages of using CAD.

This book will help those working in the industry and students starting textile courses to view specifications as an integral part of product development, quality assurance and manufacturing.

Reference: 123 $ 45.⁰⁰

order online: www.fashiondex.com/store or by phone 212 647 0051

CPSIA information can be obtained at www.ICGtesting.com
Printed in the USA
BVOW06s1519210314

348391BV00002B/5/P